Mathematical Recreations

MAURICE KRAITCHIK

SECOND REVISED EDITION

DOVER PUBLICATIONS, INC.

NEW YORK

TO

MR. DANNIE HEINEMAN

*who encouraged the author's scientific
work for more than twenty-five years*

PREFACE

In October, 1941, I was invited to give a course of lectures at the New School for Social Research in New York City on the general topic, "Mathematical Recreations." On these lectures this book is based.

It may also be regarded as a revised edition of my similar work, published in French, entitled, "La Mathématique des Jeux" ("The Mathematics of Games").* The present book is, in fact, better than a revised edition, since during nine of the intervening years (1931–1939) I was editor of *Sphinx*, a periodical devoted to recreational mathematics. This experience has made it possible to bring many improvements and much new material to the work.

Many individuals and organizations have assisted in making it possible for me to write this book. It is my grateful duty to thank them. If the reader likes this book he is in debt to those listed below:

The United States of America, which, by opening its doors for me, has deserved no small part of my thanks.

Mr. D. Heineman, who made it possible for me to come to this country, which is now the refuge of so many scientists of distressed Europe.

Dr. Alvin Johnson, Director of the New School for Social Research, who made it possible for me to bring before an American audience the results of my researches.

Mr. Donald A. Flanders, who has not only helped me to adapt the expression of my thoughts to an unfamiliar idiom, but has throughout embellished the book with the results of his own reflections. Some of the material on magic squares is due to him, particularly the methodical use of lattices; and many other pages have benefited by his explanations.

* Brussels, Stevens, 1930.

Mr. W. W. Norton and his staff, who have given their careful attention to the book, and to whom the reader is indebted for its excellent appearance. Especially I am indebted to Mr. W. L. Parker, for many valuable suggestions and for aid rendered in the preparation of the manuscript for the press.

M. KRAITCHIK

CONTENTS

10   *Contents*

CHAPTER ONE

MATHEMATICS WITHOUT NUMBERS

To most people "mathematics" is synonymous with "figuring." Actually this idea is far from the truth. Aside from the many geometrical questions which are not at all concerned with adding, subtracting, multiplying, and dividing, there are problems of quite different sorts whose solutions are obtained by the direct exercise of the powers of reasoning, without the intervention of formulas and computations. For mathematics is applied logic in its simplest and purest form. To demonstrate our contention we shall begin by examining in this first chapter a number of problems in whose solution no calculations are used.

The first question is quite easy, though not so easy as it looks.

1. I have long been an ardent chess player, yet my twelve-year-old daughter scarcely knows the moves. (The reader may be reassured; he need not know them either.) Recently two of my friends, who are chess experts, came to dinner. After dinner I played one game with each of them and lost both games, although against each I had the advantage of a pawn and the opening move. Just as we finished, my daughter came into the room. On learning of my ill success she said: "Daddy, I'm ashamed of you. I can do better than that. Let me play them! I don't want any advantage — I'll play one game with white pieces and one with black. [In chess, the white pieces always move first.] And I'll give them an advantage by playing both games at once. Still, I shall make out better than you did."

We took her up immediately on this. To my mingled delight and chagrin, she made good; she did better than I had.

How did she do it?

Solution: Let us call the experts Mr. White and Mr. Black, according to the color of the pieces each played against my daughter. Mr. White played first. My daughter copied his first move as her opening against Mr. Black at the other board. When Mr. Black had answered this move, she copied his move at the first board as her reply to Mr. White. And so on. In this way the simultaneous games against the two experts became a single game between them; my daughter served as a messenger to transmit the moves. Hence she was certain that she would either win one game and lose the other, or draw both.

The second question is also easy.

2. The inhabitants of a certain remote island are divided into two hereditary castes. To an outsider the members of these two castes look entirely alike. But those in one caste, the Arbus, always tell the truth; those in the other, the Bosnins, always tell the opposite of the truth.

To this island came an explorer who knew something of their customs, but little of their language. As he landed he met three natives — Abl, Bsl, and Crl.

"Of what caste are you?" the explorer asked Abl.

"Bhsz cjnt dkpv flgqw mrx," said Abl.

"What did he say?" asked the explorer, addressing Bsl and Crl, both of whom had learned some English.

"He say he Arbu," said Bsl.

"He say he Bosnin," said Crl.

To which castes do Bsl and Crl belong?

The solution of the problem depends on the fact that every native, whether an Arbu or a Bosnin, must always reply to a question about his caste by saying that he is an Arbu. If he really is an Arbu he will speak the truth and say so; if he is not he will lie and say that he is. Hence, Abl said that he was an Arbu, Bsl showed himself to be an Arbu by reporting Abl faithfully, and Crl proclaimed himself a Bosnin by uttering a transparent falsehood.

3. The Problem of the Three Philosophers. Wearied by their disputations and oppressed by the summer heat, three Greek philosophers lay down for a little nap under a tree in the Academy. As they slept a practical joker smeared their faces with black paint. Presently they all awoke at once and each began to laugh at the other. Suddenly one of them stopped laughing, for he realized that his own face was painted. What was his reasoning?

Solution: A, B, and C are the three philosophers. A thought: "Since B laughs he thinks his face is clean. Since he believes that, if he saw that my face was clean also, he would be astonished at C's laughter, for C would have nothing to laugh at. Since B is not astonished he must think that C is laughing at me. Hence my face is black."

4. Three unsuccessful revolutionists managed to escape across the border, where they were interned in the lockup of a small town. The sheriff's sympathies lay with the prisoners, and he sought a way to let them go free. One day he came into the jail brandishing three white disks and two black ones, and said to the prisoners: "On the back of each of you I shall pin one of these disks. None of you can see his own disk, though you can see your companions'. If any of you guesses correctly that his own disk is white he will receive his freedom. If not, he will be detained indefinitely." With this he pinned a white disk on the back of each and left them in the care of a guard. How can each of the three prisoners, A, B, and C, guess whether his disk is white?

A reasoned: "The disks of my companions are white,

so my disk may be either white or black. Suppose it were black. Then B would have gone to claim his freedom. For he would have said to himself: 'Since A's disk is black and C's is white, mine can be either. But it cannot be black, since then C would have seen that our disks were black and would have known that his must be white, since there were only two black disks. But since C has not gone to claim his freedom he must think it possible that his is black, that is, he must see that mine is white.' But B has not gone to claim his freedom, so mine must be white." All three prisoners arrived at this conclusion simultaneously, and all three escaped.

If A had completed his reasoning before the others, they would not have been able to escape. For A's escape would be possible if just one of their disks was black, so each would be tormented with the fear that his was black.

5. A telephone conversation:

"Hello. Is this OK-7-6923?"

"Yes. Who is calling, please?"

"What? You don't recognize my voice? Why, my mother is your mother's mother-in-law."

"Huh?"

What is the relationship of the speakers?

A father and his child, or a paternal uncle or aunt and his or her nephew or niece. You can reason out who is the caller and who answered the phone.

6. In a certain bitterly fought war one side summarily executed all prisoners suspected of sniping. But first the executioners amused themselves by asking each condemned man, "How are you to be killed, by shooting or by hanging? If you answer correctly you will be shot. If not, you will be hanged." Most of the prisoners were too distraught to sense the trick, but one, thinking to save himself, boldly replied, "By hanging." If the executioners had tried to keep their

word they would have been in a pretty quandary.   But need-
less to say they shot him anyway.

Problems such as these, that can be solved without numerical calculation, are really far more numerous than one might
suppose.   To this group belong the problem of the eight
queens on the chessboard and the problem of the knight, both
of which we shall examine later.   Also magic squares, which
are so fascinating and which appear to belong exclusively to
the domain of numerical calculations, may be studied without any computations.
On the other hand, certain problems appear from their
statements to be relatively innocent of extensive calculations,
but it turns out that their solution involves rather complicated number work.   The following is a good illustration of
this type of problem.

7. An honorable family of spiders, consisting of a wise
mother and eight husky youngsters, were perched on the wall
at one end of a rectangular room.   Food being scarce, owing
to the second World War, they were grumbling, when an
enormous fly landed unnoticed on the opposite wall.   If Euclid could have been summoned from his grave (location, alas,
unknown), he would have been able to show that both the
hunters and the prey were in the vertical plane bisecting the
two opposite walls, the spiders eighty inches above the center
and the fly eighty inches below.
Suddenly one young spider shouted with glee.   "Mamma!
Look!   There's a fly!   Let's catch him and eat him!"
"There are four ways to reach the fly.   Which shall we
take?" came the eager query from another.
"You have forgotten your Euclid, my darling.   There are
eight ways to reach the fly.   Each of you take a different path,
without using any other means of conveyance than your God-

given legs. Whoever reaches the goal first shall be rewarded
with the largest portion of the prey."

At the signal given by the mother the eight spiders shot
out in eight different directions at a speed of 0.65 mile per
hour. At the end of $\frac{625}{11}$ seconds they simultaneously con-
verged on the fly, but found no need of attacking it since its
heart had given way at the sight of enemies on all sides.

What are the dimensions of the room?

They have not been stated, and it does not seem clear
how to arrive at them.

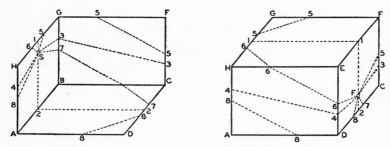

FIGURE 1. *The Spiders to the Fly: 8 Paths.*

In general the shortest distance between two points is
measured along the straight line joining them. If the given
distance is to be measured over a surface that is not plane,
the shortest path, called a geodesic, is not generally a straight
line. Sometimes there are many equally short paths, as in
the case of the shortest path between two poles on a sphere,
where any one of the infinitely many meridians joining them
will serve. Thus we may expect that the problem may have
to be examined with some care when the surface is a parallelepiped.

The key to the problem is the fact that the length of a path
on a polyhedral surface is not altered when the angles at
which the plane faces intersect are changed. In particular,
if the polyhedron may be cut along certain edges in such a

way as not to cut the path and at the same time so as to allow the surface to be spread on a plane, the shortest path on the surface of the polyhedron will become the shortest path on the plane — that is, a straight line.

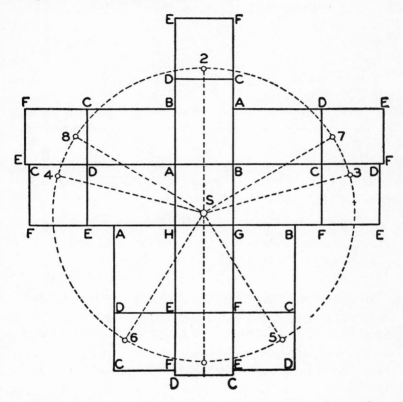

The first step is to find the distance traveled by the spiders. We use the formula

$$Distance = Velocity \times Time.$$

According to our stated conditions, the velocity is 0.65 mile per hour; but we want to get this in inches per second, since the time in our problem is given in seconds and part of the distance in inches. Calculating:

$$\frac{0.65 \text{ (mile)}}{1 \text{ (hour)}} = \frac{0.65 \times 5,280 \times 12}{60 \times 60} = \frac{41,184 \text{ (inches)}}{3,600 \text{ (seconds)}}$$

gives us our velocity. Then

$$Distance = \frac{41,184}{3,600} \times \frac{625}{11} = 650 \text{ inches.}$$

That is how far each spider traveled. But we were asked to find the dimensions of the room. Therefore, now, let us spread out its walls, ceiling, and floor onto a plane, much as if we were to open out the six faces of a cardboard box to make one flat piece. Since there are several possible paths, this must be done in all possible ways, keeping the wall from which the spiders start fixed, and laying down the others in such a way as to keep every face attached to another along a common edge. We can then see that the following eight paths are possible:

(1) Over the floor and parts of the two end walls.

(2) Over the ceiling and parts of the two end walls.

(3) Over one side wall and parts of the two end walls.

(4) Over the other side wall and parts of the two end walls.

(5) Over the ceiling and one side wall and parts of the two end walls.

(6) Over the ceiling and the other side wall and parts of the two end walls.

(7) Over the floor and one side wall and parts of the two end walls.

(8) Over the floor and the other side wall and parts of the two end walls.

Denote the three dimensions of the room by l = length, w = width, and h = height. The lengths of the various paths may then be expressed:

$$Distance = l + h = 650 \text{ inches.} \qquad (1, 2)$$

$$Distance = \sqrt{160^2 + (l + w)^2} = 650 \text{ inches.} \qquad (3, 4)$$

$$Distance = \sqrt{\left(\frac{h+w}{2}+80\right)^2 + \left(l+\frac{h+w}{2}-80\right)^2}$$

$$= 650 \text{ inches.} \qquad (5, 6, 7, 8)$$

To eliminate the radical signs, we may rewrite these equations:

$$(l+h)^2 = 650^2. \qquad (1, 2)$$

$$160^2 + (l+w)^2 = 650^2. \qquad (3, 4)$$

$$\left(\frac{h+w}{2}+80\right)^2 + \left(l+\frac{h+w}{2}-80\right)^2 = 650^2. \qquad (5, 6, 7, 8)$$

From these we find:

$$l + h = 650, \qquad (I)$$

$$(l+w)^2 = 650^2 - 160^2 = 396,900 = 630^2,$$

$$l + w = 630. \qquad (II)$$

Adding (I) and (II), we have

$$2l + h + w = 1,280,$$

whence $\qquad l + \dfrac{h+w}{2} = 640.$

The third equation now yields

$$\left(\frac{h+w}{2}+80\right)^2 = 650^2 - (640-80)^2 = 650^2 - 560^2$$

$$= 108,900 = 330^2,$$

whence $\qquad h + w = 500. \qquad (III)$

From half the sum of equations (I), (II), and (III), we get

$$l + h + w = 890,$$

from which we obtain, by subtracting (III), (I), and (II) in turn,

$$l = 390, \; w = 240, \; h = 260.$$

CHAPTER TWO

ANCIENT AND CURIOUS PROBLEMS

THE first group of problems is based on selections from the two oldest collections of problems in French literature: the first, by Chuquet (1484), the other by Clavius, author of an early treatise on algebra (1608).

1. A man spends $\frac{1}{3}$ of his money and loses $\frac{2}{3}$ of the remainder. He then has 12 pieces. How much money had he at first? (Chuquet) *Answer:* 54 pieces.

2. A bolt of cloth is colored as follows: $\frac{1}{3}$ and $\frac{1}{4}$ of it are black, and the remaining 8 yards are gray. How long is the bolt? (Chuquet) *Answer:* 19.2 yards.

3. A merchant visited three fairs. At the first he doubled his money and spent $30, at the second he tripled his money and spent $54, at the third he quadrupled his money and spent $72, and then had $48 left. With how much money did he start? (Chuquet) *Answer:* $29.

4. A carpenter agrees to work under the following conditions: He is to be paid at the rate of $5.50 a day for his work, while he must pay at the rate of $6.60 a day for lost time. At the end of 30 days he is "all square," having paid out as much as he received. How many days did he work? (Chuquet) *Answer:* $16\frac{4}{11}$.

5. In order to encourage his son in the study of arithmetic, a father agrees to pay his boy 8 cents for every problem correctly solved and to fine him 5 cents for each incorrect solution. At the end of 26 problems neither owes anything to the other. How many problems did the boy solve correctly? (Clavius) *Answer:* 10.

6. If I were to give 7 cents to each of the beggars at my door, I would have 24 cents left. I lack 32 cents of being able to give them 9 cents apiece. How many beggars are there, and how much money have I? (Clavius)

Answer: 28 beggars, $2.20.

7. A servant is promised $100 and a cloak as his wages for a year. After 7 months he leaves this service, and receives the cloak and $20 as his due. How much is the cloak worth? (Clavius) *Answer:* $92.

8. Two wine merchants enter Paris, one of them with 64 casks of wine, the other with 20. Since they have not enough money to pay the customs duties, the first pays 5 casks of wine and 40 francs, and the second pays 2 casks of wine and receives 40 francs in change. What is the price of each cask of wine, and the duty on it? (Chuquet)

Answer: 110 francs, 10 francs.

Another legacy from the Middle Ages is the Greek Anthology, a collection of short poems called epigrams. A number of these epigrams are statements of mathematical problems. Here are some examples, modernized as little as possible.

9. Polycrates speaks: Blessed Pythagoras, Heliconian scion of the Muses, answer my question: How many in thy house are engaged in the contest for wisdom performing excellently? Pythagoras answers: I will tell thee then, Polycrates. Half of them are occupied with belles lettres; a quarter apply themselves to studying immortal nature; a seventh are all intent on silence and the eternal discourse of their hearts. [These were probably chess players. — M. K.] There are also three women, among whom the superior is Theano. That is the number of interpreters of the Muses I gather round me. (xiv: 1) *Answer:* 28.

10. On a statue of Pallas: I, Pallas, am of beaten gold, but the gold is the gift of lusty poets. Charisius gave half the gold, Thespis one eighth, Solon one tenth, and Themison one twentieth, but the remaining nine talents and the workmanship are the gift of Aristodicus. How many talents of gold are wrought into the statue? (xiv: 2)

Answer: 40 talents.

11. Heracles the mighty was questioning Augeas, seeking to learn the number of his herds, and Augeas replied: "About the stream of Alpheius, my friend, are the half of them; the eighth part pasture around the hill of Cronos, the twelfth part far away by the precinct of Taraxippus; the twentieth part feed in holy Elis, and I left the thirtieth part in Arcadia; but here you see the remaining fifty herds." How many herds had Augeas? (xiv: 4)   *Answer:* 240.

12. "Best of clocks, how much of the day is past?" "There remain twice two-thirds of what is gone." (xiv: 6)

Answer: $5\frac{1}{7}$ of the 12 hours into which the Greeks divided the day; $10\frac{2}{7}$ hours if the day be considered 24 hours.

13. I am a brazen lion, a fountain; my spouts are my two eyes, my mouth, and the flat of my right foot. My right eye fills a jar in two days [1 day = 12 hours], my left eye in three, and my foot in four; my mouth is capable of filling it in six hours. Tell me how long all four together will take to fill it. (xiv: 7)   *Answer:* $3\frac{33}{37}$ hours.

14. The Graces were carrying baskets of apples, and in each was the same number. The nine Muses met them and asked them for apples, and they gave the same number to each Muse, and the nine Muses and three Graces had each of them the same number. Tell me how many they gave and how they all had the same number. (xiv: 48)

Answer: The Graces had four apples in each basket, each

gave away three, so each of the twelve had one. Any multiples will do.

15. Make me a crown weighing sixty minae, mixing gold and brass, and with them tin and much-wrought iron. Let the gold and brass together form two thirds, the gold and tin together three fourths, and the gold and iron three fifths. Tell me how much gold you must put in, how much brass, how much tin, and how much iron, so as to make the whole crown weigh sixty minae. (xiv: 49)

Answer: $30\frac{1}{2}$, $9\frac{1}{2}$, $14\frac{1}{2}$, and $5\frac{1}{2}$ minae of gold, brass, tin and iron, respectively.

16. A: "I have what the second has and the third of what the third has." B: "I have what the third has and the third of what the first has." C: "And I have ten minae and the third of what the second has." How many minae each have A, B, and C? (xiv: 51)

Answer: 45, $37\frac{1}{2}$ and $22\frac{1}{2}$ minae, respectively.

17. This tomb holds Diophantus. Ah, how great a marvel! The tomb tells scientifically the measure of his life. God granted him to be a boy for the sixth part of his life, and adding a twelfth part to this, He clothed his cheeks with down; He lit him the light of wedlock after a seventh part, and five years after his marriage He granted him a son. Alas! late-born wretched child; after attaining the measure of half his father's life, chill Fate took him. After consoling his grief by this science of numbers for four years, Diophantus ended his life. (xiv: 126)   *Answer:* 84.

18. We three Loves stand here pouring out water for the bath, sending streams into the fair-flowing tank. I on the right, from my long-winged feet, fill it full in the sixth part of a day [1 day = 12 hours]; I on the left, from my jar, fill it in four hours; and I in the middle, from my bow, in just half a day. Tell me in what a short time we should fill it, pouring water from wings, bow, and jar all at once. (xiv: 135)   *Answer:* $\frac{1}{11}$ of a day.

19. A: "Give me ten minae and I become three times as much as you." B: "And if I get the same from you I am five times as much as you." How much each are A and B? (xiv: 145)   *Answer:* $15\frac{5}{7}$ and $18\frac{4}{7}$.

20. A: "Give me two minae and I become twice as much as you." B: "And if I got the same from you I am four times as much as you." How much each are A and B? (xiv: 146)
                                    Answer: $3\frac{5}{7}$ and $4\frac{6}{7}$.

The next problem has a rather interesting origin. In the Middle Ages it was quite common for teams to compete in the solution of problems. These competitions were something like the sporting events of our time. The competitors were informed beforehand of the questions to be asked. A famous match of this sort was in 1225 when the team backed by the Emperor Frederick II opposed Leonardo of Pisa (better known as Fibonacci, that is, filius Bonaccii). The latter was the author of "Liber Abaci" (1202), probably the first book in Europe to teach the use of the decimal system. "Liber Abaci" had a wide circulation, and for more than two centuries was a standard authority and a source of inspiration for numerous writers. Fibonacci's reputation was so great that the Emperor Frederick II stopped at Pisa in 1225 in order to hold this mathematical tournament to test Leonardo's skill, of which he had heard such marvelous accounts. The team of Frederick II consisted of John of Palermo and Theodore. One of the questions posed to Fibonacci was the following:

21. Find a perfect square which remains a perfect square when increased or decreased by 5.

Solution: Fibonacci found the numbers

$$(\tfrac{41}{12})^2, \ (\tfrac{41}{12})^2 - 5 = (\tfrac{31}{12})^2, \text{ and } (\tfrac{41}{12})^2 + 5 = (\tfrac{49}{12})^2.$$

More generally, to find a square which remains a square when increased or decreased by d, we have to find three squares which form an arithmetical progression with common difference d. The squares of the numbers $a^2 - 2ab - b^2$, $a^2 + b^2$, $a^2 + 2ab - b^2$ are $a^4 - 4a^3b + 2a^2b^2 + 4ab^3 + b^4$, $a^4 + 2a^2b^2 + b^4$, $a^4 + 4a^3b + 2a^2b^2 - 4ab^3 + b^4$. They form a progression with difference $d = 4a^3b - 4ab^3 = 4ab(a^2 - b^2)$. If $a = 5$ and $b = 4$, then $d = 720$, and we have the three squares $(a^2 + b^2)^2 = 41^2$, $41^2 - 720 = 31^2$, $41^2 + 720 = 49^2$. Dividing by 12^2, we have Fibonacci's solution.

From any one solution we can form infinitely many. Thus, if we take $a = 41^2 = 1,681$, $b = 720$, we have another solution, with $d = 5(24 \cdot 41 \cdot 49 \cdot 31)^2 = 11,170,580,662,080$ and $(a^2 + b^2)^2 = 11,183,412,793,921$. The three squares in arithmetical progression are then $x - 5$, x, $x + 5$, where

$$x = \left(\frac{11,183,412,793,921}{2,234,116,132,416}\right)^2.$$

It was fortunate that Frederick II did not give Fibonacci 1, 2, 3, or 4 instead of 5, for the problem would then be insoluble.

Arabian Problems

22. Divide 10 into two parts in such a manner that if we add to each part its square root and form the product of the resulting sums, we obtain a given number.

Answer: If you are fortunate, you will be required to divide 10 as specified when the given number is 24. If the given number is anything else, you will find that plotting a curve is the simplest way to tackle the problem.

23. If a square be increased or decreased by 10, we shall have a perfect square. What is this number?

24. Find a cube which is the sum of two cubes.

25. Express 10 as the sum of two numbers in such a way that if each of them is divided by the other and the resulting quotients are added, the final sum is equal to one of the two original numbers.

26. Find three terms in continuous proportion whose sum is a square.

27. Find a square which remains a square when it is increased by 2, and when it is decreased by 2 plus its square root.

The author (Beha Eddin Mohammed ben al Hosain al Aamouli, 1547–1622) who collected these Arab problems remarks that the answers to them are not known to the learned persons of his time. In fact, some are impossible. For instance, the impossibility of No. 24 was proved by Euler. It is one case of the famous Fermat theorem: The equation $a^n + b^n = c^n$ has no solutions in integers if n is an integer greater than 2. Others were solved by Euler, while still others lead to equations of higher degree than the first which have no positive rational solutions.

28. THE PROBLEM OF THE PANDECTS. A hungry hunter came upon two shepherds, one of whom had 3 small loaves of bread, and the other 5, all of the same size. The loaves were divided equally among the three, and the hunter paid 8 cents for his share. How should the shepherds divide the money? *Answer:* 1 and 7.

There are many variants of this problem. The following (taken from an assortment in *Unterrichtsblätter für Mathematik und Naturwissenschaften*, xi, pp. 81–85), is probably the version which gave the problem its name:

29. For their common meal Caius provided 7 dishes and

Sempronius 8. But Titus arrived unexpectedly, so all shared the food equally. Titus paid Caius 14 denarii and Sempronius 16. The latter cried out against this division, and the matter was referred to a judge. What should his decision be, granting that the 30 denarii is the correct total amount.

> *Answer:* 12 denarii to Caius and 18 to Sempronius.

30. The Problem of Inheritance. A group of heirs divide their heritage as follows: The first takes a dollars and the nth part of the remainder, the second takes $2a$ dollars and the nth part of the remainder, and so on, each succeeding heir taking a dollars more than his predecessor and an nth part of the new remainder. In this manner the heritage is divided into equal parts. How many heirs are there, and how much does each receive? (This problem is attributed to Euler, but is found in Chuquet.)

Solution: There are many methods of solution for this problem, of which the following is perhaps the simplest. Let x be the whole heritage, y the portion of each heir. The first heir receives

$$a + \frac{x - a}{n};$$

the second receives

$$2a + \frac{1}{n}\left[x - \left(a + \frac{x - a}{n} \right) - 2a \right].$$

Setting these quantities equal to each other we find $x = (n - 1)^2 a$, $y = (n - 1) a$, from which the number of heirs is $x \div y = n - 1$.

Reapportionment by Decanting

31. The contents of a cask containing 8 quarts of wine is to be divided nto two equal parts, using only the cask and two empty jugs with capacities of 5 quarts and 3 quarts respectively.

Solution: The successive steps in the solution are given in the table below which lists the contents of each container at each stage. There are many variants of this problem.

Vessel	Amount of wine in each vessel, by stages							
	1	2	3	4	5	6	7	8
8-quart cask...........	8	3	3	6	6	1	1	4
5-quart jug.............	0	5	2	2	0	5	4	4
3-quart jug............	0	0	3	0	2	2	3	0

32. Three jars contain 19, 13, and 7 quarts, respectively. The first is empty, the others full. How can one measure out 10 quarts, using no other vessels?

Solution:

Jar	Amount of wine in each jar, by stages							
	1	2	3	4	5	6	7	8
19-quart	0	7	19	12	12	5	5	18
13-quart	13	13	1	1	8	8	13	0
7-quart	7	0	0	7	0	7	2	2

Jar	Amount of wine in each jar, by stages							
	9	10	11	12	13	14	15	16
19-quart	18	11	11	4	4	17	17	10
13-quart	2	2	9	9	13	0	3	3
7-quart	0	7	0	7	3	3	0	7

33. Three persons are to divide among themselves 21 equal casks, of which 7 are full, 7 are half full and 7 are empty. How can an equable division be made without pouring the wine from any casks into others in such a way that each person receives the same amount of wine and the same number of whole casks?

Answer: Either (2, 3, 2), (2, 3, 2), (3, 1, 3) or (3, 1, 3), (3, 1, 3), (1, 5, 1).

34. A slightly more difficult problem of the same nature as the foregoing is: A farmer leaves 45 casks of wine, of which 9 each are full, three quarters full, half full, one quarter full, and empty. His five nephews want to divide the wine and the casks without changing wine from cask to cask in such a way that each receives the same amount of wine and the same number of casks, and further so that each receives at least one of each kind of cask, and no two of them receive the same number of every kind of cask.

Solution: Each nephew must have nine casks and $\frac{1}{5} \times [9 + (9 \times 2) + (9 \times 3) + (9 \times 4)] = 18$ quarter casks of wine. Designate by x, y, z, t, u the respective numbers of each kind of cask which any one nephew might receive. Then we must have

$$4x + 3y + 2z + t = 18,$$
$$x + y + z + t + u = 9.$$

If we exclude all zero values we have the eight following solutions of these equations:

Solution	x	y	z	t	u
1	3	1	1	1	3
2	2	1	2	3	1
3	2	1	3	1	2
4	2	2	1	2	2
5	1	1	5	1	1
6	1	2	3	2	1
7	1	3	1	3	1
8	1	3	2	1	2

Any one of these eight solutions would satisfy any one of the nephews under the conditions of the will. But for the five nephews we need five of the solutions, one for each. And furthermore, we have only 9 of the full barrels (that is to say, $9x$), 9 of the y barrels, and so on. Hence the nephews must chose their assortments in such a way that all of their x's will be exactly 9, all of their y's also 9, and so on.

Solution 5, therefore, cannot be used. If we give one nephew 5 of the z barrels, there is no way in which we could give the other 4 nephews each a single z barrel. So we cross out solution 5, since we cannot use it. Then the sums of the successive columns are 12, 13, 13, 13, 12, so we must subtract 3, 4, 4, 4, 3 respectively. Thus we must omit two solutions for which the sums in the columns are 3, 4, 4, 4, 3.

Solution 1 cannot be eliminated. On the other hand, solutions 2 and 8, 3 and 7, 4 and 6 give these sums, so we have three fundamental sets of five solutions, each of which gives $5! = 120$ permutations among the five nephews:

$$(1, 3, 4, 6, 7), (1, 2, 4, 6, 8), \text{ and } (1, 2, 3, 7, 8).$$

Hindu Problems

35. Three men who had a monkey bought a pile of mangoes. At night one of the men came to the pile of mangoes while the others slept and, finding that there was just one more mango than could be divided exactly by three, tossed the extra mango to the monkey and took away one third of the remainder. Then he went back to sleep. Presently another of them awoke and went to the pile of mangoes. He also found just one too many to be divided evenly by three, so he tossed the extra one to the monkey, took one third of the remainder, and returned to sleep. After a while the third rose also, and he too gave one mango to the monkey and took away the number of whole mangoes which represented precisely one third of the rest.

Next morning the men got up and went to the pile. Again they found just one too many, so they gave one to the monkey and divided the rest evenly. What is the least number of mangoes with which this can be done?   *Answer:* 79.

36. Three travelers came to a tavern and ordered a dish of potatoes. When the landlord brought in the potatoes the men were all asleep. The first of the travelers to wake up ate a third of the potatoes and went back to sleep without disturbing his companions. Then another awoke and, not realizing that one of his companions had already eaten, ate a third of those that he found, and went to sleep again. Finally the third man did the same, eating a third of the potatoes that were there and going back to sleep. When the landlord came to clean the table he found 8 potatoes. How many had he prepared?   *Answer:* 27.

37. Three men play a game with the understanding that the loser is to double the money of each of the other two. After three games each has lost just once and each ends up with $24. With how much did each one start?

Answer: $39, $21, $12.

38. In an effort to equalize the wealth of all the citizens of a certain country, its government decreed that the richest man must double the wealth of every other citizen. But when this had been done it was found that only the *owners* of the n fortunes had been changed, not their *amounts*. What were the various fortunes?   (Meuris)

Answer: $a, 2a, \cdots, 2^{n-1}a$.

39. While three watchmen were guarding an orchard a thief slipped in and stole some apples. On his way out he met the three watchmen one after the other, and to each in turn he gave a half of the apples he then had, and two besides. Thus he managed to escape with one apple. How many had he stolen originally?   *Answer:* 36.

40. Three dealers in adjacent stalls at a market were selling apples of identical quality, so they had to keep their prices equal. At the end of the day Mr. Pappas had sold 10 apples, Mr. Gatta 25, and Mrs. Murphy 30, yet all had taken in the same total. How much did they charge, and how much did they take in? (After Ozanam, 1741)

Answer: The problem is possible only if the price was changed in the course of the day. Assuming just one price change, these are the ten possible basic solutions:

Solution No.	Dealer	Sales at first price			Sales at second price			Total, each dealer, cents
		No. sold	Price, cents	Amount	No. sold	Price, cents	Amount	
1	Pappas	4		24	6		6	
	Gatta	1	6	6	24	1	24	30
	Murphy	0		0	30		30	
2	Pappas	5		30	5		5	
	Gatta	2	6	12	23	1	23	35
	Murphy	1		6	29		29	
3	Pappas	6		36	4		4	
	Gatta	3	6	18	22	1	22	40
	Murphy	2		12	28		28	
4	Pappas	7		42	3		3	
	Gatta	4	6	24	21	1	21	45
	Murphy	3		18	27		27	
5	Pappas	8		48	2		2	
	Gatta	5	6	30	20	1	20	50
	Murphy	4		24	26		26	
6	Pappas	9		54	1		1	
	Gatta	6	6	36	19	1	19	55
	Murphy	5		30	25		25	

Solution No.	Dealer	Sales at first price			Sales at second price			Total, each dealer, cents
		No. sold	Price, cents	Amount	No. sold	Price, cents	Amount	
7	Pappas	10		60	0		0	
	Gatta	7	6	42	18	1	18	60
	Murphy	6		36	24		24	
8	Pappas	8		56	2		4	
	Gatta	2	7	14	23	2	46	60
	Murphy	0		0	30		60	
9	Pappas	9		63	1		2	
	Gatta	3	7	21	22	2	44	65
	Murphy	1		7	29		58	
10	Pappas	10		70	0		0	
	Gatta	4	7	28	21	2	42	70
	Murphy	2		14	28		56	

41. IMITATION PUNISHED. Two market-women were selling apples, one at 2 for 1 cent and the other at 3 for 2 cents. They had 30 apples apiece. In order to end their competition they formed a trust, pooling their stocks and selling the apples at 5 for 3 cents. This was to their advantage since under the new arrangement they took in a total of 36 cents, while under the old system they would have received a total of only 35 cents.

Their example was contagious. Two other women, who also had 30 apples apiece and who were selling them at 2 for 1 cent and 3 for 1 cent, formed a trust to sell their apples at 5 for 2 cents. But instead of the total of 25 cents which they would have taken in operating separate enterprises, their trust grossed only 24 cents. Why?

Solution: Let $\frac{b}{a}$ and $\frac{d}{c}$ be the original selling prices, and assume $\frac{b}{a}$ greater than or equal to $\frac{d}{c}$. The average price is then

$$\frac{1}{2}\left(\frac{b}{a} + \frac{d}{c}\right) = \frac{bc + ad}{2ac}.$$

But the trusts set the price

$$\frac{b + d}{a + c}.$$

The trust price will be advantageous only if

$$\frac{b + d}{a + c} > \frac{bc + ad}{2\,ac},$$

that is (after simplifications), only if

$$(bc - ad)(a - c) > 0.$$

This condition requires that both factors be positive. The expression $bc - ad > 0$ is equivalent to $\frac{b}{a} > \frac{d}{c}$, and this combined with $a - c > 0$ tells us that the trust will be advantageous only if the original prices are unequal and the denominator of the higher price is greater than that of the lower price.

It is interesting to note that when the trust price is computed by the formula

$$\frac{b + d}{a + c},$$

then whether the result of the operation is a profit or a loss depends, not upon the *values* of the differing original prices, but upon the *form* of their expression. If, as in the case above,

$$\frac{b}{a} > \frac{d}{c} \qquad \text{and} \qquad a > c,$$

so that the formation of a trust and the sale of its merchandise at the price

$$\frac{b + d}{a + c}$$

is advantageous, the advantage is lost if the second price is stated in the form $\frac{nd}{nc}$, where n is chosen so large that $a > nc$. In sum, it may be said that the formula which by chance or accident fits both the presently considered trust prices is a wholly unsound one.

42. Four men, Peter and Paul and their sons Tom and Dick, buy books. When their purchases are completed it turns out that each man has paid for each of his books a number of dollars equal to the number of books he has bought. Each family (father and son) has spent $65. Peter has bought 1 more book than Tom, and Dick has bought only 1 book. Who is Dick's father?

Solution: Let x be the number and price of the books bought by a father, y the number and price of the books bought by his son. Then, in each case, $x^2 + y^2 = 65$, since each person who bought x books paid x dollars per book, and each person who bought y books paid y dollars per book. Assuming that the number of books bought is a whole number, we have the possibility that $x = 8$, $y = 1$; $x = 7$, $y = 4$; $x = 4$, $y = 7$; $x = 1$, $y = 8$. This is as much as to say that since Dick bought 1 book, Dick's father is the man who bought 8 books. This same man who bought 8 books obviously bought 1 more book than whoever bought 7 books; Peter, we were told, bought 1 more book than Tom; then it must be Peter who bought 8 books, and accordingly Peter is Dick's father.

43. Three men — Arthur, Bernard, and Charles — with their wives — Ann, Barbara, and Cynthia — make some purchases. When their shopping is finished each finds that the average cost in dollars of the articles he or she has purchased is equal to the number of his or her purchases. Arthur has bought 23 more articles than Barbara, and Bernard has bought 11 more than Ann. Each husband has spent $63 more than his wife. Who is the husband of whom?

Answer: Arthur and Cynthia, Bernard and Barbara, Charles and Ann.

44. Every day at noon a ship leaves New York for Lisbon, and at the same instant a ship leaves Lisbon for New York. Each trip lasts exactly 192 hours, or 8 days. How many ships from Lisbon will each ship from New York meet?

Solution: A ship leaving New York on the 15th will meet at the dock the ship which left Lisbon on the 7th, and will meet all the west-bound ships thereafter until it meets in the dock at Lisbon the ship which is leaving for New York on the 23rd. Thus the east-bound ship meets 17 west-bound ships.

The solution may be found graphically with ease.

45. A double-track trolley line runs between two stations 6 miles apart. From each station cars set out for the other station every 3 minutes and proceed at uniform speed. A pedestrian leaves one station just as one car is arriving and another leaving. He walks beside the right-of-way at constant speed until he reaches the other station just as one car is arriving and another leaving. Including these 4, he saw 62 cars on his way, 19 going in the same direction and 43 in the opposite direction. What was his speed, and what was the speed of the cars? *Answer:* 4 and 10 miles per hour.

46. Stations A and B are 120 miles apart on a single-track railroad. At the same instant that a train leaves A for B at 25 miles an hour, a train leaves B for A at 15 miles an hour. Just as the first train leaves A, a fly flies from the front of the engine straight toward the other train at 100 miles an hour. On meeting the second train it immediately turns back and flies straight for the first train. So it continues to fly back and forth with undiminished speed until it is crushed in the eventual collision. How far had this marvelous fly flown before it met its glorious end?

Answer: The trains met after $\dfrac{120}{25 + 15} = 3$ hours, so the fly flew 300 miles.

47. Two pedestrians walk along the same road in the same direction. The first, walking at 4 miles an hour, starts out 8 miles in advance of the second, who walks at 6 miles an hour. As they start, the dog of one of them leaves his master and sets off for the other man at 15 miles an hour. As soon as he reaches the second man, the dog returns at once to his master, and so he continues to run back and forth until the second man overtakes the first. How far did the dog travel?

Answer: 60 miles.

48. Suppose the earth were a perfect sphere 25,000 miles in circumference, and suppose it possible to erect a telephone line on poles about the equator. Assuming that the telephone wire would then form a circle concentric with the equator, would a man be able to crawl under the wire without touching it if the total length of the wire exceeded the circumference of the earth by only 100 feet?

Answer: Easily, for the difference in diameter of the two circles would be the difference of their circumferences divided by π, or about 32 feet. Thus the poles would be about 16 feet high.

49. I have no watch, but I have an excellent clock, which I occasionally forget to wind. Once when this happened I went to the house of a friend, passed the evening in listening to the radio concert program, and went back and set my clock. How could I do this without knowing beforehand the length of the trip?

Solution: Before leaving my house I started my clock,

without bothering to set it, and I noted the exact moment A of my departure according to its reading. At my friend's house I noted the exact times, h and k, of my arrival and departure by his clock. On returning I noted the time B of my arrival according to my clock. The length of my absence was $B - A$. Of that time $k - h$ minutes were spent with my friend, so the time spent in traveling, t in each direction, was $2t = (B - A) - (k - h)$. Thus the correct time when I reached home was $k + t$.

50. I am going hunting and wish to take my gun with me on the train. The ticket agent tells me I may not take it in the coach, while the baggage man will not take it because of its excessive length (1.7 yards), since he is forbidden to accept for shipment any article whose greatest dimension exceeds 1 yard. What should I do?

Answer: Pack it diagonally in a cubic case 1 yard on a side. The length of the diagonal is $\sqrt{3} = 1.73^+$ yards.

51. A large furniture store sells 6 kinds of dining-room suites, whose prices are \$231, \$273, \$429, \$600.60, \$1,001, and \$1,501.50, respectively. Once a South American buyer came, purchased some of each kind of suite, paid the total amount due, \$13,519.90, and sailed for South America. The manager lost the duplicate bill of sale and had no other memorandum of each kind of suite purchased. Can you help him fill the order correctly? (Tarry)

Solution: Let x, y, z, t, u, v be the respective numbers of each kind of suite purchased. Then $2{,}310x + 2{,}730y + 4{,}290z + 6{,}006t + 10{,}010u + 15{,}015v = 135{,}199$. This equation can be solved most readily by congruences. With reference to the moduli m, we must have

$$9x \equiv 12 \quad (m = 13), \quad x \equiv 10.$$
$$2y \equiv 9 \quad (m = 11), \quad y \equiv 10.$$
$$6z \equiv 1 \quad (m = 7), \quad z \equiv 6.$$

$$t \equiv 4 \quad (m = 5), \quad t \equiv 4.$$
$$2u \equiv 1 \quad (m = 3), \quad u \equiv 2.$$
$$v \equiv 1 \quad (m = 2), \quad v \equiv 1.$$

Precisely the values $x = 10, y = 10, z = 6, t = 4, u = 2, v = 1$ give the desired result.

52. The water lentil reproduces by dividing into 2 every day. Thus on the first day we have 1, on the second 2, on the third 4, on the fourth 8, and so on. If, starting with one lentil, it takes 30 days to cover a certain area, how long will it take to cover the same area if we start with 2 lentils?

Answer: 29 days. For on the second day we actually begin with 2.

53. Two steamers simultaneously leave New York for Lisbon, where they spend 5 days before returning to New York. The first makes 30 miles an hour going and 40 miles an hour returning. The second makes 35 miles an hour each way. Which steamer gets back first?

Answer: The second, because $\left(\dfrac{x}{30} + \dfrac{x}{40}\right) > \dfrac{2x}{35}$.

54. A grocer attempts to weigh out identical amounts of sugar to two customers, but his scales are false. The first time he puts the weight in one pan and the sugar in the other, the second time he reverses the procedure. Does he gain or lose?

Answer: He loses. Let a and b be the unequal lengths of the arms of the scale, x the fixed weight, and y and z the amounts of sugar weighed out. Then $ax = by$ and $bx = az$, so the weight of the sugar dispensed is $\left(\dfrac{a}{b} + \dfrac{b}{a}\right)x$, which is greater than $2x$. For $\dfrac{a}{b} + \dfrac{b}{a} > 2$, $a^2 - 2ab + b^2 > 0$, and $(a - b)^2 > 0$ are equivalent statements when a and b are distinct positive quantities.

55. I am twice the age that you were when I was your age. When you get to be my age our ages will total 63 years. How old are we? *Answer:* 28 and 21.

56. The value of the expression

$$\left(x^4 + x^3 + x^2 + x + 1 + \frac{2}{x-1}\right)\left(x^4 - x^3 + x^2 - x + 1 - \frac{2}{x+1}\right)$$

will not be changed if we suppress the two fractions. Why?

Solution: If we write each factor as a fraction, the expression becomes

$$\frac{x^5 + 1}{x - 1} \cdot \frac{x^5 - 1}{x + 1},$$

which may be written,

$$\frac{x^5 - 1}{x - 1} \cdot \frac{x^5 + 1}{x + 1} = (x^4 + x^3 + x^2 + x + 1)(x^4 - x^3 + x^2 - x + 1).$$

Thus the suppression of the fractions changes the value of the factors but not of their product.

Here are three other cases where wrong operations lead to right results:

A high-school girl had to divide $a^2 - b^2$ by $a - b$. She said: "a^2 divided by a gives me a, minus divided by minus gives me plus, b^2 divided by b gives me b. So I get $a + b$." A president of the American Mathematical Society could not have found a more correct result.

An inattentive boy who was asked to simplify the fractions $\frac{16}{64}$, $\frac{26}{65}$, $\frac{19}{95}$, $\frac{49}{98}$, simply canceled the common digits in numerators and denominators and obtained the right answers, $\frac{1}{4}$, $\frac{2}{5}$, $\frac{1}{5}$, $\frac{4}{8}$.

A lazy student had to solve the simultaneous equations

$$\frac{x-2}{y-1} = \frac{3}{5} \quad \text{and} \quad \frac{x-1}{y-2} = 1.$$

He disregarded the second equation and solved the first by the following steps:

$$\frac{x-2}{y-1} = \frac{3}{5} \quad \text{gives} \quad \frac{x}{y} - \frac{2}{1} = \frac{3}{5};$$

then
$$\frac{x}{y} = \frac{2}{1} + \frac{3}{5} = \frac{2+3}{1+5} = \frac{5}{6},$$

so $x = 5$ and $y = 6$. These values satisfy both of the given equations, so the problem is solved. Can you blame him for his answer?

57. THE FALSE COIN. See page 324.

CHAPTER THREE

NUMERICAL PASTIMES

WRITE each of the numbers 1 and 100, using each of the ten digits just once.

Solution: $1 = \frac{35}{70} + \frac{148}{296}$, $100 = 50 + 49 + \frac{1}{2} + \frac{38}{76}$.

Write 31 using only the digit 3 five times.

Solution: $31 = 3^3 + 3 + \frac{3}{3}$.

These problems are freakish, for their solution rests on no general principle. They should really be classed as puzzles. We have put them here only in order to give point to our protest against their inclusion in an honest collection, so we have not dignified them by giving them numbers.

1. MISCELLANEOUS PROBLEMS

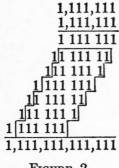

```
  1,111,111
  1,111,111
  1 111 111
 1 1 111 11
 1 11 111 1
 1 111 111
 1 1 111 11
 1 11 111 1
1 111 111
1,111,111,111,111
```

FIGURE 2.

1. Explain the identity $1,111,111^2 - (10 \times 111,111^2) = 1,111,111,111,111$.

Answer: Write out the multiplication of the first term as in Figure 2, but do not add up the partial products. The terms which are here enclosed clearly represent the product $10 \times 111,111^2$. When these have been deleted, the remaining digits represent precisely the number $1,111,111,111,111$.

2. Find four numbers such that the product of any two of them is one less than a perfect square. (Diophantus)

Solution (by Boije af Gennas): Let a, b, c, and d be the desired numbers. There are six possible products of any two of these, namely, *ab, ac, ad, bc, bd, cd.* Then if *m* and *n* are any arbitrary integers, the requirement can be stated:

$a = m,$
$b = n(mn + 2),$
$c = (n + 1)(mn + m + 2),$
$d = 4(mn + 1)(mn + m + 1)(mn^2 + mn + 2n + 1);$

$ab + 1 = (mn + 1)^2,$
$ac + 1 = (mn + m + 1)^2,$
$ad + 1 = (2m^2n^2 + 2m^2n + 4mn + 2m + 1)^2,$
$bc + 1 = (mn^2 + mn + 2n + 1)^2,$
$bd + 1 = (2m^2n^3 + 2m^2n^2 + 6mn^2 + 4mn + 4n + 1)^2,$
$cd + 1 = (2m^2n^3 + 4m^2n^2 + 6mn^2 + 2m^2n$
$$+ 8mn + 4n + 2m + 3)^2.$$

Values for *m* and *n* may be any integers. For example, $m = 2$ and $n = 1$ yield $a = 2,\ b = 4,\ c = 12,\ d = 420,\ ab + 1 = 3^2,$ $ac + 1 = 5^2,\quad ad + 1 = 29^2,\quad bc + 1 = 7^2,\quad bd + 1 = 41^2,$ $cd + 1 = 71^2.$

3. A triangular number (see p. 67) is a positive integer expressible in terms of a positive integer x in the form $\dfrac{x(x + 1)}{2}$. Find a triangular number which is the sum of the squares of two consecutive odd numbers.

Solution: We must have

$$\frac{x(x + 1)}{2} = (2y - 1)^2 + (2y + 1)^2 = 8y^2 + 2.$$

Multiplying by 8 and adding 1,

$$(2x + 1)^2 = 64y^2 + 17, \qquad \text{or} \qquad (2x + 1)^2 - 64y^2 = 17.$$

Thus we must satisfy the simultaneous equations

$$2x + 8y + 1 = 17,$$
$$2x - 8y + 1 = 1,$$

whence $x = 4$, $y = 1$. The desired number is

$$\frac{4 \cdot 5}{2} = 10 = 1^2 + 3^2.$$

4. Find a set of numbers when the product of each by the sum of all the others is known. For example, find six numbers x, y, z, t, u, v, being given

$$
\begin{aligned}
x(y + z + t + u + v) &= \ \ \ 264, \\
y(x + z + t + u + v) &= \ \ \ 325, \\
z(x + y + t + u + v) &= \ \ \ 549, \\
t(x + y + z + u + v) &= \ \ \ 825, \\
u(x + y + z + t \ + v) &= \ \ \ 901, \\
v(x + y + z + t \ + u) &= 1{,}000.
\end{aligned}
$$

Solution: Note that in each equation the sum of the two factors on the left is the sum of all the unknowns. Hence we must express each number on the right as the product of two factors in such a way that the sums of the pairs of factors are all equal. Below are given the possible decompositions of each of the given numbers into products of two factors. The pairs in boldface type are those which satisfy the requirement. Thus we find $x = 4$, $y = 5$, $z = 9$, $t = 15$, $u = 17$, $z = 20$.

$$
\begin{aligned}
264 &= 1 \times 264 \ \ = 2 \times 132 \ \ = 3 \times 88 \ \ = \mathbf{4 \times 66} = 6 \times 44 \\
&= 8 \times 33 \ \ \ \ = 11 \times 24 \ \ = 12 \times 22, \\
325 &= 1 \times 325 \ \ = \mathbf{5 \times 65} \ \ = 13 \times 25, \\
549 &= 1 \times 549 \ \ = 3 \times 183 \ \ = \mathbf{9 \times 61}, \\
825 &= 1 \times 825 \ \ = 3 \times 275 \ \ = 5 \times 165 \ \ = 11 \times 75 \\
&= \mathbf{15 \times 55} \ \ = 25 \times 33, \\
901 &= 1 \times 901 \ \ = \mathbf{17 \times 53}, \\
1{,}000 &= 1 \times 1{,}000 = 2 \times 500 \ \ = 4 \times 250 \ \ = 5 \times 200 \\
&= 8 \times 125 \ \ = 10 \times 100 = \mathbf{20 \times 50} \ \ = 25 \times 40.
\end{aligned}
$$

5. Find a four-digit number of the form $a{,}abb$ which is a perfect square. *Answer:* $7{,}744 = 88^2$.

Mr. Thebault generalized this question and proved that if the base of the notation (see p. 51) is B ($B > 4$), then the square of the number represented by cc is represented by $a,a44$ when $c = B - 2$, and $a = B - 3$.

6. Find a four-digit perfect square whose first two digits and last two digits each represent squares.

Answer: $1,681 = 41^2$, and also the squares of 40, 50, 60, 70, 80, 90.

7. Find a four-digit square which is the square of the sum of the numbers represented by its first two and last two digits.   *Answer:* 2,025, 3,025, 9,801.

8. Find a square represented by four even digits.
                               Answer: The squares of 68, 78, 80, 92.

9. Find a number equal to the cube of the sum of its digits.   *Answer:* $4,913 = 17^3$ and $5,832 = 18^3$.

10. Find a six-digit square such that the numbers represented by its first three digits and its last three digits are consecutive.

Solution: Let N be the desired number, x the number represented by one set of three digits, $x + 1$ the number represented by the other three. Then $N = 1,000x + (x + 1) = 1,001x + 1$, or $N = 1,000 (x + 1) + x = 1,001x + 1,000$. Now $1,001 = 7 \cdot 11 \cdot 13$. This shows at once that the second case is impossible since N would then leave the remainder 6 when divided by 7, and such a number cannot be a square. It also shows that in the first case N leaves the remainder 1 when divided by 7, 11, or 13. Thus N must be the square of a number y satisfying the congruences $y^2 \equiv 1$ ($m = 7, 11,$ and 13). Hence $y \equiv \pm 1$ for each modulus, so $y \equiv \pm 286 \pm 364 \pm 77$ ($m = 1,001$), the double signs being independent. Of the eight positive solutions less than 1,001, just four are such that their squares are six-digit numbers. These give

$428^2 = 183,184,\quad 573^2 = 328,329,\quad 727^2 = 528,529,\quad 846^2 = 715,716.$

11. The corresponding problem for four-digit and eight-digit numbers. (Hint: 101 is a prime, and $10,001 = 73 \cdot 137$, both of which are primes.)

Answers: $91^2 = 8,281,\quad 7,810^2 = 60,996,100,\quad 9,079^2 = 82,428,241,\quad 9,901^2 = 98,029,801.$

12. Find a number such that each digit except zero appears just once in the number and its square. (Thebault)

Solution: If x is the unknown number, then $(x + x^2) \equiv 0$ $(m = 9)$, since the sum of the nine digits is 45. There are two solutions of this congruence which satisfy the other requirements of the problem: $567^2 = 321,489$ and $854^2 = 729,316.$

13. Find a number N which yields given remainders when divided by certain given divisors.

Solution: Let $p, q, r, \cdots$ be the given divisors, which we assume to be prime to each other, and let $a, b, c, \cdots$ be the corresponding remainders. The number $M = pqr \cdots$ is divisible by every divisor, and each of the numbers $P = qr \cdots$, $Q = pr \cdots$, $R = pqs \cdots$, and so on, is divisible by every divisor but one. We must find a convenient multiple gP of P which yields the remainder 1 on division by p. Similarly we must find a convenient multiple hQ of Q which yields the remainder 1 on division by q, and so on. Then $N = gPa + hQb + \cdots \pm$ any multiple of M.

For example, an unknown number gives the remainders 4, 5, and 6 on division by 7, 11, and 13 respectively. Then $gP = 5(11 \cdot 13) = 715$, $hQ = 4(7 \cdot 13) = 364$, $kR = 12(7 \cdot 11) = 924$, so $N = 715 \cdot 4 + 364 \cdot 5 + 924 \cdot 6 \pm (n \cdot 1,001) = 10,224 \pm n \cdot 1,001 = 214,\ 1,215$, and so on.

14. I count the lines of a page of my book. Counting by

threes I find a remainder 2, by fives a remainder 2, by sevens a remainder 5. How many lines are there on the page?

Answer: 47.

15. Write the sequence of numbers one after the other in their natural order without separating them, as though one were writing a single number: 1234567891011121314 15····. Find what digit occupies a given position, say the millionth.

Solution: In the given sequence,

> the 1-digit numbers occupy the first 9 places;
> the 1- and 2-digit numbers occupy the first
> $9 + 2 \cdot 90 = 189$ places;
> the 1-, 2-, and 3-digit numbers occupy the first
> $189 + 3 \cdot 900 = 2{,}889$ places.

Proceeding thus, we find:

> numbers of from 1 to 4 digits occupy the first
>   38,889 places,
> numbers of from 1 to 5 digits occupy the first
>   488,889 places,
> numbers of from 1 to 6 digits occupy the first
>   5,888,889 places,
> numbers of from 1 to 7 digits occupy the first
>   68,888,889 places,

and so on.

Now the millionth digit is between the 488,889th place and the 5,888,889th place, hence it occupies the $(1{,}000{,}000 - 488{,}889)$th place, that is, it is in the 511,111th place among the 6-digit numbers. Dividing by 6 we get the quotient 85,185 and the remainder 1, so the desired digit occupies the first place in the 85,186th 6-digit number. Since the first 6-digit number is 100,000, the 85,186th is 185,185, whose first digit is 1, the required number.

16. How many pieces of type does a printer need in order to set up the page numbers of a 288-page book if he does not use any piece twice? *Answer:* 756.

17. Under the conditions of problem 16, how many pages are there in a book in which 15,321 pieces of type have been used to number the pages? *Answer:* 4,107.

18. With the digits 1, 2, 3, 4, 5 we can form $5! = 120$ numbers of 5 digits each, no one of which has any digit repeated. What is the sum of these numbers?

Solution: When the numbers have been arranged one below the other in order to add them, we find that each column contains the same digits as every other, though in a different order, and each column contains each of the five digits equally often, that is, $\frac{120}{5} = 24$ times apiece. Thus the sum of the digits in each column is $(1 + 2 + 3 + 4 + 5)24 = 15 \cdot 24 = 360$. When these sums are added *in their proper positions*, we get $11,111 \times 360 = 3,999,960$.

$$
\begin{array}{r}
\text{ten thousands} \quad \text{thousands} \quad \text{hundreds} \quad \text{tens} \quad \text{units} \\
3\;6\;0 \\
3\;6\;0 \\
3\;6\;0 \\
3\;6\;0 \\
3\;6\;0 \\
\hline
3,9\,9\,9,9\,6\,0
\end{array}
$$

19. Perfect Squares. Set $10^n - 1 = 9a = b - 1$, and $c = 8a + 1$. The following expressions are then perfect squares:

(1) $4ab + c = 4a(9a + 1) + 8a + 1 = (6a + 1)^2 = 66 \cdots 7^2 = 444 \cdots 888 \cdots 9$.

(2) $(a - 1)b + c = 9a^2 = (333 \cdots 333)^2 = 111 \cdots 0888 \cdots 9$.

(3) $16ab + c = 16a(9a + 1) + 8a + 1 = (12a + 1)^2 = (133\cdots3)^2 = 177\cdots688\cdots9$.

(4) $(25a + 3)b + c = (15a + 2)^2 = (166 \cdots 7)^2 = 277\cdots888\cdots9$.

2. SCALES OF NOTATION

We are so used to our decimal system of notation that we may not realize that it is possible to use positional systems based on other scales than ten. Yet it is easy to generalize the notions and rules which are the basis of our notations for numbers and for arithmetical calculations with them. Furthermore, in some cases our decimal system is not the most useful. Let us examine other scales.

If B units of any order form one unit of the next higher order, then B is the base of the scale of notation. In order to be able to write all numbers in the scale of notation with the base B we need $B - 1$ digits for the numbers 1, 2, 3, $\cdots$, $B - 1$, and the digit 0 (which is to have the same function as in the decimal system). Also we shall agree that of two digits written side by side, the one to the left indicates the number of units of order next higher than that referred to by the right-hand digit.

The use of negative digits in a positional system is little known, in spite of their utility in certain cases. In the notation of any number by the base B, any digit F which is greater than or equal to $\dfrac{B}{2}$ may be replaced by $-(B - F)$ provided the digit to its left be increased by one. Such a negative digit may be denoted by placing a minus sign ($^-$) directly over the symbol for the corresponding positive digit. Thus, for example, in the decimal system, $16 = 2\overline{4}$ (that is, 2 tens minus 4 units), $142{,}857 = 143{,}\overline{143}$, and so on.

We first give some properties of numbers which hold in all scales of notation.

1. 121 represents a perfect square in every scale with base $B > 2$. (B cannot $= 2$, since 2 is not one of the digits in the scale with base 2.)

Proof: 121 represents $B^2 + 2B + 1 = (B+1)^2$, which is represented by 11^2.

2. Similarly, 1,331 represents a perfect cube in every scale with base $B > 3$; 14,641 represents a perfect 4th power for $B > 6$, and so on.

3. The number 40,001 is divisible by 221 and by $2\bar{2}1$ in every scale having $B > 4$.

Proof: 40,001 represents

$$4B^4 + 1 = (2B^2 + 2B + 1)(2B^2 - 2B + 1),$$

and the factors are represented by 221 and $2\bar{2}1$, respectively.

In the binary scale, every number is represented as a sum of powers of 2 (including $2^0 = 1$), and the digits are 0 and 1. Thus the number six is written 110, eleven is written 1,011, one hundred is written 1,100,100, and so on. Or we may use negative digits, as in $1,0\bar{1}0$ for six, $1,1\bar{1}1$ for eleven, and so on.

In the ternary scale every number is expressed as a sum or difference of powers of 3, using the digits 0, 1, $\bar{1}$. Thus sixteen (Arabic decimal) may be denoted by $121 = 1\bar{1}\bar{1}1$.

A very well-known medieval problem whose solution may be found by using the ternary scale is the following:

4. Find the least number of standard weights needed to weigh every whole number of pounds from 1 to 40. (It is understood that the weighing machine is the simple equal-arm balance.)

Solution: Bachet de Méziriac gave the two following solutions:

Weights of 1, 2, 4, 8, 16 and 32 pounds, totaling 63 pounds.
Weights of 1, 3, 9, 27 pounds, totaling 40 pounds.

If the standard weights may be placed in one scale pan only, the first set alone gives the answer. For every number from 1 to 40 can be represented as a sum of multiples by 0 or 1 of the successive powers of 2 from the 0th (= 1) to the 5th (= 32). In fact, all numbers from 1 to 63 can be so represented.

If the standard weights may be placed in either pan, then the second set gives a more economical solution, both in the number of the standard weights and in their total weight. For every number from 1 to 40 may be represented as a sum of multiples by 0, 1, or −1 of the successive powers of 3 from the 0th to the 3rd.

Bachet's solution is correct but not complete. It was completed by Major MacMahon, who generalized the medieval problem and posed it as follows:

Find all sets of standard weights, not necessarily unequal, with which one can weigh every whole number of pounds from 1 to n, in each of the following cases: (1) If the standard weights may be placed in only one scale pan. (2) If the standard weights may be placed in either scale pan.

MacMahon added two other conditions: (a) It is not permissible to measure additional weights with the set of standard weights. (b) Each weight can be measured in just one way with these standard weights.

The solution of MacMahon's problem is based on the following theorem:

Let a product

$$(1 + x + x^2 + \cdots + x^m)(1 + x + x^2 + \cdots + x^n)$$
$$(1 + x + x^2 + \cdots + x^p) \cdots$$

be written as a polynomial,

$$1 + Ax + Bx^2 + Cx^3 + \cdots.$$

Then the coefficient of any particular power of x, say of x^k, in the expanded product is the total number of different ways in which a set of powers of *x* may be selected from the factors on the left in such a way that in each case the sum of the exponents is **k** and just one term is selected from each factor.

The solution of the first problem is given by expressing

$$1 + x + \cdots + x^n = \frac{x^{n+1} - 1}{x - 1}$$

as a product of factors of the form

$$1 + x^a + \cdots + x^{ka} = \frac{x^{(k+1)a} - 1}{x - 1}.$$

Each such factorization yields a solution consisting of *k* weights of *a* pounds each, corresponding to each factor. Thus the solutions are seen to depend upon the possible factorizations of $n + 1$.

For example, take $n = 5$.

$$\frac{x^6 - 1}{x - 1} = \frac{x^2 - 1}{x - 1} \cdot \frac{x^6 - 1}{x^2 - 1} = \frac{x^3 - 1}{x - 1} \cdot \frac{x^6 - 1}{x^3 - 1},$$

that is,

$$1 + x + \cdots + x^5 = (1 + x)(1 + x^2 + x^4)$$
$$= (1 + x + x^2)(1 + x^3).$$

The corresponding solutions are: 5 1-pound weights, 1 1-pound and 2 2-pound weights, 2 1-pound and 1 3-pound weights.

In the second case the solution is found by expressing

$$x^n + x^{n-1} + \cdots + x + 1 + x^{-1} + \cdots + x^{-(n-1)} + x^{-n}$$

$$= \frac{x^{2n+1} - 1}{x^n(x - 1)}$$

as a product of factors of the form

$$x^{ka} + x^{(k-1)a} + \cdots + x^a + 1 + x^{-a} + \cdots + x^{-(k-1)a} + x^{-ka}$$

$$= \frac{x^{(2k+1)a} - 1}{x^{ka}(x^a - 1)}.$$

Again the solution corresponding to any such factorization

consists of k weights of a pounds apiece for each such factor. In this case the types of solutions are determined by the factorizations of $2n + 1$.

To solve the problem for $n = 40$ we must find the factors of $\dfrac{x^{81} - 1}{x^{40}(x - 1)}$. The following table gives the 8 possible factorizations and the corresponding solutions in each case. It will be seen that the total weight of every set is 40 [as was to be expected from condition (a)], but the number of weights is a minimum only in Bachet's solution.

No.	No. of fac- tors	Decomposition of A	Number of weights				Total
			1 lb.	3 lb.	9 lb.	27 lb.	
1	1	$\dfrac{x^{81} - 1}{x^{40}(x - 1)}$	40	—	—	—	40
2	2	$\dfrac{x^3 - 1}{x(x - 1)} \cdot \dfrac{x^{81} - 1}{x^{39}(x^3 - 1)}$	1	13	—	—	14
3	2	$\dfrac{x^{27} - 1}{x^{13}(x - 1)} \cdot \dfrac{x^{81} - 1}{x^{27}(x^{27} - 1)}$	13	—	—	1	14
4	2	$\dfrac{x^9 - 1}{x^4(x - 1)} \cdot \dfrac{x^{81} - 1}{x^{36}(x^9 - 1)}$	4	—	4	—	8
5	3	$\dfrac{x^3 - 1}{x(x - 1)} \cdot \dfrac{x^9 - 1}{x^3(x^3 - 1)} \cdot \dfrac{x^{81} - 1}{x^{36}(x^9 - 1)}$	1	1	4	—	6
6	3	$\dfrac{x^3 - 1}{x(x - 1)} \cdot \dfrac{x^{27} - 1}{x^{12}(x^3 - 1)} \cdot \dfrac{x^{81} - 1}{x^{27}(x^{27} - 1)}$	1	4	—	1	6
7	3	$\dfrac{x^9 - 1}{x^4(x - 1)} \cdot \dfrac{x^{27} - 1}{x^9(x^9 - 1)} \cdot \dfrac{x^{81} - 1}{x^{27}(x^{27} - 1)}$	4	—	1	1	6
8	4	$\dfrac{x^3 - 1}{x(x - 1)} \cdot \dfrac{x^9 - 1}{x^3(x^3 - 1)} \cdot \dfrac{x^{27} - 1}{x^9(x^9 - 1)} \cdot \dfrac{x^{81} - 1}{x^{27}(x^{27} - 1)}$	1	1	1	1	4

5. Many people know of the trick in which one person guesses a given number on being shown in a certain table which columns of the table contain the number to be guessed. Consider the accompanying table. If a person thinks of a number and says that it is in columns 1, 4, and 16, you can tell him instantly and without looking at the table that he is thinking of 21 — you need only add $1 + 4 + 16$.

32	16	8	4	2	1	32	16	8	4	2	1
32	16	8	4	2	1	48	48	40	36	34	33
33	17	9	5	3	3	49	49	41	37	35	35
34	18	10	6	6	5	50	50	42	38	38	37
35	19	11	7	7	7	51	51	43	39	39	39
36	20	12	12	10	9	52	52	44	44	42	41
37	21	13	13	11	11	53	53	45	45	43	43
38	22	14	14	14	13	54	54	46	46	46	45
39	23	15	15	15	15	55	55	47	47	47	47
40	24	24	20	18	17	56	56	56	52	50	49
41	25	25	21	19	19	57	57	57	53	51	51
42	26	26	22	22	21	58	58	58	54	54	53
43	27	27	23	23	23	59	59	59	55	55	55
44	28	28	28	26	25	60	60	60	60	58	57
45	29	29	29	27	27	61	61	61	61	59	59
46	30	30	30	30	29	62	62	62	62	62	61
47	31	31	31	31	31	63	63	63	63	63	63

The procedure is based on the expression of the number in the binary scale. The first column contains all those numbers whose last digit in the binary notation is 1, namely all numbers of the form $2k + 1$; the next column contains all those numbers whose next-to-last digit in the binary notation is 1, namely all numbers of the form $4k + 2$ or $4k + 3$; and so on. Thus the sequence of digits in the binary notation of the number is simply the sequence of 1's and 0's corresponding to the presence or absence of the number in the respective columns.

Mr. R. V. Heath had the idea of replacing the powers of 2 by colors. He writes the numbers in the first column on a red sheet, those in the second on a white sheet, those in the third on a blue sheet, and so on. In forming the number we count 1 for the red, 2 for the white, 4 for the blue, and so on.

Mr. Perelman devised a scheme by which an automaton could be made to give the answer. The sets of numbers are written on cards weighing 1 unit, 2 units, 4 units, and so on, respectively. Then we have only to put the cards on which the number appears in the pan of an automatic weighing machine in order to read off the number.

6. There are similar methods which use the ternary scale of notation. For example, we may list in the first and second

III	II	I
5	2	1
6	3	2*
7	4	4
8	5*	5*
9	6*	7
10	7*	8*
11	11	10
12	12	11*
13	13	13
14*	14*	14*
15*	15*	16
16*	16*	17*
17*	20	19
18*	21	20*
19*	22	22
20*	23*	23*
21*	24*	25
22*	25*	26*

18	9	6	3	2	1
18	9	6	3	2	1
19	10	7	4	5	4
20	11	8	5	8	7
21	12	15	12	11	10
22	13	16	13	14	13
23	14	17	14	17	16
24	15	24	21	20	19
25	16	25	22	23	22
26	17	26	23	26	25

columns those numbers whose ternary notation has a 1 or a 2 in the last place; in the third and fourth columns, those having a 1 or a 2 in the next-to-the-last place, and so on. Or we may use negative digits, and list in a single column those numbers having a 1 or a −1 in a given position, distinguishing those which have a −1 by an asterisk. In the table at the right, page 57, a number such as 18 or 24 that is to be formed by subtraction from 27, is characterized by the fact that it appears with an asterisk in the first column from the left in which it is listed.

The binary system has many other applications. In §12 of this chapter we shall show its application to the game of Nim and to the theory of the Chinese rings.

3. TO GUESS A SELECTED NUMBER

There are innumerable ways of finding a number chosen by someone, provided the result of certain operations on it is known. We shall confine ourselves to certain typical methods in ordinary use.

1. Ask the person who has chosen the number to triple it and tell you whether the resulting product is even or odd. If it is even let him divide it by two; if odd, let him add one and divide by two. Now request him to triple the result of the second step and then tell you how many times nine goes into the result, disregarding any remainder. If x is his final answer then $2x$ or $2x + 1$ is the number he selected, according as the result of the first operation was even or odd.

The demonstration of the method is easy. If the number selected was even, say $2x$, then we have successively: $2x \cdot 3 = 6x$; $6x \div 2 = 3x$; $3x \cdot 3 = 9x$; $9x \div 9 = x$. If the number selected was odd, say $2x + 1$, then $(2x + 1)3 = 6x + 3$; $(6x + 3 + 1) \div 2 = 3x + 2$; $(3x + 2)3 = 9x + 6$; $(9x + 6) \div 9 = x$ with a remainder 6 to be discarded.

2. Think of a number. Multiply it by 5; add 6 to the product; multiply this sum by 4; add 9 to this product; multiply this sum by 5. The result is a numeral of three digits or more. Cancel the last two digits; subtract 1 from the number thus formed. The remainder is the number with which you began.

Solution: Observe that the successive multipliers have been 5, 4, and 5. Applied to x, the number thought of, they multiply it by 100; applied to the other numbers, they bring 165, a result greater than 100 but less than 200. That is,

$$[(5x + 6)4 + 9]5 = 100x + 165.$$

The last two digits of $100x + 165$ will be 65. Suppressing them, therefore, gives the number $x + 1$. Reducing this by 1 obviously gives x.

3. Someone throws two dice marked from 1 to 6, or chooses a domino, or selects two numbers, neither greater than 9. To find the numbers selected, ask the person to multiply one of them by 5, add 7, double the sum, add the other number and give the result. If you subtract 14 from this last number you have a two-digit number left whose digits are the numbers selected. (If the first number selected was 0, the result will be a single digit representing the other number.)

Hint: $2 \cdot 7 = 14$.

4. On the card table are nine cards of the same suit, from the ace to the nine, face down. Have each of several persons select a card. What cards have been drawn?

Ask the first person to double the number of his card, add 1, multiply by 5 and pass the result on to the next person. Tell him to add his number to the number given him, multiply by 2, add 1, multiply by 5 and pass the result to the next person; and so on for each person in turn.

If there are n persons, subtract the number $5\cdots5$ (composed of n digits 5) from the number obtained by the last person, and divide by 10. The result will be a number whose digits are the chosen numbers in order.

5. A person is presented with a large list of numbers from which he is to select two without telling what they are. He is then instructed to add the chosen numbers, cancel any digit in the result, add the uncanceled digits and give the total. What digit was canceled?

Solution: The list is made up only of numbers exactly divisible by 9, so the sum of its digits is a multiple of 9. To find the digit that was canceled one has only to subtract the stated total from the next larger multiple of 9. To avoid the possible ambiguity arising when the digit canceled is 0 or 9, the numbers put in the list should be so chosen that the digit 0 does not appear in the sum of any two of them.

6. For variety one may arrange to have the multiple of 9 produced by someone else. Let him think of any number he pleases. Tell him to form the sum of its digits, subtract this sum from the given number, multiply the result by any number he wishes, and then cancel any digit except 0. From the sum of the remaining digits the canceled digit may be found as before.

Here is another variant. Tell the person to add to the number selected 8 times the sum of its digits, multiply the result by an arbitrary number, cancel one digit (other than 0) in the product and tell the sum of the remaining digits. The canceled digit can be found as before. Instead of 8, one less than any multiple of 9 may be used.

Again, the first operation may be varied by asking the person to subtract from his number any number formed by rearranging its digits. Or he may add to his number two such rearrangements (which yields a multiple of 3) and then square the result. Or a quite arbitrary sequence of operations may be used, ending with multiplication by some multiple of 9.

7. How to Guess an Unknown Number from Its Remainders When Divided by a Set of Given Numbers. Suppose we use the divisors 4, 5, and 7. Let a, b, and c be the remainders after division by 4, 5, and 7 respectively. Then

$$N \equiv 105a + 56b + 120c \qquad (\text{modulus} = 4 \cdot 5 \cdot 7 = 140).$$

In order that the result be unique the number to be guessed should be required to be less than 140.

Note that the coefficient of a, 105, in the expression for N has been so chosen that it is exactly divisible by 5 and 7, and gives the remainder 1 when divided by 4. Similarly, $56 \equiv 0$ ($m = 4$ and $m = 7$); $56 \equiv 1$ ($m = 5$); and $120 \equiv 0$ ($m = 4$ and $m = 5$); $120 \equiv 1$ ($m = 7$).

If the divisors are 3, 5, and 7, and the respective remainders a, b and c, the selected number will be

$$N \equiv 70a + 21b + 15c \qquad (m = 105).$$

When the divisors are 7, 11, and 13,

$$N \equiv 715a + 364b + 924c \qquad (m = 1{,}001).$$

More generally, if p, q, r, $\cdots$ are prime each to each, and a, b, c, $\cdots$ are the respective remainders from these divisors, then numbers P, Q, R, $\cdots$ can be found so that

$$N \equiv Pa + Qb + Rc + \cdots \qquad (m = pqr \cdots).$$

To find P, form the product $qr \cdots$ of all the divisors except p, and select the lowest multiple of this product which leaves the remainder 1 on division by p. Similarly for Q, R, and so on. The number to be selected should be kept less than the product of all the divisors.

8. How to Guess a Number Less Than 1,000. Ask the

person to divide his number by 42, 48, 56, and 63, and to tell you the respective remainders, say a, b, c, d. Then

$$N \equiv 1{,}008 - (96a + 21b + 90c + 800d) \qquad (m = 1{,}008).$$

To show this, let

$$N = 42p + a = 48q + b = 56r + c = 63s + d. \quad \text{Then}$$

$$96N = 1{,}008 \cdot 4p + 96a$$
$$21N = 1{,}008 \cdot q \ + 21b$$
$$90N = 1{,}008 \cdot 5r + 90c$$
$$800N = 1{,}008 \cdot 50s + 800d$$

$$\overline{1{,}007N = 1{,}008 \cdot S \ + (96a + 21b + 90c + 800d).}$$

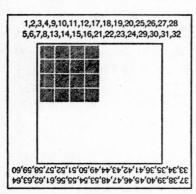

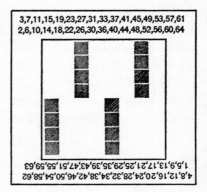

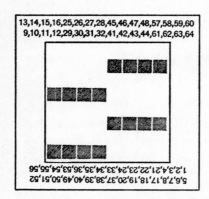

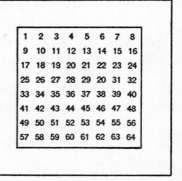

FIGURE 3. *Window Reader's Cards for Numbers 1 to 64.*

If we subtract this result from the congruence $1,008N \equiv 0$ ($m = 1,008$) and discard all but one multiple of 1,008, the desired result follows.

9. THE WINDOW READER. To assist in guessing a number from 1 to 64, four cards (three "window" cards and a

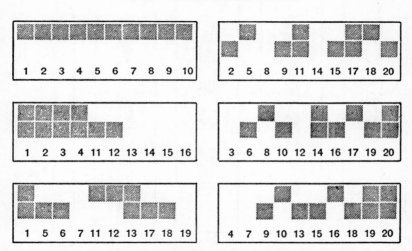

FIGURE 4. *Window Reader's Cards for Numbers 1 to 20.*

"master" card) may be prepared as in Figure 3. The shaded portions of the window cards are to be cut out, and the numbers which appear on the lower lines should be written on the back.

When a person has selected a number, give him the window cards and ask him to return them so that the selected number appears right side up on each card. Then superpose the three window cards, and they will reveal the desired number only on the master card.

In Figure 4 is given a set of six cards for use in determining a number up to 20. In this case each number appears on three of the cards. A similar set of eight cards can be devised for numbers up to 70.

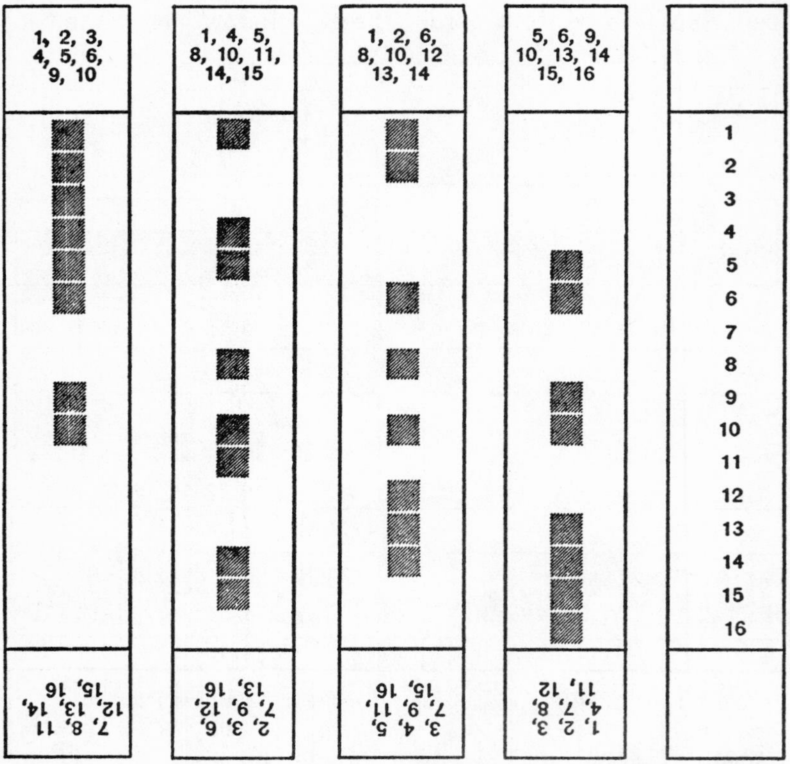

FIGURE 5. *Window Reader's Cards for Numbers* 1 *to* 16.

For numbers up to 16 the set of four cards in Figure 5 may be used.

To guess a letter of the alphabet, either seven or eight window cards and a master card may be used, respectively as in Figures 6 and 7. In the case of Figure 7, the window reader specifies the use of the cards which *do not contain* the given letter.

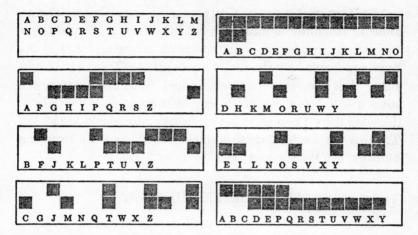

FIGURE 6. *Window Reader's Cards for the Alphabet: Seven and Master.*

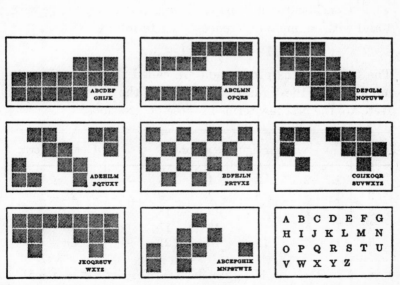

FIGURE 7. *Window Reader's Cards for the Alphabet: Eight and Master.*

10. How to Guess a Number of Three Digits (Rose-Innes). Denote the number by ABC, where A, B, and C are the digits. Ask for the remainders from division by 11 of the numbers formed by the digits arranged ABC, BCA, CAB in turn. Let the respective remainders be a, b, c. Form the sums $a + b$, $b + c$, $c + a$. If any of these is odd, increase or decrease it by 11 so as to get a positive number less than 20. Then divide each of these numbers by 2, and the resulting numbers are the digits A, B, C in order.

4. FIGURATE NUMBERS

Figurate numbers are of very ancient origin. Pascal's "Treatise on Figurate Numbers" was published in 1665; but Diophantus (about the second century A.D.) had already solved many problems concerning them.

1. Consider the arithmetical progression beginning with 1 and with common difference i. Its terms are

$$1, 1 + i, 1 + 2i, 1 + 3i, \cdots.$$

The terms of this progression are called the linear figurate numbers, or the figurate numbers of the first dimension. Here are the first few terms in these progressions:

i	Linear figurate numbers						General term
1	1	2	3	4	5	$\cdots$	n
2	1	3	5	7	9	$\cdots$	$2n - 1$
3	1	4	7	10	13	$\cdots$	$3n - 2$
4	1	5	9	13	17	$\cdots$	$4n - 3$
5	1	6	11	16	21	$\cdots$	$5n - 4$
$\cdots$			$\cdots$				$\cdots$
i	1	$1 + i$	$1 + 2i$	$1 + 3i$	$1 + 4i$	$\cdots$	$in - (i - 1)$

2. Consider now the successive sums of the terms of these progressions. These form the plane figurate numbers, or figurate numbers of the second dimension.

i	Figure	Plane figurate numbers						General term
1	Triangle	1	3	6	10	15	$\cdots$	$\frac{1}{2}n(n+1)$
2	Square	1	4	9	16	25	$\cdots$	n^2
3	Pentagon	1	5	12	22	35	$\cdots$	$\frac{1}{2}n(3n-1)$
4	Hexagon	1	6	15	28	45	$\cdots$	$n(2n-1)$
5	$\cdots$	1	7	18	34	55	$\cdots$	$\frac{1}{2}n(5n-3)$
$\cdots$	$\cdots$			$\cdots$				$\cdots$
i	$\cdots$	1	$2+i$	$3+3i$	$4+6i$	$5+10i$	$\cdots$	$\frac{1}{2}n[in-(i-2)]$

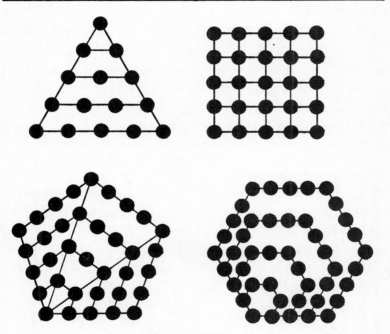

FIGURE 8. *Representation of Plane Figurate Numbers.*

The names triangular, square, pentagonal, hexagonal, and so on, are justified by the arrangements of the corresponding numbers of units shown in Figure 8.

3. If we now form the successive sums of the terms of the plane figurate numbers, the resulting numbers are the solid (pyramidal) figurate numbers, or figurate numbers of the third dimension.

i	Solid figurate numbers					General term
1	1	4	10	20	35 $\cdots$	$\frac{1}{6}n(n+1)(n+2)$
2	1	5	14	30	55 $\cdots$	$\frac{1}{6}n(n+1)(2n+1)$
3	1	6	18	40	75 $\cdots$	$\frac{1}{2}n^2(n+1)$
4	1	7	22	50	95 $\cdots$	$\frac{1}{6}n(n+1)(4n-1)$
5	1	8	26	60	115 $\cdots$	$\frac{1}{6}n(n+1)(5n-2)$
$\cdots$			$\cdots$			$\cdots$
i	1	$3+i$	$6+4i$	$10+10i$	$15+20i$ $\cdots$	$\frac{1}{6}n(n+1)[in-(i-3)]$

4. We can penetrate the fourth dimension by taking the sums of the terms of the solid progressions, which we call the figurate numbers of the fourth dimension.

i	Figurate numbers of the fourth dimension					General term
1	1	5	15	35	70 $\cdots$	$\frac{n}{4!}(n+1)(n+2)(n+3)$
2	1	6	20	50	105 $\cdots$	$\frac{n}{12}(n+1)^2(n+2)$
3	1	7	25	65	140 $\cdots$	$\frac{n}{4!}(n+1)(n+2)(3n+1)$
4	1	8	30	80	175 $\cdots$	$\frac{n^2}{6}(n+1)(n+2)$
5	1	9	35	95	210 $\cdots$	$\frac{n}{24}(n+1)(n+2)(5n-1)$
$\cdots$			$\cdots$			$\cdots$
i	1	$4+i$	$10+5i$	$20+15i$	$35+35i$ $\cdots$	$\frac{n}{4!}(n+1)(n+2)[in-(i-4)]$

5. This procedure can be generalized so as to form what we shall call figurate numbers of dimension d and difference i,

$$N_{d,i} = \frac{1}{d!} \frac{(n + d - 2)!}{(n - 1)!} [ni - (i - d)].$$

The sum of the first n terms of this sequence gives the nth figurate number of dimension $(d + 1)$ and difference i:

$$N_{d+1,i} = \sum_{i=1}^{n} N_{d,i}.$$

When $i = 1$, we have

$$N_{d,1} = \frac{1}{d!} \frac{(n + d - 1)!}{(n - 1)!} = {}_{(n+d-1)}C_d = {}_{(n+d-1)}C_{n-1},$$

that is, $N_{d,1}$ is the number of combinations of $n + d - 1$ things taken d at a time or $n - 1$ at a time.

When $i = d$ we have

$$N_{d,d} = \frac{1}{(d - 1)!} \cdot \frac{(n + d - 2)!}{(n - 1)!} \cdot n.$$

Thus

$N_{1,1} = n,$

$N_{2,2} = n^2,$

$N_{3,3} = \frac{1}{2}n^2(n + 1),$

$N_{4,4} = \frac{1}{6}n^2(n + 1)(n + 2),$

$N_{5,5} = \frac{1}{24}n^2(n + 1)(n + 2)(n + 3),$

$\cdots \qquad \cdots$

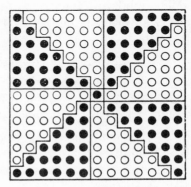

FIGURE 9. *Geometrical Interpretation of the Figurate Number of Diophantus.*

$$N_{d,d} = \frac{1}{(d - 1)!} n^2(n + 1) \cdots (n + d - 2).$$

When d is larger than 1, $N_{d,d}$ is exactly divisible by n^2.

Here is a formula due to Diophantus:

$$8T + 1 = S,$$

where T and S are corresponding triangular and square numbers. The geometrical interpretation of this is given in Figure 9. Algebraically it means,

$$8 \cdot \frac{n(n + 1)}{2} + 1 = (2n + 1)^2.$$

5. MERSENNE NUMBERS AND PERFECT NUMBERS

In 1644 Mersenne asserted that $2^n - 1$ is a prime number for $n \leq 257$ only when $n = 2, 3, 5, 7, 13, 17, 19, 31, 67, 127$ and 257.

This list contains some errors: first, the prime numbers for $n = 61$, $n = 89$, and $n = 107$ are omitted; second, the numbers for $n = 67$ and $n = 257$ are composite.

The modern theory of these numbers was founded by Lucas, who proved that $2^{127} - 1$ is a prime number. To date the following results have been obtained:

Of course $2^n - 1$ is composite when n is composite, since $2^{mp} - 1$ is divisible by $2^p - 1$.

$2^n - 1$ is known to be a prime number for $n = 2, 3, 5, 7, 13, 17, 19, 31, 61, 89, 107$, or 127.

$2^n - 1$ is completely factored for $n = 11, 23, 29, 37, 41, 43, 47, 53, 59, 67, 71, 73, 79, 113$.

n	$2^n - 1$, factors	Author
11	$23 \cdot 89$	Fermat
23	$47 \cdot 178\,481$	Fermat
29	$233 \cdot 1\,103 \cdot 2\,089$	Euler
37	$223 \cdot 616\,318\,177$	Fermat
41	$13\,367 \cdot 164\,511\,353$	Plana
43	$431 \cdot 9\,719 \cdot 2\,099\,863$	Landry
47	$2\,351 \cdot 4\,513 \cdot 13\,264\,529$	Reuschle
53	$6\,361 \cdot 69\,431 \cdot 20\,394\,401$	Landry
59	$179\,951 \cdot 3\,203\,431\,780\,337$	Le Lasseur
67	$193\,707\,721 \cdot 761\,838\,257\,287$	Cole
71	$228\,479 \cdot 48\,544\,121 \cdot 212\,885\,833$	Cunningham and Ramesam
73	$439 \cdot 2\,298\,041 \cdot 9\,361\,973\,132\,609$	Poulet
79	$2\,687 \cdot 202\,029\,703 \cdot 1\,113\,491\,139\,767$	Lehmer
83	$167 \cdot 57\,912\,614\,113\,275\,649\,087\,721$	
97	$11\,447 \cdot 13\,842\,607\,235\,828\,485\,645\,766\,393$	
113	$3\,391 \cdot 23\,279 \cdot 65\,993 \cdot 1\,868\,569 \cdot 1\,066\,818\,132\,868\,207$	Lehmer

Two or more prime factors are known (but not the complete factorisation) for $n = 151, 163, 173, 179, 181, 223, 233, 239, 251$.

n	Factors of $2^n - 1$	n	Factors of $2^n - 1$
151	18 121 · 55 871 · 165 799 · 2 332 951	223	182 187 · 196 687 · 1 466 449 · 2 916 841
163	150 287 · 704 161	233	1 399 · 135 607 · 622 577
173	730 753 · 1 505 447	239	479 · 1 913 · 5 737 · 176 383
179	359 · 1 433	251	503 · 54 217
181	43 441 · 1 164 193		

Only one prime factor is known for $n = 131, 167, 191, 197, 211, 229$.

n	Factor of $2^n - 1$	n	Factor of $2^n - 1$
131	263	197	7 487
167	2 349 023	211	15 193
191	383	229	1 504 073

$2^n - 1$ is composite but its factors are not known when $n = 101, 103, 109, 137, 139, 149, 157, 193, 199, 227, 241, 257$.

In addition some information has been gained about numbers of the form $2^n - 1$ for values of n beyond Mersenne's range. Thus, a factor is known for each of the following values of n: 263, 281, 283, 317, 337, 359, 367, 397, 419, 431, 443, 461, 463, 487, 491, 499, 547, 557, 571, 577, 593, 601, 617, 619, 641, 659, 683, 719, 743, 761, 827, 829, 839, 857, 877, 881, 883, 911, 929, 937, 941, 967.

For $2^{397} - 1$ no fewer than five divisors are known, namely 2,383, 6,353, 50,023, 53,993, 202,471, but the complete factorization is not known.

A perfect number is a number equal to the sum of all of its divisors (not including itself); for example, $6 = 1 + 2 + 3$

and $28 = 1 + 2 + 4 + 7 + 14$.   The only perfect numbers known are even numbers of the form $2^{n-1}(2^n - 1)$ in which the second factor is prime. Only the following perfect numbers are known, those obtained by setting $n = 2, 3, 5,$ 7, 13, 17, 19, 31, 61, 89, 107, 127, 521, 607, 1279, 2203, 2281.

Concerning these numbers Mersenne wrote: "On voit clairement par là combien sont rares les Nombres Parfaits et combien on a raison de les comparer aux hommes parfaits." ["We see clearly from this fact how rare are Perfect Numbers and how right we are to compare them with perfect men."]

We are in a century of materialism, and in the opinion of our time, numbers, however marvelous their properties, possess no human qualities.   But in Mersenne's time everyone believed in the intrinsic qualities of numbers, which were not only perfect, but also lucky or unlucky, good or bad, and so forth; so Mersenne's statement is not strange.

Mr. Heath has proved that every perfect number $2^{n-1}(2^n - 1)$ is a sum of cubes of 2^k odd numbers, when $k = \frac{1}{2}(n - 1)$, except for $n = 2$.   The proof is as follows:

Recall that

$$S_1 = 1 + 2 + 3 + \cdots + m = \frac{m(m + 1)}{2},$$

$$S_2 = 1^2 + 2^2 + 3^2 + \cdots + m^2 = \frac{m(m + 1)(2m + 1)}{6},$$

$$S_3 = 1^3 + 2^3 + 3^3 + \cdots + m^3 = \frac{m^2(m + 1)^2}{4} = S_1^2.$$

Then

$$S = 1^3 + 3^3 + 5^3 + \cdots + (2m - 1)^3 = \sum_{i=1}^{m}(2m - 1)^3$$

$$= \sum_{i=1}^{m}(8m^3 - 12m^2 + 6m - 1)$$

$$= 8 \cdot \frac{m^2(m+1)^2}{4} - 12 \cdot \frac{m(m+1)(2m+1)}{6} +$$
$$6 \cdot \frac{m(m+1)}{2} - m = m^2(2m^2 - 1).$$

If $m = 2^k$, $S = 2^{2k}(2^{2k+1} - 1)$. The perfect numbers are of this form for $n = 2k + 1$.

6. FERMAT NUMBERS

Fermat remarked that numbers of the form $2^m + 1$ cannot be prime when m contains an odd factor. For

$$2^{(2k+1)d} + 1 = (2^d + 1) \left[(2^d)^{2k} - (2^d)^{2k-1} + \cdots - 2^d + 1 \right].$$

He remarked also that if m has no odd factor, that is, if m is itself a power of 2, then $2^m + 1$ is a prime. Numbers of this form, $F_n = 2^{2^n} + 1$, are called Fermat numbers. They increase very rapidly: if $n = 0$, $F_n = 3$; if $n = 1$, $F_n = 5$; if $n = 2$, $F_n = 17$; if $n = 3$, $F_n = 257$; if $n = 4$, $F_n = 65,537$. For $n = 5$ we obtain a 10-digit number. To us such a number does not seem very large, and we have methods which enable us to decide quickly whether it is prime or composite. But in Fermat's time this investigation was difficult, and Fermat did not carry it out. He merely stated that all numbers of this form are prime — an assertion which was disproved by Euler almost a century later. Euler found that $F_5 = 2^{32} + 1$ is divisible by 641.

Here is an elegant proof of this result which may be carried through with little numerical calculation.

$$641 = 625 + 16 = 5^4 + 2^4 = (5 \cdot 2^7) + 1.$$

(This is the only calculation to be verified.) Then we have, modulo 641,

$$5 \cdot 2^7 \equiv -1, \quad 5 \cdot 2^8 \equiv -2, \quad 5^4 \cdot 2^{32} \equiv 2^4, \quad -16 \cdot 2^{32} \equiv 16,$$

whence

$$2^{32} \equiv -1, \quad \text{or } 2^{32} + 1 \equiv 0, \quad \text{modulo 641.}$$

The table below gives all results known up to this time.

n	F_n	Date	Author
0–4	primes	1665	Fermat
5	$641 \cdot 6700417$	1732	Euler
6	$274177 \cdot 67280421310721$	1880	Landry
7 8	$\begin{bmatrix} \text{composite, but the} \\ \text{factors are unknown} \end{bmatrix}$	1909	$\begin{cases} \text{Morehead} \\ \text{Western} \end{cases}$
9	divisible by $37 \cdot 2^{16} + 1$	1903	Western
11	divisible by $39 \cdot 2^{13} + 1$ and $119 \cdot 2^{13} + 1$	1899	Cunningham
12	divisible by $7 \cdot 2^{14} + 1$, $397 \cdot 2^{16} + 1$, $973 \cdot 2^{16} + 1$	1879	Pervouchine, Western
15	divisible by $579 \cdot 2^{21} + 1$	1925	Kraitchik
18	divisible by $13 \cdot 2^{20} + 1$	1903	Western
23	divisible by $5 \cdot 2^{25} + 1$	1878	Pervouchine
36	divisible by $5 \cdot 2^{39} + 1$	1886	Seelhof
38	divisible by $3 \cdot 2^{41} + 1$	1903	Cunningham
73	divisible by $5 \cdot 2^{75} + 1$	1905	Morehead

Quite unexpectedly Gauss found that this question was connected with the problem of inscribing a polygon in a circle. Gauss proved that the only regular polygons constructible with ruler and compass are those for which the number of sides is $m = 2^k \cdot F_n \cdot F_{n'} \cdots$, where $k = 0, 1, 2, \cdots$ and the Fermat numbers are all distinct primes.

The first five prime Fermat numbers are $2^1 + 1$, $2^2 + 1$, $2^4 + 1$, $2^8 + 1$, $2^{16} + 1$. If we multiply $1 = 2^1 - 1$ into these numbers we obtain successively $2^2 - 1$, $2^4 - 1$, $2^8 - 1$, $2^{16} - 1$, $2^{32} - 1$, the latter being the product of the first five prime Fermat numbers. $2^{32} - 1$ has the following 32 divisors:

1	257	65,537	16,843,009
3	771	196,611	50,529,027
5	1,285	327,685	84,215,045
15	3,855	983,055	252,645,135
17	4,369	1,114,129	286,331,153
51	13,107	3,342,387	858,993,459
85	21,845	5,570,645	1,431,655,765
255	65,535	16,711,935	4,294,967,295

Thus, in order that a regular polygon be constructible with ruler and compass, it is necessary and sufficient that the number m of its sides be the product by a power of 2 of one of the above numbers or of a product of prime Fermat numbers at least one of which is greater than $2^{1024} + 1$.

7. CYCLIC NUMBERS

We define a cyclic number, or a cyclic set of numbers, as follows: Let $A_1 = a_1a_2\cdots a_{n-1}a_n$ be an n-digit number in a positional notation with base B. (We include the possibility that some of the first digits may be 0's.) Then the n numbers represented by the n cyclic permutations of the digits of A_1, namely A_1, $A_2 = a_2\cdots a_na_1$, $\cdots$, $A_n = a_na_1\cdots a_{n-1}$, are said to form the cyclic set generated by A_1. Thus 142,857 generates the cyclic set 142,857, 428,571, 285,714, 857,142, 571,428, 714,285 in any scale of notation with base $B \geqq 9$.

If the scale is on the base $B = 10$ it may be shown that 142,857 is the period in the decimal expansion of $\frac{1}{7}$: that is,

$$\tfrac{1}{7} = 0.142857142857142857142\cdots;$$

and that the succeeding numbers of the cycle are the periods in the decimal expansion of $\frac{x}{7}$, where $x = 3, 2, 6, 4,$ and 5 respectively.

The sum of the cyclic set $A_1, \cdots, A_n$ is $S\cdot\dfrac{B^n - 1}{B - 1}$, where $S = a_1 + \cdots + a_n$, the sum of the digits, and B is the base of the scale of notation. It follows from this that if p is a divisor of $\dfrac{B^n - 1}{B - 1}$, the sum of the remainders from division by p of the n numbers is 0. Also, if one of these numbers is divisible by p, so are the others. For example, in the decimal scale the numbers 41,205, 12,054, 20,541, 5,412, 54,120 are all divisible by 41, which is a divisor of $\dfrac{10^5 - 1}{10 - 1} = 11,111$.

Here are some problems on cyclic sets of numbers in the decimal scale.

1. A number ends with the digit 2. If we move the 2 from the last place to the first, the new number is twice the original. What is it?

Solution: Let N be the number and n the number of its digits. Then

$$\frac{N-2}{10} + 2 \cdot 10^{n-1} = 2N,$$

whence $19N = 2(10^n - 1)$. Hence n must be chosen so that 19 divides $10^n - 1$. $n = 18, 36, 54, \cdots$, and $N = 105\,263\,157\,894\,736\,842$, or any number formed by repeating these digits. The fundamental sequence is the period in the decimal expansion of $\frac{2}{19}$.

2. A number begins with the digit 3. If this digit be transposed to the last place, the new number is $\frac{1}{3}$ of the original. What is it?

Answer: $3\,103\,448\,275\,862\,068\,965\,517\,241\,379$, or any number formed by a finite number of repetitions of this sequence of digits.

3. What number ending in 4 is multiplied by 4 when the final digit is transposed to the first place?

Answer: $102\,564$ is the smallest solution.

4. What number ending in 4 is doubled when the final digit is transposed to the first position?

Answer: $210\,526\,315\,789\,473\,684$ is the smallest solution.

The number $142\,857$ is the only number such that every cyclic permutation of it is a multiple of it. This number, its double, and numbers formed from either of them by an arbitrary number of repetitions of its sequence of digits are the only ones which generate more than one multiple of themselves in the sequence of their cyclic permutations.

8. AUTOMORPHIC NUMBERS

A number is called automorphic in the scale of notation with base B if all of its powers end in the same digits in this scale of notation.* If n is the number of digits appearing at the end of every power of the automorphic number N, we have $N^x \equiv N$ (modulo B^n), for $x > 0$. But this will be satisfied if $N^2 \equiv N$ (modulo B^n).

Suppose first that B is a prime. Then the congruence $N^2 \equiv N$ (modulo B^n) has only the solutions $N \equiv 0$ and $N \equiv 1$ (modulo B^n).

Now suppose B composite, say $B = 6 = 2 \cdot 3$. The congruence $N^2 \equiv N$ (modulo 6^n) may be replaced by the simultaneous congruences, $N^2 \equiv N$ (modulo 2^n) and $N^2 \equiv N$ (modulo 3^n). These have the solutions, $N \equiv 0$ or 1 (modulo 2^n) and $N \equiv 0$ or 1 (modulo 3^n), from which we find four solutions modulo 6^n. Of these, two are trivial, namely $N \equiv 0$ and $N \equiv 1$ (modulo 6^n). The other two are given by $N \equiv 0$ (modulo 2^n) and 1 (modulo 3^n), or $N \equiv 1$ (modulo 2^n) and 0 (modulo 3^n). Thus the numbers (in the scale with base 6) which end in 4, 44, 344, and so on or in 3, 13, 213, and so on, are automorphic.

In the usual scale of notation, with base $10 = 2 \cdot 5$, we find similarly the trivial solutions, $N \equiv 0$ and $N \equiv 1$ (modulo 10^n), and the true automorphic numbers given by $N \equiv 0$ (modulo 2^n) and 1 (modulo 5^n), or $N \equiv 1$ (modulo 2^n) and 0 (modulo 5^n). Thus numbers ending in 6, 76, 376, $\cdots$, or in 5, 25, 625, $\cdots$, are automorphic.

* The terminology as regards cyclic numbers and automorphic numbers is not as yet fixed by usage. The lexicographers of Webster's New International Dictionary, Second Edition, describe as cyclic numbers or circular numbers those numbers which are here called automorphic; they do not define the term automorphic as it applies to numbers. Of necessity, we must therefore define the terms and use them according to our definitions.

The last digits may be either

$$3\ 740\ 081\ 787\ 109\ 376$$
$$6\ 259\ 918\ 212\ 890\ 625.$$

9. PRIME NUMBERS

As one goes out in the sequence of natural numbers, prime numbers become more and more rare. For example, there are 26 prime numbers between 0 and 100, only 21 between 100 and 200, and no more than 4 between 10^{12} and $10^{12} + 100$.

In spite of the rarity of the primes, they exist among numbers no matter how large. We can never name the largest prime number, but only the largest known prime number, that is to say, the largest number whose primality has been proved.

Euler proved that $2^{31} - 1$ is a prime number, and this was the largest known prime number for a century, until Landry, Lucas, Lehmer, Powers and other authors of our time broke Euler's record.

Now we know many numbers greater than Euler's number. *Sphinx* at one time listed all known isolated prime numbers greater than 10^{12}, and all prime numbers between $10^{12} - 10,000$ and $10^{12} + 10,000$. This catalogue contains nine numbers greater than 10^{19}, one of which was shown by Lehmer to be incorrect. The other eight are:

The factor of $(3^{105} - 2^{105})$, $(2^{96} + 1) \div (2^{32} + 1)$, $(10^{23} - 1) \div 9$, $5.2^{75} + 1$, $2^{89} - 1$, $(10^{31} + 1) \div 11$, $2^{107} - 1$, $2^{127} - 1$.

Moreover Miller and Wheller proved that $k.(2^{127} - 1) + 1$ is a prime for $k = 114, 124, 388, 408, 498, 696, 738, 744, 780, 934$ and 978, as well as $180.(2^{127} - 1)^2 + 1$, and Mr. Ferrier proved that $(2^{148} + 1) \div 17$ is prime.

Mr. R. M. Robinson proved with the electronic machine the primality of $2^n - 1$ for $n = 521, 607, 1279, 2203, 2281$.

Each of these numbers has its history, and the proof of its

primality has in most cases required great labor from its discoverers.

10. MULTIGRADE

A multigrade is a relation between numbers. It is of the form

$$\sum a^x = \sum b^x$$

and holds good for more than one value of x. The simplest multigrade is

$$1^x + 2^x + 6^x = 4^x + 5^x,$$

which holds for $x = 1$ or 2, inasmuch as $1 + 2 + 6 = 4 + 5$ and $1^2 + 2^2 + 6^2 = 4^2 + 5^2$. One can find multigrades which hold for as many values of x as one pleases. Here is a very useful theorem.

Given a multigrade

$$\sum_{i=1}^{m} a_i^x = \sum_{i=1}^{m} b_i^x, \qquad 1 \leq x \leq p,$$

we can form a new multigrade,

$$\sum_{i=1}^{m} a_i^x + \sum_{i=1}^{m} (b_i + c)^x = \sum_{i=1}^{m} b_i^x + \sum_{i=1}^{m} (a_i + c)^x, \qquad 1 \leq x \leq p + 1,$$

where c is any constant.

This is a very efficient method of forming multigrades for arbitrarily high powers. For example, we may start with the identity $1 + 9 = 4 + 6$. If we take $c = 1$ we have $1^x + 5^x + 7^x + 9^x = 2^x + 4^x + 6^x + 10^x$, $x = 1, 2$. Or we may take $c = 2$ and get $1^x + 8^x + 9^x = 3^x + 4^x + 11^x$, $x = 1, 2$. From the latter, with $c = 1$, we find $1^x + 5^x + 8^x + 12^x = 2^x + 3^x + 10^x + 11^x$, $x = 1, 2, 3$. We can continue, letting c have any succession of values, as $c = 7, 4, 8, 1, 13, 11, \cdots$.

11. CRYPTARITHMETIC

Under the title "Cryptarithmie" (which we have translated as "Cryptarithmetic") the journal *Sphinx* published, from 1931 to 1939, many problems concerning the restoration of mathematical operations. The name is due to Minos (Vatriquant) who first used it in *Sphinx* in May, 1931. Minos prefaced his problem with the following remark: "Cryptographers ... put figures in place of letters. By way of reprisal we have put letters in place of figures." A "cryptarithm" is, then, an arithmetical operation — such as an addition, a multiplication, or a division — in which the digits have been replaced by letters or other symbols, and one is challenged to find the original numbers.

Although Minos originated the name, problems of this sort were known earlier, and there are better examples in "La Mathématique des Jeux" (1930). Here are two.

1. I was sitting before my chess board pondering a combination of moves. At my side were my son, a boy of eight, and my daughter, four years old. The boy was busy with his home work, which consisted of some exercises in long division, but he was rather handicapped by his mischievous sister, who kept covering up his figures with chess men. As I looked up, only two digits remained visible. I have put down the division in Figure 10 just as I saw it. Can you calculate the missing digits for my little boy without annoying his sister by removing the chess men?

Solution: This is particularly easy. First, observe that the five-digit quotient forms only three products with the divisor. Therefore two of the five digits must be 0's. These cannot be the first or last, since both obviously form products. They are therefore the second and fourth digits, those covered by the white bishops. Furthermore, the two-digit divisor, when multiplied by 8, gives a two-digit product; but when multiplied by another number, the one concealed under the first white rook, it gives a three-digit product; therefore the hidden multiplier must be larger than 8, consequently 9. Both the first and last digits in the quotient give three-digit products with the two-digit divisor, wherefore both must be 9's. We now have established the quotient: it is 90,809. Let us find the divisor, covered up beneath the two white knights. When multiplied by 8 it forms a two-digit product; when multiplied by 9 it forms a three-digit product. It must, therefore, be 12; $8 \cdot 12 = 96$, $9 \cdot 12 = 108$; neither 10, 11, 13, nor any larger number meets these requirements. The numbers under the remaining chess pieces are readily found.

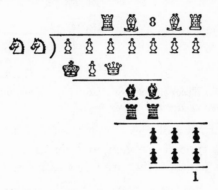

FIGURE 10. *Reconstruct the Division Problem, Finding the Numbers Hidden under the Chess Men.*

2. Discover the numbers concealed under the chess men in the division of Figure 11. Although only one digit is given, we are further told that the sum of the digits of the divisor leaves a remainder 7 when divided by 9, and the sum of the digits of the quotient leaves a remainder 3 when divided by 9.

Solution: The third digit of the quotient is 0, its first digit is not less than 4, and its last digit is greater than 4. Since the sum of the digits of the quotient is of the form $9k + 3$, that is, one of the numbers 3, 12, 21, 30, and so on, it is plain that 21 is the only possible value of this sum. Hence the sum of the first and last digits is $17 = 8 + 9$, so the quotient is 8,409.

The divisor is between $1,000 \div 9 = 111^{+}$ and $1,000 \div 8 = 125$. As it is of the form $9k + 7$ it must be either 115 or 124.

It cannot be 115 because the second digit of the quotient would then have to be greater than 4. Hence the division is $1{,}042{,}716 \div 124 = 8{,}409$.   (A. Lapierre)

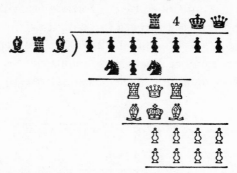

FIGURE 11.   *Reconstruct the Division Problem, Finding the Numbers Hidden under the Chess Men.*

M. Pigeolet, one of the directors of *Sphinx*, was a great master of this type of problem, and contributed many cryptarithms to its pages. Here are a few samples.

3. $ODER = 18(DO + OR)$.   *Answer:* 1,926.

4.
$$
\begin{array}{r}
ABC \\
ABC \\
\hline
DEFC \\
CEBH \\
EKKH \\
\hline
EAGFFC
\end{array}
$$
    Answer: 685^2.

5.
$$
\begin{array}{r}
ABC \\
DE \\
\hline
FEC \\
DEC \\
\hline
HGBC
\end{array}
$$
    Answer: 125·37.

6.
$$
\begin{array}{r}
ABCDE \\
CEDBA \\
\hline
* * * * * \\
* * * * * * \\
* * * * * * \\
* * * * *D \\
* * * *B \\
\hline
* * * * * * * * *
\end{array}
$$
    Answer: 18,497·47,981.

7.
$$
\begin{array}{r}
ABC \\
BAC \\
\hline
* * * * \\
* *A \\
* * *B \\
\hline
* * * * * *
\end{array}
$$
    Answer: 286·826.

8. $QUI)\overline{TRO\,UVE}(C\,ECI$ (*" Who can find this ? "*)

```
   * * *
   ─────
   * * *
   * * *
   ─────
   * * *
   * *E
   ─────
   * * *
   * * E
   ─────
```

Answer: 986,304 ÷ 132.

12. ARITHMETICAL GAMES

1. THE BATTLE OF NUMBERS. This is a game for two players, A and B. Before they begin play the players agree on two fixed numbers, the "play limit" p and a considerably larger "game limit" Q, and they decide who is to begin. Suppose A starts. He selects a number greater than zero and not greater than p. To this number B then adds a number not greater than p. A then adds to this total a number not greater than p. And so on in turn. The first one to reach the total Q is the winner.

Let us call the total obtained after any play a *position*, the position being *held* by the player who reaches that total. A position will be called *strategic* if the holder of that position can force his opponent to lose, no matter how the opponent plays from then on.

Any position H when $(H + p) \geqq Q$ is obviously hopeless; the opponent can play a number p or smaller which makes his position equal to Q, that is, to victory. But if a position S is such that $S + p + 1 = Q$, the holder of position S, say A, has his opponent B helpless; for whatever number B may add to S, from 1 to p, A's next play from p to 1 will bring A to Q and to victory. So the decisively strategic position is S when $S + p + 1 = Q$, or otherwise stated, when $S = Q - (p + 1)$.

Now if strategic position S guarantees victory when $S = Q - (p + 1)$, then it becomes the object of a player to get in position S, hence to get into a still earlier position S' from which he cannot be prevented from achieving S. Just as the strategic position S was calculated by subtracting $(p + 1)$ from Q, so the earlier strategic position S' may be calculated by subtracting $(p + 1)$ from S; or we may say $S' = Q - 2(p + 1)$. A still earlier strategic position S'' is equal to $Q - 3(p + 1)$. Reasoning thus backwards from Q toward the starting position 0, it can be seen that a player can put himself in a position early in the game from which (always assuming that he plays correctly) he can proceed to successive strategic positions and victory despite anything his opponent may do.

If $p = 10$ and $Q = 100$, the strategic positions are 89, 78, 67, 56, 45, 34, 23, 12 and 1. Hence the first to play may make certain of winning by taking the strategic position 1. But if he selects any other number, his opponent can call the tune by occupying the position 12. It is easy to see how one may make sure of continuing to occupy strategic positions once he has gained one.

The game seems to have been played originally with the limits 10 and 100. Bachet de Méziriac (1613) noted that it could be varied by changing either or both of the limits. He also remarked that if the game limit is 100, the first player can always win under the play limit 8, since the first strategic position is still 1, but with the play limit 9, the second player can always win since the first strategic position is then 10. He goes on to recommend playing this game against those who do not understand its theory; even then, he warns, if an adversary is clever, one must not always take the strategic positions, since the adversary will then discover them himself. Instead, Bachet advises waiting until near the end of the game before capturing a strategic position.

There are many modifications of the game.

First, we may agree that the game limit may not be exceeded, and that the first to reach it loses. This plan changes the strategic positions. For example, if $p = 10$ and $Q = 100$, the strategic numbers are 99, 88, $\cdots$, 22, 11; in this case the second player can always win. This variant may be played with a pile of chips, each player being allowed to take off not more than so many. The last player to remove a chip from the pile loses.

The game may be complicated by assigning different play limits to each player. In this case, however, the player with the larger play limit can always arrange to win. Let A have the larger play limit p, B the smaller play limit m. If A can once manage to occupy a position strategic for him he can never be ousted from such positions, since B must add a number $r < p$ and A can then add $p + 1 - r$, which is greater than 0 and not greater than p. In the early stages of the game, if B does not occupy a position strategic for A, then A has only to add a number less than or equal to p. If, however, B does occupy one of A's strategic positions, A can add 1, leaving B $p(> q)$ units from A's next strategic position. After B has added $r(< p)$, A then adds $p - r$.

Another variation is provided by requiring each player to have both an upper and a lower play limit. Thus A may be required to choose a number x such that $p \leq x \leq q$, and B to choose a number y such that $r \leq y \leq s$. In this case neither player may be able to reach the game-limit exactly, so we may define the winner as the one who first equals or exceeds the game limit, or else as the one who last remains below it. An analysis similar to that in the previous paragraph shows that the player with the higher upper limit can arrange to win.

It is interesting to note an application of this last case in the ritual of tossing up the bat to determine who gets first innings or who gets first choice in choosing teams for a scratch game of baseball. But neither contestant knows the play limits of his opponent, nor is the first position fixed by these limits, so the result is pretty much a matter of chance. There is also a European custom of a similar nature, called in Belgium by the Walloon word "guiser." In such games as soccer or hockey, in order to determine which team defends which goal or which team first takes the offensive, the two captains take positions a little apart. Then they take turns in advancing toward each other, each by the length or width of his own foot. The first to place his foot on that of his adversary wins.

If the battle of numbers be played with more than two players it loses its mathematical interest, for the result of the game cannot be decided by the first moves. But it must be admitted that in this case the loss of mathematical interest is more than compensated by the gain in sporting interest, for who wants to play for long a game whose result he can always foresee?

2. NIM. This game may be regarded as a generalization of the battle of numbers, and, like it, has a complete mathematical analysis.

The game is played by two persons, playing alternately. An arbitrary number of objects, say chips, is distributed into just three heaps in an arbitrary way. Each player in his turn is to take as many chips as he wishes (but at least one) from any heap he wishes. The last one to remove a chip is the winner.

We define the expressions *position*, *holding* a position, and *strategic* position as in the battle of numbers. A position will be denoted by the set of three numbers (a, b, c) representing in order the number of chips in each pile. In nim, as in the battle of numbers, strategic positions are independent of the player holding them, and are characterized by the fact that if a player A occupies a strategic position, his opponent B cannot capture a strategic position on his next play, but A can obtain a new strategic position on his next play, regardless of what B does.

The winning principle in nim rests on the following theorem: *Let the numbers of a position* (*a, b, c*) *be written in the binary scale of notation. Then the position* (*a, b, c*) *is strategic if and only if the sum of the digits in each place is even.* (For example, (5, 43, 46) is strategic since

$$\begin{array}{ll}
\text{decimal} \quad 5 = \text{binary} & 101 \\
\text{decimal} \quad 43 = \text{binary} & 101{,}011 \\
\text{decimal} \quad 46 = \text{binary} & \underline{101{,}110} \\
& 202{,}222
\end{array}$$

It is to be noticed that we do not "carry over" from one column to the next; only the sums of the individual columns are considered.)

First we shall show that every position which can be reached in one play from a position of this type is not of this type. For by the rules just one of the piles or numbers *a, b, c* is changed. Such a change produces in the binary notation of the number changed a redistribution of the digits 0 and 1; that is, at least one 1 must become a 0 or one 0 must become a 1. Hence in at least one column the sum of the digits is changed by 1, that is from an even number to an odd.

Next we show that in one play a position which is not of this special type can be made so. Find the first column from the left for which the sum of the digits is odd, either 1 or 3. If this sum is 1, then just one of the three piles or numbers has a 1 in this place, and that is the number which must be changed; if the sum is 3, each of the three piles has a 1 in this place, and any one of the piles may be changed. Having decided which number is to be changed, replace the 1 in this position by a 0 and alter the digits following it by interchanging 1's and 0's in such a way that the new sums of digits are even in every column. Since the first digit from the left which was altered in the number was reduced, this means that the new number is less than the original, and hence the change in digits is equivalent to a subtraction. Thus a single subtraction from just one of the three numbers, or taking a chip or chips from one pile, alters an unstrategic position to a position of the strategic type.

To complete the proof of the theorem we have only to observe that the winning position $(0, 0, 0)$ is of the same special type as the strategic positions. As a result of the first two paragraphs of the proof it is clear that once a player captures a position of this special type he cannot be dislodged from it, and it is equally clear that any sequence of such positions must ultimately lead to the winning position. Furthermore, these special positions are the only ones which can be maintained. Thus these are the only strategic positions.

It is clear that every sequence of strategic positions must ultimately lead to a position of the type $(0, n, n)$. From here the sequence must lead to $(0, 1, 1)$ and then to $(0, 0, 0)$.

Here is a list of the strategic positions [other than those of type $(0, n, n)$] for any game in which each pile has at most 15 chips.

1, 2, 3	2, 4, 6	3, 4, 7	4, 8,12	5, 8,13	6, 8,14	7, 8,15
1, 4, 5	2, 5, 7	3, 5, 6	4, 9,13	5, 9,12	6, 9,15	7, 9,14
1, 6, 7	2, 8,10	3, 8,11	4,10,14	5,10,15	6,10,12	7,10,13
1, 8, 9	2, 9,11	3, 9,10	4,11,15	5,11,14	6,11,13	7,11,12
1,10,11	2,12,14	3,12,15				
1,12,13	2,13,15	3,13,14				
1,14,15						

In general the initial position is not strategic, so the player who begins has the advantage, since he can make his position strategic. Only if the initial position is strategic is the advantage with the second player.

3. CHINESE RINGS. The Chinese rings are a toy, consisting of a fixed number of rings (usually from 5 to 8) hung
on a bar in such a way that the ring at the right end may be
taken off or put on the bar at pleasure, but any other can be
taken off or put on only when the next one to its right is on

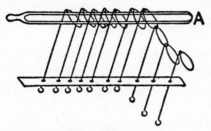

FIGURE 12.   *Chinese Rings.*

and all the others to its right are off. The order of the rings
is fixed. Only one ring can be taken off or put on at a time,
except that the two rings at the extreme right can be put on
or taken off together. When we operate with these rings
separately we shall say that we work the slow way; when the

(1)	*	*	*	*	*	*	*
(2)	*	*	*	*	*	*	0
(3)	*	*	*	*	*	0	*
(4)	*	*	*	*	*	0	0
(5)	*	*	*	0	*	0	0

FIGURE 13.   *Taking Chinese Rings off the Bar; the * Indicates
a Ring on the Bar,* 0 *a Ring off.*

two are put on or taken off together, we shall say we work
the fast way.

Let us denote the position of the rings by a set of asterisks
(*) and zeros (0) in order, * if the ring is on the bar, 0 if it is
off. In the accompanying figure, for a toy with 7 rings, position (1) indicates that all rings are on the bar. We can pass
from position (1) to position (2) *or* to position (3) in one step,

but not from (2) to (3). Position (4) can be obtained in two ways: (a) the fast way, taking the last two rings from (1) at the same time; (b) the slow way, from (1) to (3), and then taking off the last ring. Position (5) can be obtained from (4) in one step.

The following tables give the successive positions assumed in taking all the rings of a 7-ring toy off the bar by the two methods:

```
        First: The Slow Way                    Second: The Fast Way

*******  0 00000  0       0   00   0 0    *******
      0  0 0000   0      00   00   0          0 0   0 00000  0              00     0
    0 0  0 000    0  0 00     00  00            0   0 000    0      00      00   0 0
      0  0 000 0  0   0 0     00  000         000   0 000 0  0  0 00        00   0
     00  0 00  0  0   0       00 000        0 000   0 00   0  0   0         00  000
    000  0 00    0    0   0   000 000       0  0    0 00      0   0   0     000 000
  0 000  0 00 0  0    0  0 0  000  00       0 0 0   0 00 00   0  00 0       000 0
   0 00  0 00 00 0    00  0   000  0 0      0   0   0 0  00   0  00         000 0 0
    0 0  0 0 00   0   00      000    0      0       0 0       0  0000       000   0
  0 0 0  0 0 0    0   000     000           0       0 0    0  00 0000       000
    0 0  0 0      00 0000     000  0       0  00    0 0 0 0  00 00          000  00
      0  0 0   0  00 000      000  00      00 00    0 0 0    00 00 0        0000 00
    0 0  0 0 0 0  00 00       0000 00      00       0 0 000  00 0  0        0000
   0 00  0 0 0    00 00 0     0000 0       00  0    0   000  00 0           0000  0
  00 00  0 0 00   00 0  0     0000         000 0    0     0  00 0 00        00000 0
  00 0   0 0 000  00 0        0000  0      000     0    0 0  00    00       00000
   00    0   000  00 0 0 0    00000 0      00000   0       0  00            0000000
  00  0  0    00  00 0 0 00   00000
  000 0  0     0  00 0  0 00  000000
   000  0 0 0 0   00     00   0000000
  0000   0     0  00
  00000  0
```

M. Gros gave a very simple rule for counting the number of steps needed to pass from one position to another. In order to derive this rule we shall use his notation for the positions. For a toy with n rings each position is denoted by an n-digit number in the binary scale (including numbers which begin with one or more 0's), each place in the number being reserved for a symbol, 0 or 1, to denote the position of a particular ring. To those places in the binary number which correspond to rings *on* the bar are assigned alternate 1's and 0's, starting with a 1 at the left and disregarding the other rings. If the first ring from the left is off, the digit 0 is assigned to this ring's place in the number. If any other ring is off, we assign to its place the same digit which the ring to its left has; that is to say, the digit to the left of its place is repeated. In this way the set of all positions corresponds uniquely to the set of all numbers from 0 to $2^n - 1$, inclusive. The table compares the notation for four arrangements.

No.	Position of rings (* = on, 0 = off)	Cros notation
1	* 0 * * 0 0 0	1 1 0 1 1 1 1
2	* 0 0 * 0 0 0	1 1 1 0 0 0 0
3	* 0 * * 0 0 *	1 1 0 1 1 1 0
4	* 0 * * 0 * *	1 1 0 1 1 0 1

It can easily be shown that, starting from any position, the operation of taking off a ring which is in position to be taken off either increases or decreases the corresponding number by 1, and similarly for putting on a ring. Conversely, if the number corresponding to a given position is greater than 0, then the position corresponding to the next smaller number can be obtained by putting on or taking off one ring; and in like manner a number less than the maximum can be increased by 1. Since the object of the game is to reduce the number $10101\cdots$ to $00000\cdots$ in the fewest possible number of steps, this may be accomplished in just $10101\cdots$ operations. According to whether n is even or odd this number is $\frac{1}{3}(2^{n+1} - 2)$ or $\frac{1}{3}(2^{n+1} - 1)$. These results are for the slow way.

To find the number of steps by the fast way note that we save 2 steps out of every 8; except at the end, where we save 1 step out of 2 if n is even, 1 step out of 5 if n is odd. From this we find that the number of steps is $2^{n-1} - 1$ if n is even, 2^{n-1} if n is odd.

4. THE TOWER OF HANOI. The theory of the Chinese

rings suggested the idea of this toy to Mr. Claus, mandarin of the College of Li-Sou-Stian (anagram for Mr. Lucas, then a professor at the Lycée Saint-Louis). Three pegs are fastened to a stand; there are 8 (sometimes 6, 7, or 9) wooden or cardboard disks, each with a hole in its center. The disks are of different radii, and at the start of the game all are placed on one peg in order of size, the biggest at the bottom. The problem is to shift the pile from one peg to another by a succession of steps, at each step moving just one disk, and seeing to it that at no stage is any disk underneath a larger one. All three pegs may be used.

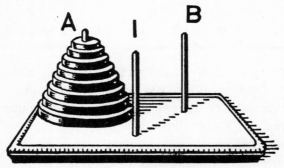

FIGURE 14. *The Tower of Hanoi.*

The problem can always be solved and is very similar to that of the Chinese rings. If the tower has n disks, $2^n - 1$ steps are necessary.

The inventor of the game told the following story about it:

The Mandarin Claus from Siam says that during his travels in connection with the publication of the works of Fer-Fer-Tam-Tam [Fermat] he saw in the great temple at Benares, beneath the dome which marks the center of the world, a brass plate in which are fixed three diamond needles, each a cubit high and as thick as the body of a bee. On one of these needles God placed at the Creation sixty-four disks of pure gold, the largest disk resting on the brass plate, the others getting smaller and smaller up to the top. This is the Tower of Brahma. Day and night unceasingly the priests transfer the disks from one diamond needle to another according to the fixed and immutable laws of Brahma, which require that the priests on duty must not move more than one disk at a time, and that no disk may be placed on a needle which already holds a smaller disk. When the sixty-four disks shall have been thus transferred from the needle on which at the Creation God placed them to one of the other needles, then towers, temple, and priests alike will crumble into dust, and with a thunderclap the world will vanish.

If we suppose that the priests can make one transfer every second, with never a mistake, they must work for $2^{64} - 1 =$ 18,446,744,073,709,551,615 seconds, or more than 500,000 million years.

We can rest easy. The end of the world will not come tomorrow.

13. JOSEPHUS' PROBLEM

1. During the cruel wars between the Moors and the Venetians, a Moorish ship was returning to Africa laden down with booty and captives, the latter to be sold as slaves. During its passage the ship encountered a severe storm, and the captain ordered that half of the 30 captives be thrown overboard to save the ship and the crew. To choose the victims supposedly without favor, the 30 prisoners (of whom 15 were men and 15 were women) were placed in a circle, and every 9th person was thrown overboard. But the captain, a gallant and wily man, placed the women so that all of them were saved. What places did the women occupy?

The solution can easily be found empirically. The women must occupy the places numbered 1, 2, 3, 4, 10, 11, 13, 14, 15, 17, 20, 21, 25, 28, 29.

Many similar questions can be solved in the same manner.

2. According to legend the famous Jewish historian Josephus saved his life by such a stratagem; the story of Josephus has indeed become the type for the problem. After the Romans had captured Jotapat, Josephus and 40 other Jews took refuge in a cave. His companions were resolved to die rather than fall into the hands of their conquerors. Josephus and one friend, not wishing to die yet not daring to dissent openly, feigned to agree. Josephus even proposed an arrangement by which the deaths might take place in an orderly manner. The men were to arrange themselves in a circle; then every third man was to be killed until but one was left, and he must commit suicide. Josephus so placed himself and his friend that they alone escaped.

Answer: Josephus and his friend must occupy places 16 and 31.

3. From among 36 guilty persons there were 6 whom Caligula wanted to punish. He wanted to free the rest if it could be done with an appearance of impartiality. He arranged all 36 in a circle and punished every tenth. In what places did he put the 6 victims?   *Answer:* 4, 10, 15, 20, 26, 30.

4. A suit of 13 cards, the ace, king, queen, jack, 10, $\cdots$, 2 of spades, is arranged in a certain order. The first card is taken off the pack, the second is put at the bottom, the third is taken off, the fourth is put at the bottom, and so on. What was the original order if the order in which the cards were taken off was ace, king, queen, jack, 10, $\cdots$, 2?

Answer: Ace, 3, king, 7, queen, 4, jack, 6, 10, 2, 9, 5, 8.

CHAPTER FOUR

ARITHMETICO–GEOMETRICAL QUESTIONS

In many geometrical problems we must find geometrical elements whose measures are integers. Nearly all these questions lead back to the Pythagorean relation connecting the lengths of the sides of a right triangle: *In any right triangle the square on the hypotenuse is equal to the sum of the squares on the other two sides.* We shall examine this question from the beginning.

1. The algebraic expression of the Pythagorean relation is $x^2 + y^2 = z^2$, where z is the length of the hypotenuse and x, y are the lengths of the legs of the right triangle. If we were to examine the algebraic relation completely we should have to admit irrational and even imaginary values of x, y, and z. However, the most interesting and difficult problems arise when the numbers are required to be rational. The relation is trivial if any of the numbers is zero; and since only their squares appear in the relation the numbers may just as well be considered to be positive. Finally, if any of the numbers are fractions the relation connecting the set of numbers is equivalent to a relation connecting integers obtained from the original set by clearing the equation of fractions. As a result of all these considerations we shall give the following definition:

A Pythagorean number-triple (x, y, z) or, more briefly, a right triangle (x, y, z) is a set of three positive integers connected by the relation $x^2 + y^2 = z^2$. In this notation z will always refer to the number whose square is the sum of the squares of the other two; that is, z may be taken as the length of the hypotenuse.

A further possible restriction is useful. If the three numbers have a common factor the Pythagorean relation continues to hold when this common factor has been removed. Unless the contrary is stipulated we shall assume that all common factors have been removed. The right triangle is then said to be primitive.

2. Since neither x nor y is zero, z must be larger than either. Furthermore $x \neq y$, for if $x = y = a$, then $z^2 = 2a^2$ and $z = a\sqrt{2}$, that is, z is not rational.

If the triangle is primitive, the length of one of the legs must be even and that of the other must be odd. If both were even, the hypotenuse would also be even and the triangle would not be primitive. Suppose, contrariwise, that both were odd, say $x = 2h + 1$, $y = 2k + 1$. Then $x^2 = 4h^2 + 4h + 1 = 4(h^2 + h) + 1$. Whether h is even or odd, $h^2 + h = h(h + 1)$ is even, say $h^2 + h = 2u$, since either h or $h + 1$ is even. Hence $x^2 = 4 \cdot 2u + 1 = 8u + 1$. Similarly, y^2 can be written $8v + 1$. Then

$$z^2 = 8(u + v) + 2 = 2[4(u + v) + 1].$$

Since the second factor is odd, z cannot be rational.

If the right triangle is primitive we shall therefore assume that x is the even number. If the right triangle is not primitive, its numbers may be expressed as the multiples of a primitive right triangle (x', y', z') by a common integral multiplier n, and we shall assume that x is n times the even number x'.

3. The Fundamental Problem. Find three relatively prime numbers x, y, z, rational integers satisfying the relation $x^2 + y^2 = z^2$. (x, y, z are relatively prime if they have no common factor.)

We have seen that we may assume x even and y and z odd.

Since
$$y^2 = z^2 - x^2 = (z + x)(z - x),$$

both $z + x$ and $z - x$ are odd. Further, they have no common divisor. For every common divisor of $z + x$ and $z - x$ is a common divisor of their sum, $2z$, and their difference, $2x$, and hence is a divisor of the greatest common divisor of $2z$ and $2x$. If z and x had a common divisor it would divide y and the triangle would not be primitive. Hence $2z$ and $2x$ have only the common divisor 2. Hence $z + x$ and $z - x$ could have only the common divisor 2, which is impossible since both are odd.

From this it follows that each of the factors $z + x$ and $z - x$ is itself a perfect square, so we may write $z + x = m^2, z - x = n^2$. Since $z + x$ and $z - x$ are both odd, so are m and n. Hence $m + n$ and $m - n$ are both even, and we may set

$$\frac{m + n}{2} = a, \qquad \frac{m - n}{2} = b,$$

that is, $m = a + b, n = a - b$. Then

$$z + x = a^2 + b^2 + 2ab,$$
$$z - x = a^2 + b^2 - 2ab,$$

so $z = a^2 + b^2$, $x = 2ab$, and $y = a^2 - b^2$. It is also easy to see that x and y (and hence x, y, and z) will have a common factor if and only if either a and b have a common factor, or both a and b are odd.

The results of the preceding paragraphs may be summed up thus: (x, y, z) is a primitive right triangle if and only if x, y, and z can be expressed by the formulas $x = 2ab$, $y = a^2 - b^2$, $z = a^2 + b^2$, where a and b are any two relatively prime integers such that $a > b$ and one is even and the other odd. (It is understood that in the notation (x, y, z) the largest number is z and the even number is x.) It is also true that under these conditions no two distinct pairs (a, b) yield the same set (x, y, z).

Now we can solve some problems about right triangles.

4. Given the hypotenuse z of a right triangle, find the legs of the triangle.

Solution: The relation $z = a^2 + b^2$ determines a and b. From them we can calculate $x = 2ab$ and $y = a^2 - b^2$.

It is shown in the theory of numbers that if z is composite then z can be represented as the sum of two squares without a common factor if and only if each of its factors can be so represented. Hence we must first examine the cases in which z is a prime.

First: If $z = 2$ we must have $a = b = 1$. This solution does not give us a primitive triangle, but it will be useful later.

Second: If z is a prime of the form $4k + 1$ it can be shown that there is just one solution for the equation $a^2 + b^2 = z$.

Third: If z is a prime of the form $4k - 1$ there are no solutions.

If z is composite there are two more cases to consider:

Fourth: If z has a prime factor of the form $4k - 1$ there are no solutions unless every such prime factor occurs to an even degree. In the latter case we can write $z = t^2 w$, where every prime factor of t is of the form $4k - 1$ and no prime factor of w is of that form. The solutions will then be of the form (ta', tb'), where (a', b') are solutions of $w = x^2 + y^2$.

Fifth: If z has no prime factors of the form $4k - 1$ there will be several solutions, which may be derived from the expressions of the separate prime factors as sums of squares. To see how this is done let $z = uv$, and suppose that $u = a^2 + b^2$, $v = c^2 + d^2$. Then

$$
\begin{aligned}
z = uv &= (a^2 + b^2)(c^2 + d^2) \\
&= a^2c^2 + b^2d^2 + a^2d^2 + b^2c^2 \\
&= (a^2c^2 \pm 2acbd + b^2d^2) + (a^2d^2 \mp 2adbc + b^2c^2) \\
&= (ac + bd)^2 + (ad - bc)^2 = (ac - bd)^2 + (ad + bc)^2.
\end{aligned}
$$

Thus from two prime factors we can find solutions for their product; from these and the solutions for another prime we can find solutions for the product of the three primes, and so on.

Examples: (1) $z = 29 = 4 \cdot 7 + 1 = 5^2 + 2^2$ only. Hence $x = 2 \cdot 5 \cdot 2 = 20$, $y = 5^2 - 2^2 = 21$, so $(x, y, z) = (20, 21, 29)$.

(2) $z = 145 = 5 \cdot 29 = (2^2 + 1^2)(5^2 + 2^2) = (2 \cdot 5 \pm 1 \cdot 2)^2 + (2 \cdot 2 \mp 1 \cdot 5)^2 = 12^2 + 1^2 = 8^2 + 9^2$. Hence $(x, y, z) = (24, 143, 145)$ or $(144, 17, 145)$.

(3) $z = 58 = 2 \cdot 29 = (1^2 + 1^2)(5^2 + 2^2) = 7^2 + 3^2$ only. $(x, y, z) = (40, 42, 58)$. This triangle is not primitive, as was to be expected from the fact that z is even.

(4) $z = 1{,}105 = 5 \cdot 13 \cdot 17 = (2^2 + 1^2)(3^2 + 2^2)(4^2 + 1^2) = (8^2 + 1^2)(4^2 + 1^2) = (7^2 + 4^2)(4^2 + 1^2) = 33^2 + 4^2 = 31^2 + 12^2 = 32^2 + 9^2 = 24^2 + 23^2$. Hence $(x, y, z) = (264, 1{,}073, 1{,}105)$, $(744, 817, 1{,}105)$, $(576, 943, 1{,}105)$, or $(1{,}104, 47, 1{,}105)$.

(5) $z = 385 = 5 \cdot 7 \cdot 11$. This problem has no solution.

5. Given the even leg of a primitive right triangle, find the other two sides.

Solution: The problem can be solved only when x is divisible by 4. For $x = 2ab$, and just one of the numbers a, b is even. Having given $x = 4m$, we factor $2m$ into a product of two unequal factors without common factor in all possible ways, take the larger as a, the smaller as b, and determine y and z.

Examples:

$4m$	a	b	(x, y, z)
4	2	1	(4, 3, 5)
8	4	1	(8, 15, 17)
12	6	1	(12, 35, 37)
12	3	2	(12, 5, 13)
16	8	1	(16, 63, 65)
20	10	1	(20, 99, 101)
20	5	2	(20, 21, 29)

6. Given the odd leg of a primitive right triangle, find the other two sides.

Solution: Since $y = a^2 - b^2 = (a + b)(a - b)$, we factor y into a product of two unequal, relatively prime factors in all possible ways, and in each case take the larger factor as $a + b = u$, the smaller as $a - b = v$. Then

$$a = \frac{u + v}{2}, \qquad b = \frac{u - v}{2},$$

and both are integers since both u and v are odd.

Examples:

y	$a + b$	$a - b$	a	b	(x, y, z)
3	3	1	2	1	(4, 3, 5)
5	5	1	3	2	(12, 5, 13)
15	15	1	8	7	(112, 15, 113)
15	5	3	4	1	(8, 15, 17)

7. Find a right triangle whose legs are consecutive integers.

Solution: $y - x$ is either $+1$ or -1, so $(a^2 - b^2) - 2ab = (a - b)^2 - 2b^2 = \pm 1$. We may set $a - b = u$ and $b = v$ (then $a = u + v$), and our problem now is to solve the equation $u^2 - 2v^2 = \pm 1$ in integers. (This is a particular case of what is usually called Pell's equation.) In the theory of numbers it is shown that this equation can be solved by expressing $\sqrt{2}$ as an infinite continued fraction,

$$\sqrt{2} = 1 + \cfrac{1}{2 + \cfrac{1}{2 + \cdots}} = (1, 2, 2, 2 \cdots).$$

If we cut off this continued fraction at any point the value of the resulting fraction is an irreducible simple fraction called a convergent. Thus $1 = \frac{1}{1}$ is the first convergent, $1 + \frac{1}{2} = \frac{3}{2}$ is the second,

$$1 + \cfrac{1}{2 + \frac{1}{2}} = \frac{7}{5}$$

is the third, and so on. The next two convergents are $\frac{17}{12}$ and $\frac{41}{29}$. If we set the numerator of any convergent equal to u and its denominator equal to v, then u and v satisfy $u^2 - 2v^2 =$ $+1$ or -1 according to whether $\frac{u}{v}$ is an even or odd convergent. The first few solutions of our problem are, then,

$a - b$	b	a	(x, y, z)
1	1	2	(4, 3, 5)
3	2	5	(20, 21, 29)
7	5	12	(120, 119, 169)
17	12	29	(696, 697, 985)
41	$\cdots$	$\cdots$	

8. Find a primitive right triangle whose hypotenuse exceeds its even leg by 1.

Solution: From $z - x = 1$ we have $a^2 + b^2 - 2ab = (a - b)^2 = 1$. Since $a > b$, we must have $a - b = 1$; that is, b and a must be consecutive integers.

9. Find a right triangle whose area is equal to its perimeter.

Solution: We must have $\frac{xy}{2} = x + y + z$, that is,

$$ab(a^2 - b^2) = 2ab + a^2 + b^2 + a^2 - b^2 = 2a(a + b),$$

so $b(a - b) = 2$. Hence we must have either $b = 2, a - b = 1,$ $a = 3$, or $b = 1, a - b = 2, a = 3$. Thus there are just two such triangles: (12, 5, 13) and (6, 8, 10), with perimeters and areas 30 and 24 respectively.

10. FURTHER PROPERTIES OF PRIMITIVE RIGHT TRIANGLES.

First: One leg of a primitive right triangle is divisible by 3. For if a or b is divisible by 3, $x = 2ab$ is divisible by 3. If neither a nor b is divisible by 3, then $y = a^2 - b^2$ is, since the squares of both a and b are of the form $3k + 1$.

Second: One of the sides of a primitive triangle is divisible by 5. We shall prove this by showing that the product of the three sides is divisible by 5. This product is

$$2ab(a^2 - b^2)\ (a^2 + b^2) = 2ab(a^4 - b^4).$$

if a or b is a multiple of 5, so is $2ab$. If neither a nor b is a multiple of 5, then $a^4 - b^4$ is. For a is then of one of the forms $5k \pm 1$, $5k \pm 2$. If we expand the fourth power of each of these by the binomial theorem, we find at once that a^4 is of the form $5h + 1$. Similarly for b^4.

Third: The area of a primitive right triangle is divisible by 6, and the product of its sides by 60. For x is divisible by 4, x or y is divisible by 3, and x, y, or z is divisible by 5. Hence the area, $\frac{xy}{2}$, is divisible by $\frac{4 \cdot 3}{2}$, and xyz is divisible by $4 \cdot 3 \cdot 5$.

11. TRIGONOMETRIC RELATIONS. A primitive right triangle will be called elementary or composite according as its hypotenuse is prime or composite.

An angle is called arithmetical if all of its trigonometric functions are rational. (The multiples of 90° are considered to be arithmetical although some of their trigonometric functions do not exist.) We shall show that an angle is arithmetical if and only if it is an angle of a primitive right triangle, or differs from such an angle by a multiple of 90°.

Let (x, y, z) be the sides of a primitive right triangle, and let X, Y, Z be the angles opposite the respective sides. Z is the right angle, and X and Y are the acute angles. Since all the angles are determined by either acute angle we shall call Y *the* angle of the right triangle. Then

$$\sin Y = \frac{y}{z} = \frac{a^2 - b^2}{a^2 + b^2} = \cos X,$$

$$\cos Y = \frac{x}{z} = \frac{2ab}{a^2 + b^2} = \sin X,$$

$$\tan Y = \frac{y}{x} = \frac{a^2 - b^2}{2ab} = \cot X,$$

$$\sin Z = 1, \qquad \cos Z = 0, \qquad \tan Z = \infty.$$

and the other trigonometric functions of these angles are the reciprocals of those given. Thus all the trigonometric functions of all the angles of a primitive triangle are rational and the angles are arithmetical. Let A be an arithmetical angle. If A is a multiple of 90° the theorem is trivial. If A is not a multiple of 90° we know from the reduction formulas of trigonometry that there is a positive acute angle B, differing from $\pm A$ by a multiple of 90°, whose trigonometric functions have the same numerical values as those of A. Let $\sin B = \frac{y}{z}$, $\cos B = \frac{x}{z}$. Then $x^2 + y^2 = z^2$ and B lies in an integral right triangle.

An angle B is arithmetical if and only if $\tan \frac{B}{2}$ is rational. For if $\tan \frac{B}{2} = \frac{m}{n}$, then

$$\tan B = \frac{2mn}{m^2 - n^2} \qquad \text{and} \qquad \tan (B - 90°) = \frac{n^2 - m^2}{2mn}.$$

Some multiple of 180° added to one of the angles B, $B - 90°$ is acute and belongs to an integral right triangle. The converse is obvious.

Since the trigonometric addition formulas are rational functions of the trigonometric functions of the angles added or subtracted, it is clear that the sum and difference of arithmetical angles are arithmetical. More generally, if A, B, C, $\cdots$ are arithmetical angles, and h, k, l, $\cdots$ are integers (positive, negative or zero), then the linear function $hA + kB + lC + \cdots$ of the given angles is arithmetical.

12. Let (x, y, z) and $(x', y', z') = (2cd, c^2 - d^2, c^2 + d^2)$ be two elementary triangles. We found on page 98 that the triangles with hypotenuse zz' are

$$(2ef,\ e^2 - f^2,\ e^2 + f^2) \qquad \text{and} \qquad (2gh,\ g^2 - h^2,\ g^2 + h^2),$$

where $\qquad e^2 + f^2 = (ac + bd)^2 + (ad - bc)^2$

and $\qquad g^2 + h^2 = (ac - bd)^2 + (ad + bc)^2.$

If the smaller angle of (x, y, z) is greater than the smaller angle of (x', y', z'), then it can easily be shown that the smaller angle of the first of these new triangles is the difference of the smaller angles of the original triangles, and the smaller angle of the second is their sum.

If $z = z'$, then $ad - bc = 0$ and only the second triangle exists. In this case the smaller angle of the new triangle is twice the smaller angle of the original.

13. HERONIAN TRIANGLES. A Heronian, or arithmetical, triangle is one whose sides and area are all rational. Hence the altitudes are also rational. The triangle is accordingly called by some mathematicians a rational triangle. If the vertices are A, B, C, the lengths of the opposite sides are a, b, c, the semiperimeter $\frac{1}{2}(a + b + c)$ is s, the area is K, and the radius of the inscribed circle is r, then we know from geometry that

$$r = \frac{K}{s}, \quad \tan\frac{A}{2} = \frac{r}{s-a}, \quad \tan\frac{B}{2} = \frac{r}{s-b}, \quad \tan\frac{C}{2} = \frac{r}{s-c},$$

so these quantities are all rational and the angles are arithmetical. One can also show quite easily that the radii of the circumscribed and escribed circles are rational.

Since the angles of a Heronian triangle are arithmetical, a perpendicular from a vertex to an opposite side forms two rational right triangles whose sum or difference is the given triangle. By using this fact we can form any desired Heronian triangle which is not a right triangle by combining two rational right triangles of different shapes. Let $(x, y, z) = (2ab,\ a^2 - b^2,\ a^2 + b^2)$ and $(u, v, w) = (2cd,\ c^2 - d^2,\ c^2 + d^2)$ be two such primitive triangles. If we form triangles similar to these and having a leg of one equal to a leg of the other, we can form two Heronian triangles by bringing the equal legs into coincidence and letting the unequal legs lie on a common perpendicular to the common leg, either on the same side of it or on opposite sides. Since either leg of one right triangle can be used with either leg of the other, four such

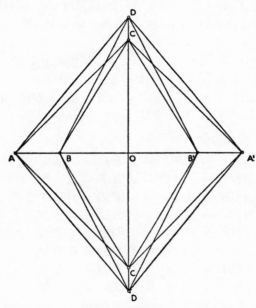

FIGURE 15. *Heronian Triangles in Combination.*

pairs of Heronian triangles can be formed; that is, any pair of dissimilar rational right triangles gives rise to eight dissimilar scalene Heronian triangles. In addition, two dissimilar isosceles Heronian triangles can be formed from a single rational right triangle.

Figure 15 exhibits these results in a beautifully symmetric pattern. Using the triangles (x, y, z) and (u, v, w), we form the triangles (ux, uy, uz), (vx, vy, vz), (xu, xv, xw), (yu, yv, yw). These can then be arranged as in the figure, where

$$OA = OA' = xu = 4abcd,$$
$$OB = OB' = yv = (a^2 - b^2)(c^2 - d^2),$$
$$OC = OC' = yu = 2cd(a^2 - b^2),$$
$$OD = OD' = xv = 2ab(c^2 - d^2).$$

Then $AB = A'B'$, $AB' = A'B$, $CD = C'D'$ and $CD' = C'D$ are formed from these by taking sums and differences. (In a figure based on different right triangles the relative positions of A and B may be interchanged, as may those of C and D.) Also,

$$AC = AC' = A'C = A'C' = zu = 2cd(a^2 + b^2),$$
$$AD = AD' = A'D = A'D' = xw = 2ab(c^2 + d^2),$$
$$BC = BC' = B'C = B'C' = yw = (a^2 - b^2)(c^2 + d^2),$$
$$BD = BD' = B'D = B'D' = zv = (a^2 + b^2)(c^2 - d^2).$$

The scalene triangles are:

$$ABC = ABC' = A'B'C = A'B'C',$$
$$AB'C = AB'C' = A'BC = A'BC',$$
$$ABD = ABD' = A'B'D = A'B'D',$$
$$AB'D = AB'D' = A'BD = A'BD',$$
$$CDA = CDA' = C'D'A = C'D'A',$$
$$CD'A = CD'A' = C'DA = C'DA',$$
$$CDB = CDB' = C'D'B = C'D'B',$$
$$CD'B = CD'B' = C'DB = C'DB'.$$

The isosceles triangles are:

$$AA'C = AA'C',$$
$$AA'D = AA'D',$$
$$BB'C = BB'C',$$
$$BB'D = BB'D',$$

to which the following are respectively similar:

$$DD'B = DD'B',$$
$$CC'B = CC'B',$$
$$DD'A = DD'A',$$
$$CC'A = CC'A'.$$

In addition there are four Heronian parallelograms (parallelograms with rational sides, diagonals, and areas):

$$ACA'C', \quad ADA'D', \quad BCB'C', \quad BDB'D'.$$

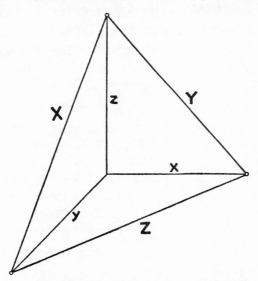

FIGURE 16. *Diagonals and Edges of Three Faces of a Cuboid.*

We may obtain the same result by starting with two arithmetical angles, A, B, given by

$$\sin A = \frac{p^2 - q^2}{p^2 + q^2} \quad \text{or} \quad \frac{2pq}{p^2 + q^2},$$

$$\sin B = \frac{r^2 - s^2}{r^2 + s^2} \quad \text{or} \quad \frac{2\,rs}{r^2 + s^2}.$$

When any pair of values of $\sin A$ and $\sin B$ has been selected, the larger acute angle may be taken as interior or exterior to the triangle, so eight different triangles may be formed.

Again, we may start with the circumscribed circle of radius R, using the relations

$$\frac{a}{\sin A} = \frac{b}{\sin B} = \frac{c}{\sin C} = 2R.$$

The triangles will then be determined by the sines of the arithmetical angles A and B as before.

14. Find a cuboid (rectangular parallelepiped) in which the edges and the diagonals of the faces are all rational. This is a more difficult problem. (See Fig. 16.)

We can take $x = a(4b^2 - c^2)$, $y = b(4a^2 - c^2)$, $z = 4abc$, where a, b, c are the sides of a rational right triangle: $a = m^2 - n^2$, $b = 2mn$, $c = m^2 + n^2$. Then

$$X = b(4a^2 + c^2), \qquad Y = a(4b^2 + c^2), \qquad Z = c^3.$$

These formulas do not give the complete solution. Here are some that cannot be obtained from them:

x	85	187	195	231	275	855	1,105	1,155	1,155	$\cdots$
y	132	1,020	748	792	252	2,640	9,360	1,100	6,300	$\cdots$
z	720	1,584	6,336	160	240	832	35,904	1,008	6,688	$\cdots$

From any solution we can derive a new one by taking $u = yz$, $v = zx$, $w = xy$.

CHAPTER FIVE

THE CALENDAR

TIME can be measured only by observing the motions of bodies that move in unchanging cycles. The only motions of this nature are those of the heavenly bodies, which continue in their courses with inimitable constancy and limitless duration. Hence we owe to astronomy the establishment of a secure basis for the measurement of time by determining the lengths of the day, the month, and the year. The week of seven days is an artificial unit, though it has been used from time immemorial.

For measuring astronomical periods of time longer than the day, two systems have been in common use. One uses the lunation as the fundamental cycle, a lunation being the time from one new moon to the next. The other is based on the sun's year, and it is this which we shall study.

The first difficulty is that the length of the year is not commensurable with the length of the day, for the year contains about 365.242199 days. The history of the calendar is the history of the attempts to adjust these incommensurable units in such a way as to obtain a simple and practicable system.

Our calendar story goes back to Romulus, the legendary founder of Rome, who introduced a year of 300 days divided into 10 months. His successor, Numa, added two months. This hardly scientific calendar was used for the following six and a half centuries until Julius Caesar introduced a more exact year of 365.25 days. The difficulty of the extra quarter of a day was handled by making the length of the ordinary

year just 365 days and making every fourth year a leap year
of 366 days. The Julian calendar spread abroad with other
important features of Roman culture, and was generally used
until 1582.

The Julian year was a little too long, and by 1582 the ac-
cumulated error amounted to 10 days. A second reform,
instituted by Pope Gregory XIII, compensated for the error
and required that for the future the last year of each century
should not be a leap year unless the number of the century
were divisible by 4. Thus, 1700, 1800, 1900, 2100, · · · are
not leap years, but 2000 is.

Gauss gave a formula for finding the day of the week corresponding to a given date. This formula is:

$$W \equiv D + M + C + Y \ (\text{modulo } 7),$$

where W is the day of the week (starting with Sunday = 1),
D is the day of the month, and M, C, and Y are numbers depending on the month, the century and the year, respectively. The values of M, C, and Y are given in the tables
on page 111.

In determining the value of Y, the number of the year
must be diminished by one if the month is January or
February.

Many tables and mechanisms have been devised to solve
this problem. We shall give two of the simplest, which are
nomograms.

The first is shown in Figure 17.

To find the day of the week corresponding to a given date,
on Figure 17, proceed as follows:

1. Write the given date as a set of four numbers — the
day of the month (called the Date in the first scale of the
nomogram), the month (third scale), the first two numbers
of the year (called the Century in the fourth scale), and the
last two numbers of the year (called the Year in the first

Month	M
January	0
February	3
March	3
April	6
May	1
June	4
July	6
August	2
September	5
October	0
November	3
December	5

First Two Digits of the Year	C

Gregorian Calendar

First Two Digits	C
15, 19, 23, · · ·	1
16, 20, 24, · · ·	0
17, 21, 25, · · ·	5
18, 22, 26, · · ·	3

Julian Calendar

First Two Digits	C
00, 07, 14, · · ·	5
01, 08, 15, · · ·	4
02, 09, 16, · · ·	3
03, 10, 17, · · ·	2
04, 11, 18, · · ·	1
05, 12, 19, · · ·	0
06, 13, 20, · · ·	6

Last Two Digits of the Year									Y
00	06		17	23	28	34		45	0
01	07	12	18		29	35	40	46	1
02		13	19	24	30		41	47	2
03	08	14		25	31	36	42		3
	09	15	20	26		37	43	48	4
04	10		21	27	32	38		49	5
05	11	16	22		33	39	44	50	6
51	56	62		73	79	84	90		0
	57	63	68	74		85	91	96	1
52	58		69	75	80	86		97	2
53	59	64	70		81	87	92	98	3
54		65	71	76	82		93	99	4
55	60	66		77	83	88	94		5
	61	67	72	78		89	95		6

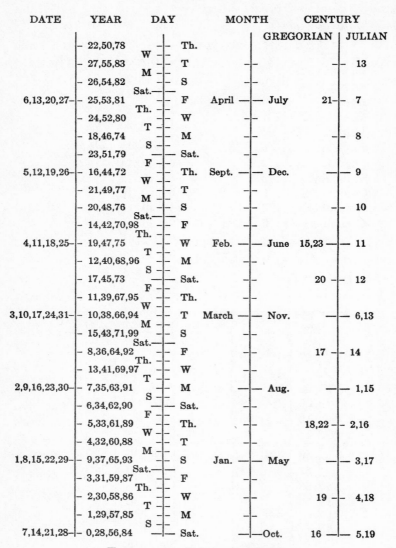

DATE	YEAR	DAY	MONTH	CENTURY	
				GREGORIAN	JULIAN
	– 22,50,78				
	W				
	– 27,55,83	–– T			–– 13
	M				
	– 26,54,82	–– S			
	Sat.––				
6,13,20,27–	– 25,53,81	–– F	April ––	– July 21–	–– 7
	Th.				
	– 24,52,80	–– W			
	T				
	– 18,46,74	–– M			–– 8
	S				
	– 23,51,79	–– Sat.			
	F				
5,12,19,26–	– 16,44,72	–– Th.	Sept. ––	– Dec.	–– 9
	W				
	– 21,49,77	–– T			
	M				
	– 20,48,76	–– S			–– 10
	Sat.––				
	– 14,42,70,98	–– F			
	Th.				
4,11,18,25–	– 19,47,75	–– W	Feb. ––	– June 15,23 ––	– 11
	T				
	– 12,40,68,96	–– M			
	S				
	– 17,45,73	–– Sat.		20 –	– 12
	F				
	– 11,39,67,95	–– Th.			
	W				
3,10,17,24,31–	– 10,38,66,94	–– T	March ––	– Nov.	–– 6,13
	M				
	– 15,43,71,99	–– S			
	Sat.––				
	– 8,36,64,92	–– F		17 –	– 14
	Th.				
	– 13,41,69,97	–– W			
	T				
2,9,16,23,30–	– 7,35,63,91	–– M		– Aug.	–– 1,15
	S				
	– 6,34,62,90	–– Sat.			
	F				
	– 5,33,61,89	–– Th.		18,22 –	– 2,16
	W				
	– 4,32,60,88	–– T			
	M				
1,8,15,22,29–	– 9,37,65,93	–– S	Jan. ––	– May	–– 3,17
	Sat.––				
	– 3,31,59,87	–– F			
	Th.				
	– 2,30,58,86	–– W		19 –	– 4,18
	T				
	– 1,29,57,85	–– M			
	S				
7,14,21,28–	– 0,28,56,84	–– Sat.	––Oct.	16 ––	– 5,19

FIGURE 17. *Perpetual Calendar.*

scale). *For the months January and February the Year should be diminished by 1.*

2. With a straight edge, join the point on the first scale given by the Date with that given by the Month on the third scale, and mark the point of intersection with the second scale.

3. Join the point thus found with the point on the fourth scale given by the Century, and mark the point of intersection with the third scale. (Use the heading Gregorian or Julian for the Century, according to whether the date is New Style or Old Style. The date of adoption of the new calendar varies in different countries, but was 1582 for most of Europe.)

4. Join the point found in (3) with the point given by the Year in the first scale. The point of intersection with the second scale gives the day of the week.

Another arrangement is shown in Figure 18.

For successful use of the calendar in Figure 18, its plan and terminology need to be well understood. Observe that it consists of three concentric rings intersected by seven radii. Each radius is identified by the name of a day of the week. Where each radius intersects the innermost ring is a set of numbers; these are Year numbers — 42 for 1842, 1942, and so on, is at the point where this ring meets the Tuesday radius. Again, where each radius cuts the intermediate ring, more numbers are found, prefixed either by a J (for Julian) or a G (for Gregorian; these are Century numbers, as 19 for 1942, and Gregorian 19 is found where the Friday radius cuts the intermediate ring. Where the radii meet the outer ring, the month names are found inside and the day-of-the-month numbers (Dates) outside. We have then to consider *Dates, Months, Centuries,* and *Years* in order to find the day of the week on which a known date fell or is to fall. A ruler and pencil may be needed at first; after a little practice they can be laid aside; points mentioned in these instructions are always ring-radius intersections, and the required parallels are easy to visualize. Now proceed, for any date, as follows:

1. Locate the Date and the Month on the outer ring; if

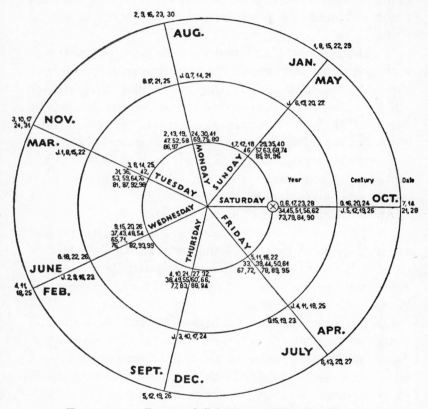

FIGURE 18. *Perpetual Calendar, Radius-ring Type.*

they are two points, draw a line between them; if they coincide, draw a tangent.

2. Locate the Century on the intermediate ring. Through this point draw a line parallel to the line already drawn, until it intersects the intermediate ring at another point; if this line is tangent to the ring, then the starting point is also the

"other point." In any case, the point found will be a ring-radius intersection.

3. From the point just found, follow the radius to the inner ring. Then locate the Year, which will be found at some

DETAIL FINDER FOR PERPETUAL CALENDAR

Item	Sun.	Mon.	Tues.	Wed.	Thurs.	Fri.	Sat.
Date of month (outer ring)	1	2	3	4	5	6	7
	8	9	10	11	12	13	14
	15	16	17	18	19	20	21
	22	23	24	25	26	27	28
	29	30	31				
Gregorian century (intermediate ring)		17		18		15	16
		21		22		19	20
		25		26		23	24
Julian century (intermediate ring)		0	1	2	3	4	5
	6	7	8	9	10	11	12
	13	14	15	16	17	18	19
	20	21	22	23	24	25	26
	27						
Year (inner ring)						→	00
	1	2	3	→	4	5	6
	7	→	8	9	10	11	→
	12	13	14	15	→	16	17
	18	19	→	20	21	22	23
	→	24	25	26	27	→	28
	29	30	31	→	32	33	34
	35	→	36	37	38	39	→
	40	41	42	43	→	44	45
	46	47	→	48	49	50	51
	→	52	53	54	55	→	56
	57	58	59	→	60	61	62
	63	→	64	65	66	67	→
	68	69	70	71	→	72	73
	74	75	→	76	77	78	79
	→	80	81	82	83	→	84
	85	86	87	→	88	89	90
	91	→	92	93	94	95	→
	96	97	98	99			

intersection of this inner ring and a radius. (If the month is January or February, use the preceding year.) Draw a line between these two points on the inner ring; if they coincide, then draw a tangent to the inner ring. (If they coincide on Saturday, then Saturday is the week day sought.)

4. Now find the point where the Saturday radius cuts the inner ring, and through this Saturday point draw a line parallel to the line just drawn. The two lines may coincide; in any case, the line will meet the inner ring at some radius-ring intersection. The week day on this latter radius is the week day of the Date with which we began. If the last line drawn is tangent to the inner ring at the Saturday intersection, then the day is Saturday.

To help in locating such details as Date of the month, Year number and Century number, a table has been prepared. If there is any difficulty in locating a Year, say 45, it may be looked up in the detail-finding table, which will show that Year 45 is at the intersection of the inner ring and the Saturday radius.

CHAPTER SIX

PROBABILITIES

THE serious investigation of the laws of chance began with Pascal and Fermat in the seventeenth century. Our first problem is a more general statement of a question brought to Pascal by the Chevalier de Méré, a gambler friend of Pascal. It was this problem which started Pascal on his researches in the field of probability.

1. THE UNFINISHED GAME. A and B are playing a game in which a point is scored for either A or B at the end of each play, and the first to win N points wins the game. Thus there are no drawn games. The game is interrupted when A needs a points in order to win, and B needs b points. How should the stakes be divided between the players?

Solution: Let m and $n = 1 - m$ be the respective probabilities that A and B will win any one point, and p and $q = 1 - p$ their respective chances of winning the game at the time the game stopped. Then the stakes should be divided in the ratio $p:q$, where

$$p = m^a\left[1 + \frac{a}{1}n + \frac{a(a+1)}{1\cdot 2}n^2 + \cdots + \frac{a(a+1)\cdots(a+b-2)}{(b-1)!}n^{b-1}\right],$$

$$q = n^b\left[1 + \frac{b}{1}m + \frac{b(b+1)}{1\cdot 2}m^2 + \cdots + \frac{b(b+1)\cdots(b+a-2)}{(a-1)!}m^{a-1}\right].$$

If the game is one in which $m = n = \frac{1}{2}$, as in matching pennies or cutting for the high card, then the relative values of p and q may be listed in such a table as the following:

		p				
		$a = 1$	$a = 2$	$a = 3$	$a = 4$	$a = 5$
	$b = 1$	128	64	32	16	8
	$b = 2$	192	128	80	48	28
q	$b = 3$	224	176	128	88	58
	$b = 4$	240	208	168	128	93
	$b = 5$	248	228	198	163	128

Each entry in this table corresponds to the value of p for the given values of a and b, but the probabilities have all been multiplied by a common factor in order to eliminate fractions. Since the value of p for given (a, b) is the same as the value of q when a and b are interchanged, the ratio of the respective chances of A and B when A needs a games and B needs b games is the ratio of the entry under (a, b) to the entry under (b, a) and the stakes should be divided accordingly.

Example: A and B, who are considered to be equally proficient tennis players, begin a match for a prize of $1,000, which is to go to the first one to win 3 sets. At the end of the third set, when A has won 1 game and B has won 2, the match has to be called off because of bad weather. How should the money be divided?

Answer: In the table we find the entry 64 under $a = 2$ and $b = 1$, and the entry 192 under $a = 1$, $b = 2$. Hence the money should be divided in the ratio $64:192 = 1:3$, so A should receive $250 and B $750.

2. A Dice Problem. What is the probability of throwing a twelve in n throws of two dice?

Solution: In any one throw of two dice there are 36 equally likely results, since any one of the 6 faces of one die may come up with any one of the 6 faces of the other. Just one of these possibilities produces a twelve, namely the appearance of the six on each die. Hence the probability of throwing a twelve in one throw is $\frac{1}{36}$, the probability of throwing something else is $\frac{35}{36}$. If we make n throws there are 36^n equally likely cases, favorable and unfavorable, of which 35^n are unfavorable. Hence the probability of throwing at least one twelve in n throws is

$$\frac{36^n - 35^n}{36^n} = 1 - \left(\frac{35}{36}\right)^n.$$

If we want this probability to be $\frac{1}{2}$, we must have $(\frac{35}{36})^n = 1 - (\frac{1}{2}) = \frac{1}{2}$, whence

$$n = \frac{\log 2}{\log 36 - \log 35} = 24.605\cdots.$$

Thus it is slightly advantageous to bet even money on throwing a twelve in 25 throws, but slightly disadvantageous to bet on its occurrence in 24 throws.

This problem also was proposed to Pascal by the Chevalier de Méré. Here is an extract of a letter that Pascal wrote to Fermat about it:

I have not time to send you the demonstration of a difficulty that astonished M. de Méré. He is very bright, but he is no geometer; and that, as you know, is a great defect. He told me that he had the following difficulty with numbers: If one wagers on the throwing of a six with a single die, it is advantageous to wager that the six will come up once in 4 throws. But if one wagers on throwing twelve with two dice, there is a disadvantage in wagering that it will occur in 24 tries. Nevertheless, 24 is to 36 (which is the product of the number of faces of the two dice) as 4 is to 6 (the number of faces on one die). To him this was a great scandal, and this it was which made him say loudly that arithmetical theorems are not always true, and that arithmetic contradicts itself.

3. BRIDGE HANDS. Many interesting mathematical questions arise in connection with the game of bridge. Here we are concerned only with the probabilities of various distributions of cards among the hands. Other questions will be dealt with in Chapter Nine.

The likelihood that any particular given distribution will occur is in general very slight. For instance, the probability that each player will have a complete suit is $\dfrac{(13!)^4 4!}{52!}$, that is, 1 to 2,235,197,406,895,366,368,301,560,000.

Here are the probabilities for the different distributions of the cards in one hand.

Distribution	Probability	Distribution	Probability
4–3–3–3	0.1054	7–3–3–0	0.0027
4–4–3–2	.2151	7–5–1–0	.0011
4–4–4–1	.0299	7–6–0–0	.0001
5–3–3–2	0.1552	8–2–2–1	
5–4–3–1	.1293	8–3–1–1	
5–4–2–2	.1058	8–3–2–0	0.0047
5–5–2–1	.0317	8–4–1–0	
5–4–4–0	.0124	8–5–0–0	
5–5–3–0	.0090	9–2–1–1	
6–3–2–2	0.0564	9–2–2–0	
6–4–2–1	.0470	9–3–1–0	
6–3–3–1	.0345	9–4–0–0	
6–4–3–0	.0133	10–1–1–1	
6–5–1–1	.0071	10–2–1–0	0.0002
6–5–2–0	.0065	10–3–0–0	
6–6–1–0	.0007	11–1–1–0	
7–3–2–1	0.0188	11–2–0–0	
7–2–2–2	.0052		
7–4–1–1	.0039	12–1–0–0	
7–4–2–0	.0036	13–0–0–0	

Some interesting conclusions can be drawn from this table. For instance, one can determine the probability that at least one suit will not be represented, that is, that the hand will be blank in one suit. Similarly, one may find the probability of having at least one singleton, or of having a 9-card suit. The next table lists the probabilities that some suit will be represented in the hand by just *n* cards.

Cards in suit	Probability	Cards in suit	Probability
0	0.0510	4	0.3508
1	.3055	5	.4434
2	.5381	6	.1655
3	.1054	7	.0354
		8	.0047
		9–13	.0002
	1.0000		1.0000

Here is a table telling what hopes one may have of finding trumps in the dummy:

Trumps in bidder's hand	Probability of the occurrence in the dummy of just *n* trumps								Total
	$n = 1$	$n = 2$	$n = 3$	$n = 4$	$n = 5$	$n = 6$	$n = 7$	$n = 8$	
4	–	–	–	.2219	.0908	.0211	.0027	.0001	0.3366
5	–	–	.3057	.1738	.0544	.0091	.0007	.0000	0.5437
6	–	.3336	.2355	.1024	.0230	.0025	.0001	–	0.6971
7	.2621	.3574	.2279	.0712	.0103	.0005	–	–	0.9294

4. The Error Curve. In many applications of probabilities one must use the error curve (Figure 19), whose equation is $y = Ae^{-bx^2}$. This curve may be thought of as arising in the following way. Suppose an experimenter has to measure a certain quantity. He is able to read off measurements from his instrument to within a certain degree of accuracy, say 0.0001 inch. Successive measurements of the same quantity will not ordinarily produce the same readings. If he marks off on the x-axis of a co-ordinate system equally spaced points for the possible readings (say one for each .0001 inch in the vicinity of the expected value), and takes as ordinate at each such point the number of times the corresponding reading has occurred, the greater the total number of readings the more closely will the ordinates come to assuming the shape of the error curve when they have been

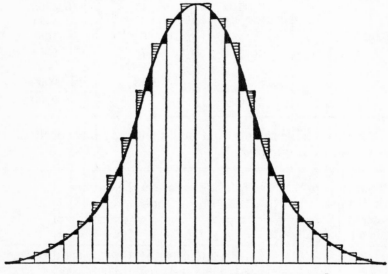

FIGURE 19. *The Error Curve:* $y = Ae^{-bx^2}$. *

joined by a smooth curve. The constants A and b permit one to adjust the steepness of the curve to fit varying conditions.

Halton's apparatus (illustrated in Figure 20) enables one to find the curve mechanically. It consists of an inclined board into which have been fixed a great many pins as obstacles. At the top is a reservoir of shot with a hole at the middle of its lower edge. When the hole is opened the shot roll down the board, hitting the nails as they pass. At the bottom of the board are narrow straight-sided compartments,

* From *Mathematics for the Million*, by Lancelot T. Hogben, published by W. W. Norton & Company, Inc., New York.

into some one of which each shot must eventually roll. As the shot pile up in these compartments, the tops of the piles form an error curve.*

5. CRAPS. Two dice are thrown. If the total turned up is 7 or 11 (a natural), the thrower wins and retains the dice

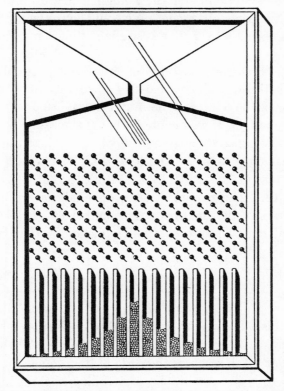

FIGURE 20. *Halton's Pin-and-ball Apparatus for Producing the Error Curve.*

for another throw. If the total is 2, 3, or 12 (craps), the thrower loses, but retains the dice. If the total is any other number the play is incomplete. The number just thrown is called the thrower's point, and the thrower must continue

* The error curve is also known as the normal distribution curve and the probability curve.

to throw in the effort to make the point, that is, to throw this number again before he throws a 7. If he is successful, he wins and retains the dice. But if not, that is, if the point never reappears and a 7 is thrown, the thrower loses on the throw of 7 and the dice pass to the next player. It is possible that neither the point nor the 7 might come up, but, as we shall see, the probability that play could continue in this way for an appreciably long time is so slight that it may be disregarded.

Consider first the probability of throwing a particular total on a single throw. There are $6 \cdot 6 = 36$ equally likely ways in which one of the 6 faces of die A and one of the 6 faces of die B may come up. If we denote by (a, b) the respective numbers of spots exposed on the two dice, we see that the total 2 can appear only as $(1, 1)$, the total 3 as $(1, 2)$ or $(2, 1), \cdots$, the total 6 as $(1, 5)$, $(2, 4)$, $(3, 3)$, $(4, 2)$, $(5, 1), \cdots$, the total 12 as $(6, 6)$, The results of such an analysis are listed in the following table, in which the number of ways in which each total may be thrown (the frequency of that total) is given.

Total	2	3	4	5	6	7	8	9	10	11	12
Frequency	1	2	3	4	5	6	5	4	3	2	1

From this table we can draw all the conclusions needed in the theory of the game. First, the probability of throwing a particular total, say 5, is the ratio of its frequency to 36, in this case $\frac{4}{36} = \frac{1}{9}$. Again, the probability of throwing some one of several totals, say of throwing a 2, a 3, or a 12, is the sum of the probabilities of the separate totals, $\frac{1}{36} + \frac{2}{36} + \frac{1}{36} = \frac{4}{36} = \frac{1}{9}$. The probability of making a point, say of throwing a 5 before throwing a 7, is the ratio of the frequency of the point to the sum of the frequency of the point plus the frequency of 7: in the case of making 5, $\dfrac{4}{4+6} = \dfrac{4}{10} = \dfrac{2}{5}$.

Finally, the probability of throwing a point *and* then of making it is the product of the separate probabilities: for example, $(\frac{1}{9})(\frac{2}{5}) = \frac{2}{45}$ is the probability that the thrower will win by throwing a 5 and making his point. In this way we arrive at the following table of all possible results of one play:

Result of play		Probability	
The thrower wins			
by throwing a natural:	7 or 11	$\dfrac{6+2}{36} = \dfrac{2}{9} = \dfrac{220}{990}$	
by throwing and making	6 or 8	$2 \cdot \dfrac{5}{36} \cdot \dfrac{5}{5+6} = \dfrac{25}{198} = \dfrac{125}{990}$	
by throwing and making	5 or 9	$2 \cdot \dfrac{4}{36} \cdot \dfrac{4}{4+6} = \dfrac{4}{45} = \dfrac{88}{990}$	
by throwing and making	4 or 10	$2 \cdot \dfrac{3}{36} \cdot \dfrac{3}{3+6} = \dfrac{1}{18} = \dfrac{55}{990}$	
in any one of these ways		$\dfrac{488}{990}$	$\dfrac{244}{495}$
The thrower loses			
by throwing craps:	2, 3, or 12	$\dfrac{1+2+1}{36} = \dfrac{1}{9} = \dfrac{55}{495}$	
by throwing and losing	4 or 10	$2 \cdot \dfrac{3}{36} \cdot \dfrac{6}{3+6} = \dfrac{1}{9} = \dfrac{55}{495}$	
by throwing and losing	5 or 9	$2 \cdot \dfrac{4}{36} \cdot \dfrac{6}{4+6} = \dfrac{2}{15} = \dfrac{66}{495}$	
by throwing and losing	6 or 8	$2 \cdot \dfrac{5}{36} \cdot \dfrac{6}{5+6} = \dfrac{5}{33} = \dfrac{75}{495}$	
in any one of these ways			$\dfrac{251}{495}$

From these results it appears that the thrower is at a slight disadvantage, since the odds against him are 251 to 244. This is interesting in the light of the almost universal feeling among players (even honest ones) that they would rather hold the dice. The game is made equitable if the dice go from player to player according to the rules given above.

The sum of the probabilities given above is 1, which de-notes certainty. That would seem to say that if the calculations are correct any play is bound to end. This is not quite the proper interpretation. Suppose a 4 is thrown. What is the probability that the player will never make his point? This question is essentially meaningless. We have no experience which would lead us to suppose that the thrower would live more than 100 years to carry on the attempt, and 100 years is a short time in the history of the earth. Instead, let us see what is the probability that the play would continue without issue for a large number of throws, say 100. The probability that neither 4 nor 7 will turn up in one throw is $1 - \dfrac{3+6}{36} = \dfrac{3}{4}$. The probability that neither will turn up in 100 consecutive throws is then $(\frac{3}{4})^{100} = 0.0000000000003$, approximately. Thus it is not very likely that the play would go on without result for even an hour. In general, the probability that the attempt to make the point will go on without result for n throws is $(\frac{3}{4})^n$, a quantity which steadily decreases as n increases, and which can be made as near to 0 as one wishes by taking n sufficiently large. This is what we mean by saying that the probability that the play will never end is 0, or that the play is certain to end.

6. THE GAME OF OVER TEN. This game is played with three dice. The thrower wins if the total of the points turned up in a single throw is over 10, and he loses if the total is 10 or under.

An analysis similar to that given for craps shows that the various throws have the following frequencies:

Total....	3	4	5	6	7	8	9	10
or.....	18	17	16	15	14	13	12	11
Frequency	1	3	6	10	15	21	25	27

It is clear that the game is fair since the totals over 10 have the same frequencies as those under 11.

7. THE POOL. A group of $n + 1$ players are said to form a pool in connection with a game for two players when they play under the following conditions. The players are numbered from 1 to $n + 1$ and play is begun by player 1 and player 2. The winner of this match then plays number 3, the winner of the second match plays number 4, and so on, each loser being replaced by the player whose number follows his (unless player h is defeated by player $h + 1$, in which case player h is replaced by player $h + 2$). In the order of play, player $n + 1$ is followed by player 1. The matches continue until one player has defeated all the others in *succession*, that is, until one player has won n straight games.

This scheme is not practical if the number of players is large, or if drawn games are frequent. Sometimes the pool can be concluded only if players drop out.

8. POLISH BANK. In this game, as in Russian Bank and baccara, each player (or punter, as he is called) plays against the banker. After bets have been made at even money, the banker deals from a pack of one or more decks of playing cards. Three cards are dealt face up to each punter, and one to the banker. A punter wins only if one of his cards is higher than the banker's and in the same suit. But any punter who receives a valueless hand (such as the lowest three cards of one suit, or the lowest card in each of three suits) is customarily dealt another hand.

The advantage of the banker is very great. Suppose the game is played with a pack of 32 cards, from the 7 to the ace in each suit. Let a ($0 \leq a \leq 21$) be the number of cards the punter can beat, and n_a the frequency of a (the number of different hands which can beat just a cards). The respective frequencies (whose total is $\dfrac{32 \cdot 31 \cdot 30}{1 \cdot 2 \cdot 3} = 4{,}960$) are:

a	n_a	a	n_a	a	n_a
0	20	8	492	16	84
1	60	9	484	17	60
2	120	10	456	18	40
3	200	11	408	19	24
4	288	12	340	20	12
5	420	13	252	21	4
6	448	14	144		
7	492	15	112		

Disregarding the valueless hands, the total number of possible games is

$$29 \cdot \sum_{a=1}^{21} n_a = 29 \cdot 4{,}940 = 143{,}260.$$

The total number of games which the player can win is

$$\sum_{a=1}^{21} a n_a = 42{,}540.$$

Hence the probability that a punter will win a game is $42{,}540 : 143{,}260 = 0.297$, or about $3 : 10$.

9. RUSSIAN BANK. Two like packs of 32 cards each are used. The banker sells to each punter as many cards from one pack as the punter desires, at a fixed price per card. When the punters have bought their cards, the banker turns up 9 cards from the other pack. He pays the cards which match his as follows:

> 1 times the stake on his first 2 cards,
> 2 times the stake on his next 2 cards,
> 3 times the stake on his next 2 cards,
> 4 times the stake on his next 2 cards,
> 9 times the stake on his last card.

If the punter's card happens to be matched by one of the first two cards, it is customary for him to leave his stake and exchange his card for another. Also, the bottom card of the deck is usually not used. Thus the banker can sell 29 cards and must pay 27 times the price of each card, which gives him an advantage of 29:27, or about 1.074.

10. BACCARA. The banker deals two cards to the punter and two to himself. The punter may either stand pat or ask for an additional card. The banker has the same rights, but he has the advantage of knowing before he decides whether the punter has asked for another card and what the card was, in case the punter has taken a third card. Each face card counts ten, and the others count according to the number of their pips; if the sum of the cards in a hand equals or exceeds 10 or 20, the 10 or 20 is not counted; that is, in valuing a hand, 10 or 20 counts for 0. The winner is the one with the highest total. If one of the players receives 8 or 9 with two cards, no cards are drawn and the winner is declared on the basis of the cards dealt.

J. Bertrand discussed the following question: If the punter's first two cards give him a count of 5, should he ask for a third card? Bertrand does not give a single direct answer. His conclusions are:

(1) If the punter stands pat and the banker knows that he usually does so, the respective probabilities that the player will win, draw, or lose are 0.445, 0.086, 0.469.

(2) If the punter asks for a card and the banker knows that this is his practice, the corresponding probabilities are 0.444, 0.121, 0.435.

(3) If the punter stands pat and the banker thinks the punter would usually ask for another card under the circumstances, the probabilities are 0.490, 0.095, 0.415.

(4) If the punter asks for a card and the banker believes he would usually stand pat with a 5, the probabilities are 0.447, 0.127, 0.426.

Could we calculate the advantage of disguising our thoughts?

11. Trente et Quarante. This game is played with a large pack of cards containing several complete decks. Face cards count 10, the others according to the number of their pips. To the first of two players the banker deals cards face up, one after the other, until the total points are just over 30. The banker then deals to the second player in the same way. The player with the higher total wins. If the totals are equal the game is a draw unless the total is 31, in which case the banker takes half the stake. This is his only advantage.

The probability that 31 points will be dealt to one hand was found by Bertrand to be 0.148. If one disregards the cards already dealt in the first hand, the probability that the second hand will also total 31 is $(0.148)^2 = 0.022$. Poisson calculated this probability, taking into account the cards dealt in the first hand. His result does not differ through the third decimal place.

At Monte Carlo and in some other clubs the game is played slightly differently, under the name of rouge-et-noir (red and black). The cards are dealt into two rows, called the black and the red, and each must have a total between 31 and 40, the winning row being that with the lower total. Bets may be placed on red, on black, on color, or on reverse; the two last risks refer to whether the first card dealt has or has not the same color as the winning row. As before, the banker takes half the stakes if both rows total 31, but the game is drawn if the sums are equal and are greater than 31. In some cases the player may take out insurance against double 31's at the rate of 1 per cent.

12. Roulette. Roulette is one of the favorite games of commercial gambling houses. The wheel at Monte Carlo is divided into 37 equal compartments numbered from 0 to 36, and the players may wager that the ball will fall in some one of them, or in any one of certain sets of them. The rate of payment is based on the assumption that there are 36 compartments, so that the bank has a small constant advantage. In addition, whenever the ball falls into the 0, all even bets are withheld and put in play on the next turn. In America there is usually a second 0 (sometimes even a third), which probably represents the price of " protection."

Gamblers have expended great ingenuity in devising schemes for losing their money, and roulette has always been one of the most prolific sources of such "winning systems." Here is one.

Suppose the player wishes to ensure winning an average of 1 unit at each play. For the sake of simplicity let us suppose that he plays always one of the combinations, such as red, black, even, or odd, which returns 1 for 1 to the winner. He begins by betting 1 unit. If he wins the round is closed, and he again bets 1 unit. If he loses, he bets enough so that if he wins he gets back his initial loss and 2 units more. If he wins the increased bet, this round is closed and he again bets 1 unit. If he loses, he must bet enough to cover his losses and make 3 units more, and so on. Let $x_1, x_2, \cdots, x_n$ be the amounts of the successive bets necessary to complete a round of n plays, that is to ensure winning just n units in n plays of which the first $n-1$ are losses and the nth is a win. Then we must have:

$$x_1 = 1, \qquad -x_1 + x_2 = 2, \qquad -x_1 - x_2 + x_3 = 3, \cdots,$$
$$-x_1 - x_2 - \cdots - x_{n-1} + x_n = n.$$

Hence

$$x_1 = 1, \qquad x_2 = 3, \qquad x_3 = 7, \qquad \cdots, \qquad x_n = 2^n - 1.$$

Again, if the player always bets on a play which returns 2 for 1, the stakes in the successive plays of a successful round of n plays are determined by the following equations:

$$2x_1 = 1, \, -x_1 + 2x_2 = 2, \cdots, \, -x_1 - x_2 - \cdots - x_{n-1} + 2x_n = n.$$

From these we find

$$x_1 = \tfrac{1}{2}, \qquad x_2 = \tfrac{5}{4}, \qquad \cdots,$$

That the author may rest easy of nights, he warns the reader to note that in such "winning systems" the rate of winning is slow, the rate of losing fast. *Facilis est descensus Averni.*

13. THE BALLOT-BOX PROBLEM.   In counting the ballots in an election contest between two candidates, what is the probability that the eventual winner will always lead his opponent?

Answer: If m votes are cast for the winner and n for the loser, the probability is $\dfrac{m-n}{m+n}$.

14. THE NEEDLE PROBLEM.   A needle is thrown at random upon a horizontal plane on which have been drawn a set of equally spaced parallel lines.   What is the probability that the needle will meet one of the lines?

Answer: If a is the distance between the lines and l ($\leq a$) is the length of the needle, the probability is $\dfrac{2l}{a\pi}$.   An experimental checking of this formula gave satisfactory results.

15. A TRIANGLE PROBLEM.   From a point M inside an equilateral triangle ABC perpendiculars MD, ME, MF are drawn to each of the sides.   What is the probability that a triangle can be drawn having segments of lengths MD, ME, MF as sides?

Solution: In order that the sum of any two of the three distances should be greater than the third it is necessary that the point M lie inside the triangle joining the mid points of the sides of the triangle ABC.   Since the area of the inner triangle is one fourth that of the original triangle, the probability is $\frac{1}{4}$.

The same result is obtained for the probability that when a stick is broken into three pieces a triangle can be formed from the pieces. The length of the stick may be taken as the altitude of the equilateral triangle.

16. THE PARADOX OF THE NECKTIES. Each of two persons claims to have the finer necktie. They call in a third person who must make a decision. The winner must give his

a \ b	1	2	3	4	· · ·	x
1	0	1	2	3		
2	1	0	1	2	A loses, B gains.	
3	2	1	0	1		
4	3	2	1	0		
· · ·		A gains, B loses.			0	
x						0

necktie to the loser as consolation. Each of the contestants reasons as follows: " I know what my tie is worth. I may lose it, but I may also win a better one, so the game is to my advantage."

How can the game be to the advantage of both?

The question can be put in an arithmetical form. Two people agree that they will compare the number of pennies in their purses, and that the one who has the greater number must give the difference to the other. In case of a tie, no money is transferred.

Discussion: From the point of view of the contestants the conditions of the game are symmetrical, so each has a probability of $\frac{1}{2}$ of winning. In reality, however, the probability is not an objectively given fact, but depends upon one's knowledge of the circumstances. In the present case it is wise not to try to estimate the probability.

We shall show that the game is no more advantageous for one than for the other. Let player A have a pennies in his pocket, and the other B have b pennies, and suppose that neither number exceeds a certain large fixed number x, say the total number of pennies which have been coined to date. If all cases are equally probable, the possible gains of player A (given above the diagonal row of zeros) are the same as his possible losses (given below the diagonal row of zeros), since the table is symmetric with respect to this row.

17. THE HORSES. Sometimes we can overcome luck and obtain a result which is independent of chance. An interesting example occurs in betting on horse races, when odds are quoted on the various horses in the race. It is possible to place wagers in such a way that the result of the betting will be profitable (or costly) whatever the result of the race.

If the odds quoted on a horse are "a to b," this means that the estimated probability that the horse will win is $\dfrac{b}{a+b} = p$. If the bettor wagers $x(= by)$ dollars, and the horse wins, the bettor receives $(a+b)y = by \div \dfrac{b}{a+b} = \dfrac{x}{p}$ dollars.

Let $p_1, \cdots, p_n$ be the respective estimated probabilities for the various horses in the race as determined by the quoted odds. Let $x_1, \cdots, x_n$ be the amounts which should be bet on each horse so that the result of the betting will be known in advance. If the ith horse wins, the bettor spends $S = x_1 + \cdots + x_n$ and receives $\dfrac{x_i}{p_i}$, so his net gain is $g = \dfrac{x_i}{p_i} - S$, whence $\frac{x_i}{p_i} = S + g$. Since this is to be true whatever horse wins, we must have

$$S + g = \frac{x_1}{p_1} = \cdots = \frac{x_n}{p_n} = \frac{S}{p_1 + \cdots + p_n}.$$

If we denote the sum $p_1 + \cdots + p_n$ by p, then $x_1 = \frac{p_1 S}{p}$, $\cdots, x_n = \frac{p_n S}{p}$, and $g = \frac{S}{p} - S$.

Hence the bettor may view the race with calm detachment if he has placed a wager on each horse proportionate to its estimated chance of winning. He will have an actual profit if $p < 1$, a loss if $p > 1$. Of course, the bookmakers arrange their odds so that $p > 1$, but perhaps the bettor will be consoled by the fact that it makes no difference which horse wins.

18. THE SAINT PETERSBURG PARADOX. A and B play under the following conditions: A is to toss a coin until it falls heads, at which time the game is to stop and A is to pay B 2^{n-1} dollars, where n is the number of throws. How much should B stake on the game?

Let us calculate the value of B's expectation. He has probability $\frac{1}{2}$ of winning \$1, probability $\frac{1}{4}$ of winning \$2, $\frac{1}{8}$ of winning \$4, and in general he has probability $\frac{1}{2^n}$ of winning 2^{n-1} dollars. Hence the value of his expectation is

$$\frac{1}{2} \cdot 1 + \frac{1}{4} \cdot 2 + \frac{1}{8} \cdot 4 + \cdots + \frac{1}{2^n} \cdot 2^{n-1} + \cdots = \frac{1}{2} + \frac{1}{2} + \frac{1}{2} + \cdots,$$

which is a limitless infinite sum. Thus no matter how much B pays, he buys a bargain.

This unexpected result engaged the attention of many mathematicians of the eighteenth and nineteenth centuries. We shall give the results of the speculations of some of them.

D'Alembert wrote to Lagrange: "Your memoir on games

makes me very eager that you should give us a solution of the Petersburg problem, which seems to me insoluble on the basis of known principles."

Condorcet and Poisson thought that the game contains a contradiction. A enters into an engagement which he cannot keep. If heads does not come until the hundredth throw, then B's profit will be a mass of gold bigger than the sun, and A has deceived B by his promise.

Bertrand gives the following commentary:

This observation is correct, but it does not clarify anything. If we play for pennies instead of dollars, for grains of sand instead of pennies, for molecules of hydrogen instead of grains of sand, the fear of becoming insolvent may be diminished without limit. This should not affect the theory, which does not require that the stakes be paid before every throw of the coin. However much A may owe, the pen can write it. Let us keep the accounts on paper. The theory will triumph if the accounts confirm its prescriptions. Chance will probably, we can even say certainly, end by favoring B. However much B pays for A's promise, the game is to his advantage, and if B is persistent it will enrich him without limit. A, whether he is solvent or not, will owe B a vast sum.

If we had a machine which could throw 100,000 coins a second and register the results, and if B paid $1,000 for every game, B would have to pay $100,000,000 every second*; but in spite of this, after several trillion centuries he will make an enormous profit. The conditions of the game favor him and the theory is right.

This statement can be explained without extended calculation. Suppose, to avoid too large numbers, that A agrees to play 10^9 games. Let us see how much B may expect to receive without assuming particularly good luck.

"Among the 10^9 games we can expect that 500 million will end on the first throw and yield B only $1 apiece. It is not unusual for heads to fall once in two tries. If the number is less, B is in luck, which we do not assume. The other 500 million games all begin

* Since B pays by the game and not by the throw, he will not ordinarily pay the full amount every time; for many of the throws will represent continuations of uncompleted games.

with a throw of tails, so A must throw again. In half of these games we may expect the coin to fall heads, and for each of these games B will receive $2. Thus again he may expect 500 million dollars. The remaining 250 million games begin with two throws of tails. In half of these we may expect heads on the third throw, and for each of these 125 million games B receives $4, again a total of $500 million. We may continue in this way for thirty times in all (since $2^{10} = 1024$, 10^9 is approximately equal to 2^{30}), so that for all the games B will receive about $15 billion. Luck may aid him and increase this amount, or it may abuse him and decrease it; but if he stakes $15 a game he has a good chance not to lose.

If A has to play only a hundred games the chances are different. B, staking $15 a game, has more chance to lose. The conditions of the game are still to his advantage, but his advantage comes from possible large profits whose probabilities are small. But if A promises to play 10^{12} games instead of 10^9, B could risk $20 on each game instead of $15 ($10^{12} = 2^{40}$, approximately), with a good chance of recovering $20 \cdot 10^{12}$, without counting in this approximation the possibility of winning immense sums, which should be kept in mind in accurate calculations.

The most singular answer to the supposed paradox is that of Daniel Bernoulli, who was the first to recall the problem from oblivion. It was originally proposed by his cousin Nicholas.

According to Daniel Bernoulli, $100 million added to an already acquired fortune of $100 million is not sufficient to double the original fortune. What new advantages can it procure? Accordingly he replaces the notion of mathematical expectation by that of moral expectation, in the calculation of which the worth of a fortune depends not only on the number of dollars it contains, but also on the satisfactions that it can give.

Here is the solution proposed by Bernoulli. If a given fortune x is increased by an amount dx, the worth of the increase is $\dfrac{dx}{x}$. Hence if my fortune increase from an amount *a* to an amount *b*, I have gained an advantage which can be measured by

$$\int_a^b \frac{dx}{x} = \log_e b - \log_e a = \log_e \frac{b}{a}.$$

No account was ever settled in such a manner. But thanks to the approbation of eminent persons, the theory of moral expectation brought no less fame to Daniel Bernoulli than did his admirable works on physics.

The eloquent Buffon increased the importance attached to Bernoulli's idea. The miser, Buffon said, is like the mathematician. Both value money by its numerical quantity. The reasonable man disregards both its mass and numerical measure. He sees only the advantages that he can derive from it. His reasoning is better than the mathematician's. The nickel that the poor man puts aside for his living expenses or the nickel that completes the banker's million have the same value for the miser and for the mathematician. The miser will grab it with equal pleasure, the mathematician will count it with the same unit. But the reasonable man will count the nickel of the poor man as a dollar, and the dollar of the banker as a nickel.

Quételet adds: "Thus a thousand dollars possesses the same importance for a man who has only two thousand, as 500 thousand has for the owner of a million."

Bertrand comments as follows: "If one seek to escape the reproach of avarice by this lofty disdain of all fortune beyond one's needs, he merits a still heavier charge. A man who possesses one million and gains a second will change his manner of life very little, if at all. Is this the only fruit of riches for one who is not miserly? If Buffon's reasonable man is not a cynical egotist he can find some use other than hoarding for those millions we suppose him to possess. We could double his fortune, multiply it by ten, and double it again, without diminishing the constant increase in the good that he can do. Does there exist no family that he may enrich or no misery that he may relieve, are there no great works that he may create or cause to be created? If he is wise he will avoid gambling heavily, even if the game is fair; but if, rich as he is, he does not take $100,000 to the roulette table every day, it is the fear of loss that stops him, rather than the disdain of profit."

We shall end these quotations by stating that Bertrand's solution is the most reasonable. B's stake depends upon the number of games that A is obliged to play. If this number is n, B's stake is $\dfrac{\log n}{2 \log 2}$.

Other solutions of this problem have been given. Here is one of American origin (T. C. Fry, New York, 1928).

The conditions of the game are changed in such a manner that A's loss in each game is limited. A must pay B 2^n dollars for each game if heads first appears on the $(n + 1)$st throw, and if 2^n is lower than a given limit, for instance, 10^6. If heads does not appear within 21 tries, A's stake remains at 10^6, no matter how many more throws are required ($2^{20} = 1,048,576 > 10^6$).

Under these conditions B's stake is

$$\left[\sum_{n=1}^{20} \left(\frac{1}{2}\right)^{n+1} \cdot 2^n \right] + \left[\sum_{n=21}^{\infty} \left(\frac{1}{2}\right)^{n} \cdot 10^6 \right].$$

The first term is 10, the second is $\dfrac{10^6}{2^{20}} = 0.95$. Thus the total stake is $10.95.

19. A and B play heads or tails. A begins. If he throws heads he wins the stake and the game is finished. If not, B throws, and wins if he throws heads within two tries. If he fails, A may have three tries; and so on. The first player to throw heads wins.

The respective probabilities of winning are 0.609 for A and

0.391 for B. In order to have an equitable game the stakes must be in this ratio, 609:391.

20. THE GAMBLER'S RUIN. If two persons play constantly against each other, one of them will end by ruining the other, whether the game be fair or not. The probability that they can play a given number n of games approaches 0 as n increases. For example, if one plays heads or tails at the rate of a dollar a game, he has a probability bordering on certainty (actually 0.999) of losing \$100,000 if he plays $\dfrac{2 \cdot 10^{16}}{\pi}$ games; and a probability of 0.9 of losing \$100 in 624,000 games.

Though these results seem reassuring, ruin is certain. Furthermore, it was assumed that the accounts were not settled until the end of the game. Under ordinary conditions one must put up his stake before each game, so it is not the ultimate loss which should be considered, but the maximum.

In an equitable game two players whose fortunes are a and b have the respective probabilities $\dfrac{a}{a+b}$ and $\dfrac{b}{a+b}$ of ruining each other. If the game is not equitable, let p and q be the respective probabilities for each to win a game. Then the probability that the first player will ruin the second is $\dfrac{x^a - 1}{x^{a+b} - 1}$, where x is found from the equation $px^{a+b} - x^a + q = 0$.

If the game is not equitable the least advantage is sufficient not merely to avoid ruin but to ensure a profit. This is the case in roulette, where the banker has the advantage of the 0. It is also the case with insurance companies.

21. A man stakes $\dfrac{1}{m}$ of his fortune on each play of a game whose probability is $\frac{1}{2}$. He tries again and again, each time staking $\frac{1}{m}$ of what he possesses. After $2n$ games he has won n times and lost n times. What is his result?

Solution: After $2n$ games he will have

$$A\left(1 + \frac{1}{m}\right)^n\left(1 - \frac{1}{m}\right)^n = A\left(1 - \frac{1}{m^2}\right)^n < A,$$

A being the amount with which he began. He always loses.

CHAPTER SEVEN

MAGIC SQUARES

1. DEFINITIONS

A MAGIC square is a square array of n^2 distinct positive integers with the property that the sum of the n numbers lying in any horizontal, vertical, or main diagonal line is always the same. In the accompanying illustration, for example, the

1	12	7	14
8	13	2	11
10	3	16	5
15	6	9	4

FIGURE 21.

horizontals give the sums $1 + 12 + 7 + 14 = 8 + 13 + 2 + 11 = 10 + 3 + 16 + 5 = 15 + 6 + 9 + 4 = 34$, the verticals give $1 + 8 + 10 + 15 = 12 + 13 + 3 + 6 = 7 + 2 + 16 + 9 = 14 + 11 + 5 + 4 = 34$, and the main diagonals give $1 + 13 + 16 + 4 = 14 + 2 + 3 + 15 = 34$.

It would be possible to admit negative numbers and fractions, but no real generality would be gained thereby. On the one hand, a magic square remains magic if the same number is added to every number in the square, wherefore a square with negative numbers can be changed to one with only positive numbers by adding a sufficiently large positive number to every number in the square. On the other hand, a magic square also remains magic when every one of its numbers is multiplied by the same constant (not zero), wherefore we can readily change a magic square containing fractions into one containing only integers by multiplying every number by a suitable constant. Hence we shall admit only positive integers.

Usually magic squares are required to be formed from the first n^2 natural numbers, which we may call the *normal* case. We shall have so little occasion to deal with other types that we shall ordinarily omit the specification " normal." In this normal case the constant sum of the horizontal, vertical and main diagonal lines is $\frac{1}{2}n(n^2 + 1)$, and is called the *magic constant*. Any set of n distinct numbers from 1 to n^2 whose sum is the nth magic constant is called a *magic series*.

The number n of rows (and of columns) of the square is called its *order*. The rows and columns will be called *orthogonals*. The term *diagonal* will be generalized as follows: A line from the upper left to the lower right corner of the square cuts across the numbers forming one of the main diagonals, consisting of just one number from each row and from each column. If we draw lines parallel to this line through the pth element from the bottom in the first column from the left, and through the pth element from left in the top row. the two lines together cross n elements, one from each row and from each column, and these will be said to form a *broken* diagonal. These are called the *downward* diagonals. The *upward* diagonals are similarly defined. In Figure 21, the broken upward diagonals are (6, 16, 11, 1), (9, 5, 8, 12) and (4, 10, 13, 7). A square of order n has just n upward and n downward diagonals.

A square that fails to be magic only because one or both of the main diagonal sums differs from the orthogonal sums will be called *semimagic*. On the other hand there are squares, called *panmagic*, in which *all* diagonal sums are equal to all orthogonal sums.

A magic square is called *bimagic* if the square formed by

replacing each of its numbers by its second power is also magic. A bimagic square is *trimagic* if the third powers of its elements form a magic square. And so on. Such squares may be called *multimagic*.

2. TRANSFORMATIONS

Any square array may be subjected to certain geometric transformations which affect one's manner of looking at the

FIGURE 22. *Transformations of a Square by Plane Rotation and Reflection.*

array rather than the interrelations of the objects contained in it. These transformations form a group generated by two fundamental operations — rotation through a right angle

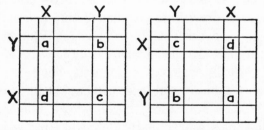

FIGURE 23. *Transformation by Interchange of Rows.*

and reflection in a mirror. Starting from any one array, seven others may be obtained in this manner. Figure 22 shows such a set. Any two members of such a set may be called *equivalent*. In discussing magic squares equivalent squares are usually not considered as distinct.

Sometimes a square array keeps a distinctive property (for example, a panmagic square remains panmagic) under cyclic interchange of rows or of columns or both. Cyclic interchange of rows may be expressed geometrically by supposing the array to be inscribed on a cylinder so that the top and bottom rows meet. Any row may then be considered the bottom row. Cyclic interchange of both rows and columns

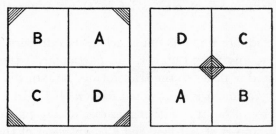

FIGURE 24. *Transformation by Interchange of Quarters, Even Order.*

may be obtained by inscribing the array on a torus (anchor ring).

A magic square remains magic if any two rows equidistant from the center are interchanged, provided that the two col-

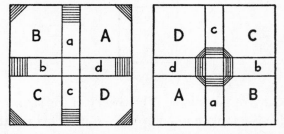

FIGURE 25. *Transformation by Interchange of Quarters, Odd Order.*

umns at that same distance from the center are also interchanged. Figure 23 shows the manner in which such a transformation affects the elements at the intersections of the transposed rows and columns. Repetition of this transformation for all such sets of four orthogonals results in a rotation of the original square through 180°.

Another transformation which does not affect the magic property may be described as the interchange of diagonally opposite quarters of the square. The description is exact for squares of even order (Figure 24), but must be modified slightly for squares of odd order in the manner shown in Figure 25.

A magic square remains magic when its numbers are subtracted from any fixed number. In particular, if the square is normal and of order n, the transformed square will be normal if every element is subtracted from $n^2 + 1$. In a normal magic square of order n, either member of any pair of numbers whose sum is $n^2 + 1$ is called a *complement* of the other. The square resulting from this last transformation may be called the complement of the original square.

3. MAGIC SQUARES OF THE THIRD ORDER

To date it has not been possible to give completely general methods of construction or complete enumeration of

a	b	c
d	e	f
g	h	i

FIGURE 26.

magic squares of all orders. The theory of the squares of the third order is simple and complete, so it seems worth while to sketch it here.

The magic constant is 15.

We can show at once that the central number must be 5. Denote the elements of the square as in Figure 26. If we add together the two orthogonals and two diagonals containing e, we find

$$3e + (a + b + c + d + e + f + g + h + i) = 3e + 45 = 60,$$

whence $e = 5$. This has the further consequence that $a + i =$

$b + h = c + g = d + f$, that is, that complementary pairs lie in the same central line.

Next we can show that 1 cannot occur in a corner. Suppose $a = 1$, so that $i = 9$. But now neither 2, 3, nor 4 can occupy the same orthogonal with 1, since there is no number large enough to occupy the third position. This leaves only two positions open for these three numbers, which is a manifestly impossible condition. Hence 1 and 9 must occupy a common orthogonal through the center, say $b = 1$, $h = 9$.

8	1	6
3	5	7
4	9	2

6	1	8
7	5	3
2	9	4

2	7	6
9	5	1
4	3	8

4	3	8
9	5	1
2	7	6

2	9	4
7	5	3
6	1	8

4	9	2
3	5	7
8	1	6

6	7	2
1	5	9
8	3	4

8	3	4
1	5	9
6	7	2

FIGURE 27. *Equivalent Magic Squares.*

Not only can 3 not occupy the same line with 1, it cannot lie in the same line with 9, since the third number would also have to be 3. Hence neither 3 nor its complement 7 may occupy a corner. Suppose we set $d = 3$, $f = 7$.

At least two of the three numbers in each orthogonal have now been fixed, so the remaining elements of the square are completely determined. If we choose the locations of 1, 3, 7, 9 in all possible ways, subject to the restrictions above, we obtain just the 8 equivalent squares of Figure 27. Thus there is only one fundamental normal magic square of order 3.

Similar considerations suffice to show that in order that any nine distinct numbers be capable of forming a magic square it is necessary and sufficient that they form three

three-termed arithmetic progressions whose first terms are in arithmetic progression. If these conditions are satisfied there is essentially only one magic square derivable from these nine numbers, and one of the equivalent forms may be written as in Figure 28.

$m + x$	$m - (x + y)$	$m + y$
$m - (x - y)$	m	$m + (x - y)$
$m - y$	$m + (x + y)$	$m - x$

Figure 28.

From this it follows at once that no square of order 3 can be either panmagic or multimagic.

4. ELEMENTARY METHODS OF CONSTRUCTION

We have remarked before that no completely general methods of construction exist for magic squares of all orders. For squares of odd order there are methods of great generality which we shall describe in §6. Here, however, are some simple special methods which enable one to construct some magic squares of any order. (We might remark here that it is obviously impossible to find a magic square of order 2, and the magic square of order 1 is trivial. Hence, when we speak of magic squares of any order n, we assume $n > 2$.)

De la Loubère gave the following method for constructing a magic square of odd order: Write 1 at the top of the middle column. Fill in, in order, the remaining positions of the upward broken diagonal through 1 with the numbers 2, $\cdots$, n. (The effect of this is to put 2 at the bottom of the next column to the right, since this is where the upward continuation of this broken diagonal starts.) When this broken diagonal has been filled with the successive numbers 1, $\cdots$, n, write $n + 1$ in the cell immediately below the cell containing n and fill in the remaining positions of the new upward diagonal with the numbers $n + 2, \cdots, 2n$. Continue this procedure. Each time a diagonal is filled write the next number immediately below the one before and fill the remaining positions in the new diagonal with successive numbers, proceeding al-

17	24	1	8	15
23	5	7	14	16
4	6	13	20	22
10	12	19	21	3
11	18	25	2	9

8	1	6
3	5	7
4	9	2

30	39	48	1	10	19	28
38	47	7	9	18	27	29
46	6	8	17	26	35	37
5	14	16	25	34	36	45
13	15	24	33	42	44	4
21	23	32	41	43	3	12
22	31	40	49	2	11	20

47	58	69	80	1	12	23	34	45
57	68	79	9	11	22	33	44	46
67	78	8	10	21	32	43	54	56
77	7	18	20	31	42	53	55	66
6	17	19	30	41	52	63	65	76
16	27	29	40	51	62	64	75	5
26	28	39	50	61	72	74	4	15
36	38	49	60	71	73	3	14	25
37	48	59	70	81	2	13	24	35

FIGURE 29.   *Generation of Magic Squares Using De la Loubère's Procedure.*

ways upward.   Figure 29 illustrates the application of this method.

It is to be noted that the middle number always lies in the center of the square.

The method of Bachet de Méziriac is similar.   His starting point is the cell directly over the center of the square.   When a diagonal ends he begins the new diagonal in the same column two cells higher.   Figure 30 gives squares of orders 3, 5, 7, and 9 constructed by this method.

Devedec has given a slightly more complicated method for forming magic squares of any even order. We start with the numbers written in what will be called *fundamental* position, that is to say, written in a square in oraer from left to right and up, so that the bottom row is 1, 2, $\cdots$, n, the row above

23	6	19	2	15
10	18	1	14	22
17	5	13	21	9
4	12	25	8	16
11	24	7	20	3

8	1	6
3	5	7
4	9	2

46	15	40	9	34	3	28
21	39	8	33	2	27	45
38	14	32	1	26	44	20
13	31	7	25	43	19	37
30	6	24	49	18	36	12
5	23	48	17	42	11	29
22	47	16	41	10	35	4

77	28	69	20	61	12	53	4	45
36	68	19	60	11	52	3	44	76
67	27	59	10	51	2	43	75	35
26	58	18	50	1	42	74	34	66
57	17	49	9	41	73	33	65	25
16	48	8	40	81	32	64	24	56
47	7	39	80	31	72	23	55	15
6	38	79	30	71	22	63	14	46
37	78	29	70	21	62	13	54	5

FIGURE 30. *Generation of Magic Squares Using the Procedure of Bachet de Méziriac.*

is $n + 1$, $\cdots$, $2n$, and so on. The numbers are now written in the magic square as indicated in Figure 31, where:

O indicates an element that is in the same position here as in the fundamental square.

\ indicates an element that, in the fundamental square, occupied the position symmetric to this with respect to the center.

| indicates an element that, in the fundamental square, occupied the position symmetric to this with respect to the horizontal median.

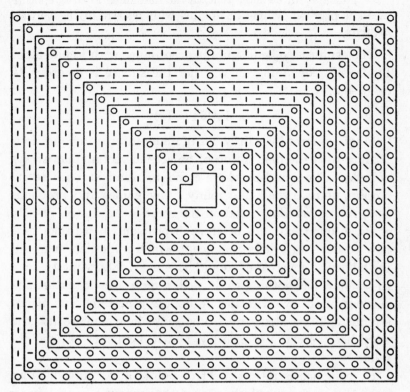

FIGURE 31. *Generation of Magic Squares of Even Order by the Method of Devedec.*

FIGURE 32.

FIGURE 33.

— indicates an element that, in the fundamental square, occupied the position symmetric to this with respect to the vertical median.

The center is to be filled in in accordance with Figure 32 or Figure 33, depending on whether the square is of order $4k$ or $4k + 2$.

5. LATTICES

Magic squares form only one of many interesting questions dealing with the disposition of objects in rectangular arrays of cells. Chess and checkers come to mind at once as examples, and we shall find many other games and problems that are, or may be, based on the same idea. It will greatly assist in our treatment of all such problems if we take time now to develop briefly a concept which underlies them all: the lattice. (The reader should be warned that what we have to say now has nothing to do with a more recent mathematical use of the word lattice to denote a certain type of abstract algebraic structure. The sense in which we use the word has the claim of priority, and it has never become obsolete.)

By a lattice is meant a set of points at a finite distance from each other, regularly spaced throughout a space of any number of dimensions. Thus a one-dimensional lattice is a set of points equally spaced along a whole line. A two-dimensional lattice may be described as the set of points of intersection of one set of equally spaced parallel lines with another such set in the same plane. (The spacings of the two sets of parallels need not be the same.) Similarly, a three-dimensional lattice can be obtained as the set of points of intersection of three intersecting sets of equally spaced parallel planes.

The basic configuration, in terms of which all the lattices with which we shall deal can be described, is the set of points

in one-, two-, or three-dimensional space whose co-ordinates
are integers, positive, negative, or zero. Any point of such
a lattice may be denoted by its co-ordinates, (x), (x, y) or
(x, y, z), depending on the dimension. We shall confine ourselves almost wholly to lattices lying in a plane. We shall
suppose then that our basic lattice is the set of all points
(x, y) having x and $y = 0, \pm 1, \pm 2, \cdots$

It is useful to attach a second meaning to the symbol
(x, y), in that (x, y) may be thought of as representing the motion of translation from the origin $(0, 0)$ to the lattice point
(x, y), or the parallel motion in the same direction from any
lattice point (a, b) to the lattice point $(a + x, b + y)$. In this
sense we shall call (x, y) a *motion*, and x and y its *direction
numbers*. The motion opposite to a motion (x, y) is $(-x,
-y)$, and will be denoted by $-(x, y)$. The result of two suc-
cessive motions, (x, y) and (t, u), is the motion $(x + t, y + u)$,
which will be expressed by $(x, y) + (t, u)$. The motion
(nx, ny) resulting from n repetitions of the motion (x, y) will be
denoted by $n(x, y)$. Thus we may have a single motion expressed as a linear combination of other motions, as $(x, y) =
a(t, u) + b(v, w) + c(p, q)$, where a, b, c are signed integers.

Keeping in mind the double significance of the symbol
(x, y), we may add a motion to a fixed point and interpret the
result as the point obtained by moving in the given way from
the given point. Thus $(a, b) + (t, u)$ may be interpreted to
mean the result of moving t units horizontally and u units
vertically from the point (a, b) to the point $(a + t, b + u)$.
This is particularly important when we add to a fixed point
the indefinite repetitions of one or more motions. Thus
$(x, y) = (a, b) + r(t, u), r = 0, \pm 1, \pm 2, \cdots$, may be used to denote the points (x, y) obtained from (a, b) by indefinite
repetitions of the motion (t, u) in either direction. For
example, $(x, y) = (1, 2) + r(3, -4)$ represents the points
$(1, 2), (4, -2), (-2, 6), (7, -6), (-5, 10)$, and so on.

In full generality the points $(x, y) = (a, b) + r(t, u)$ are those having co-ordinates $x = a + rt$, $y = b + ru$ for all integral values of r. This shows that these points are just those points of the basic lattice which lie on the line with slope $\dfrac{u}{t}$ through the point (a, b). These points obviously form a one-dimensional lattice in the plane. It is equally obvious that every one-dimensional lattice composed of points in the basic plane lattice can be represented by such a notation. For if (a, b) and (c, d) are any two consecutive points on the one-dimensional lattice we can take $(t, u) = (c - a, d - b)$ and write $(x, y) = (a, b) + r(c - a, d - b)$.

Hence we shall call the set of points with co-ordinates $(x, y) = (a; b) + r(t, u)$ the (one-dimensional) lattice with *origin* (a, b) *generated* by the motion (t, u), or having direction numbers t, u. If the lattice goes through $(0, 0)$ it may just as well be expressed by $r(t, u)$, unless we have particular occasion to think of some one of its points as a starting point.

From what has been said about the one-dimensional case it is easy to guess the interpretation of the expression $(a, b) + r(t, u) + s(v, w)$. If (t, u) and (v, w) are motions in different lines, which will be the case if and only if $t:u \neq v:w$, that is if $tw - uv \neq 0$, the points whose co-ordinates are given by $(x, y) = (a, b) + r(t, u) + s(v, w)$ form a two-dimensional lattice of points drawn from the fundamental lattice, and every such lattice can be so expressed. (If the directions of the motion are not distinct it can be shown that the expression generates a one-dimensional lattice, which may then be expressed by a single motion.) Such a lattice will be said to have (a, b) as origin and to be generated by the motions (t, u) and (v, w). As before, if $(0, 0)$ lies in the lattice we shall usually denote the lattice by $r(t, u) + s(v, w)$. For example, the basic lattice may be represented by $(x, y) = r(1, 0) + s(0, 1)$.

We shall call the one-dimensional lattices obtained by fixing the value of either r or s in the expression $(a, b) + r(t, u) + s(v, w)$ the *orthogonals* of the lattice, those with fixed s being the *rows*, those with fixed r the *columns*. (This agrees with our earlier definitions for magic squares whenever the lattice is the basic lattice.) The diagonals are then easily expressed. For the motion $(t, u) + (v, w)$ goes across one diagonal of any fundamental parallelogram, and $(t, u) - (v, w)$ goes across the other. Hence the lattice $(a, b) + r(t + v, u + w) + s(t - v, u - w)$ forms the complete set of diagonals in both directions, and a diagonal in one direction or the other is obtained by fixing the value of either s or r.

All this has to do with points spread over the whole plane. Most of our problems will concern points in a square or a rectangle. In certain cases we may have to limit our applications of this method to those lattice points lying in a rectangle of given size by requiring, say, that $1 \leq x \leq m$ and $1 \leq y \leq n$. In the vast majority of cases this is not necessary. Instead we can adopt the following procedure: Suppose the fundamental configuration in which we are interested is a rectangular array of cells, m on one side and n on the other. Let a whole plane be covered with repetitions of this figure by successive horizontal and vertical displacements. The central points of the cells will then form a basic plane lattice. It will be more convenient, however, to think of these points (or the cells themselves) as being covered by a basic lattice, usually in such a way that the cells of the first column from the left lie under the points with $x = 1$ and $1 \leq y \leq n$, while the cells of the bottom row lie under the points having $1 \leq x \leq m$ and $y = 1$. In this way the cells of the fundamental figure are *covered* by the lattice points (x, y) for which x lies in the range 1 to m and y in the range 1 to n. The cells of any repetition of the fundamental figure then lie under the points (x, y) for which the values of x differ from the numbers 1 to m by some fixed multiple of m, and the values of y differ from the numbers from 1 to n by some fixed multiple of n. Since, after all, the repetitions of the figure are essentially the figure itself, we may then consider a cell of the figure to be covered by all the points $(a + rm, b + sn)$, where (a, b) is the point covering the cell in its initial position, and r and s are any two integers.

From one point of view, then, this procedure associates with each cell of the fundamental configuration a lattice $(a, b) + r(m, 0) + s(0, n)$ of points from the basic lattice. From another point of view, and this is the one that we shall usually adopt, the different points of the lattice $(a, b) + r(m, 0) + s(0, n)$ are not considered as being distinct. That is, two points whose x-co-ordinates differ by a multiple of m and whose y-co-ordinates differ by a multiple of n are considered to be identical. This can be expressed by saying that the x-co-ordinates are taken with respect to the modulus m, and the y-co-ordinates with respect to the modulus n. Such a lattice will be called a basic lattice with respect to the modulus $[m, n]$. When, as is most often the case, $m = n$, we shall speak of the basic lattice with respect to the modulus m.

Very few modifications of the theory are necessary in order to take care of modular lattices. One point is worth noting, however. Suppose we have in the basic lattice with respect to the modulus $[m, n]$ a lattice $(a, b) + r(t, u) + s(v, w)$ and a lattice $(a, b) + r'(t, u) + s'(v, w)$, where $r \equiv r'$, modulo m, and $s \equiv s'$, modulo n. If these two lattices are drawn in the nonmodular plane they may look different. But if all the points covered by each lattice are brought back to the corresponding points of the fundamental rectangle it will be found that each of the two lattices covers precisely the same set of points. Such lattices will not, then, be considered distinct in the modular sense. In particular, the direction of a one-dimensional lattice will be denoted by the direction numbers after they have been reduced by the moduli. For example, in a basic lattice with respect to the modulus $[3, 5]$ the one-dimensional lattice $r(4, 7)$ is the same as the lattice $r(1, 2)$, and may be thought of as generated by the motion $(1, 2)$.

6. REGULAR MAGIC SQUARES OF ODD ORDER

We shall give now a very general method which enables us to write a great variety of magic squares of any odd order. Because of the simplicity of the law governing the positions of the numbers in the square, magic squares formed by this method may be called *regular*. For simplicity we consider first the case in which the order is a prime number.

1. SQUARES OF PRIME ORDER p. We begin with the p^2 numbers $1, \cdots, p^2$ in fundamental position (that is, written in a square in order from left to right and up). This fundamental square, which is never magic, is then covered by a basic lattice with respect to the modulus p. [In applying the method it is best (at least at first) to represent the basic lattice in nonmodular form.] The co-ordinates of (the cell containing) a number $m = h + (k - 1)p$ in fundamental position are then (h, k). For example, 1 is covered by the point $(1, 1)$, p is covered by $(p, 1)$, $2p + 1$ is covered by $(1, 3)$, p^2 is covered by (p, p).

Consider a one-dimensional lattice: $(x, y) = (a, b) + r(t, u)$. If neither t nor u is divisible by p this lattice will cover just p distinct cells of the fundamental square, one from each row and one from each column. Not only that, but the numbers occupying these cells will form a magic series. If t is divisible by p but u is not, the lattice will cover the cells of that column of the fundamental square containing (a, b). In this case numbers occupying these cells will form a fundamental series only if they lie in the central column, that is, if $b = \dfrac{p+1}{2}$. Similarly, if u alone is divisible by p the lattice will cover the cells of a row of the fundamental square, and the corresponding numbers will form a magic series only if this is the middle row, for which $a = \dfrac{p+1}{2}$. Clearly, if both t and u are divisible by p the lattice will cover only the cell (a, b) in the fundamental square, and will be quite useless.

The basic idea of the method of finding regular magic

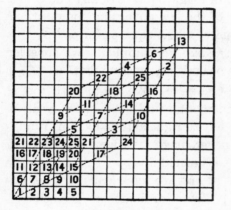

FIGURE 34. *Magic Square and Lattice.*

squares now begins to show itself. We want to cover the cells of the fundamental square with a two-dimensional lattice, $(x, y) = (a, b) + r(t, u) + s(v, w)$, whose rows, columns, and principal diagonals are magic series. To make sure that the lattice covers every cell of the fundamental square we must select t, u, v, w so that $tw - uv$ is not divisible by p; otherwise we shall find that only p of the cells are covered. If this has been taken care of, and if p does not divide $t, u, v,$ or w, the square whose rows and columns are the rows and columns of the lattice will then be at least semimagic. Figure 34 shows how this method is applied when $p = 5$, using the lattice $(1, 1) + r(2, 1) + s(1, 2)$.

Of course it is not sufficient to have magic series in the rows and columns. We must also take care of the diagonals. The set of upward diagonals is generated by the motion $(t + v, u + w)$, and the other set by $(t - v, u - w)$. If it happens that none of the numbers $t + v, t - v, u + w, u - w$ is divisible by p, then every diagonal in each direction will be a magic series, so the square will be not only magic, but panmagic. That is the case with the square in Figure 34 whose diagonals

43	44	45	46	47	48	49
36	37	38	39	40	41	42
29	30	31	32	33	34	35
22	23	24	25	26	27	28
15	16	17	18	19	20	21
8	9	10	11	12	13	14
1	2	3	4	5	6	7

20	28	29	37	45	4	12
32	40	48	7	8	16	24
44	3	11	19	27	35	36
14	15	23	31	39	47	6
26	34	42	43	2	10	18
38	46	5	13	21	22	30
1	9	17	25	33	41	49

FIGURE 35.

are generated by $(3, 3)$ and $(-1, 1)$. It is also the case in the square of order 7 (Figure 35) generated by the lattice $(x, y) = (1, 1) + r(1, 1) + s(2, -2)$. Its diagonals are generated by $(3, -1)$ and $(-1, 3)$.

Suppose, however, that one set of diagonals is composed of rows or columns of the fundamental square. For example, in the square of order 5 determined by $(x, y) = (1, 1) + r(1, 2) + s(1, -1)$, the diagonals are generated by $(2, 1)$ and $(0, 3)$. (This square is shown in the upper 5 rows of Figure 36.) Here all the upward diagonals are magic series, but only one of the downward diagonals is, and that one is not a main diagonal. The one downward diagonal which is a magic series is, we know, the one that consists of the central row or column of the fundamental square — in any case, the one that contains the central number of the fundamental square. The semimagic square can then be made magic by permuting the rows cyclically so as to bring this number, $\dfrac{p^2 + 1}{2} = 13$, into the main diagonal. The lower five rows of Figure 36 show the result of this operation. It will be seen also that from this square we can get four other magic squares by per-

10	16	2	13	24
14	25	6	17	3
18	4	15	21	7
22	8	19	5	11
1	12	23	9	20
10	16	2	13	24
14	25	6	17	3

FIGURE 36.

muting cyclically both rows and columns so as to bring the "13" into every position along the downward main diagonal.

This shifting of rows and columns is simple enough for a small square, but would be very laborious for a large one. We can avoid the difficulty by ensuring at the start that the central number, $\dfrac{p^2 + 1}{2}$, of the fundamental square is on the desired main diagonal. This can be done by properly choosing the origin of the generating lattice. This will surely be accomplished if the central cell $\left(\dfrac{p+1}{2}, \dfrac{p+1}{2}\right)$ of the fundamental square becomes the central cell of the new square. For this we must have

$$a + \frac{p-1}{2}t + \frac{p-1}{2}v \equiv \frac{p+1}{2}, \qquad \text{modulo } p,$$

$$b + \frac{p-1}{2}u + \frac{p-1}{2}w \equiv \frac{p+1}{2}, \qquad \text{modulo } p,$$

that is,

$$a \equiv \frac{t+v+1}{2}, \qquad b \equiv \frac{u+w+1}{2}, \qquad \text{modulo } p.$$

Shifting the origin of the lattice will also ensure success when both sets of diagonals are rows and columns of the fundamental square. Figure 37 shows how the square of order 5 generated by $(x, y) = (1, 1) + r(1, 2) + s(1, -2)$ can be made magic by shifting rows and columns. The same effect would have been produced by taking $(4, 3)$ as the origin of the lattice. Here the generators of the diagonals are $(2, 0)$ and $(0, 4)$.

15	21	7	18	4		
24	10	16	2	13		
8	19	5	11	22		
17	3	14	25	6		
1	12	23	9	20	1	12
15	21	7	18	4	15	21
24	10	16	2	13	24	10
8	19	5	11	22	8	19
17	3	14	25	6	17	3

FIGURE 37.

It is clear that distinct lattices may generate equivalent squares. For example, the squares generated by

$$(x, y) = (a, b) + r(t, u) + s(v, w)$$

and

$$(x, y) = (b, a) + r(u, t) + s(w, v)$$

will be equivalent. The curious reader might determine for himself what effect the transformations generating equivalent squares have on the generating lattice. By such means one

can determine how many nonequivalent regular magic
squares of a particular prime order p there are. In Figure
38 are given the four nonequivalent panmagic squares of
order 5 from which all others can be derived by certain
permutations of rows and columns.

2. REGULAR SQUARES OF ODD COMPOSITE ORDER m. Relatively few modifications are required to apply the proce-

18	24	5	6	12
10	11	17	23	4
22	3	9	15	16
14	20	21	2	8
1	7	13	19	25

15	18	21	4	7
24	2	10	13	16
8	11	19	22	5
17	25	3	6	14
1	9	12	20	23

20	22	4	6	13
9	11	18	25	2
23	5	7	14	16
12	19	21	3	10
1	8	15	17	24

13	17	21	5	9
25	4	8	12	16
7	11	20	24	3
19	23	2	6	15
1	10	14	18	22

FIGURE 38. *Basic Panmagic Squares of Order 5.*

dures for generating magic squares of odd prime order to
squares of odd composite order. Essentially they may be
expressed by changing the restriction "divisible by p" to
"not prime to m." Thus a lattice

$$(x, y) = (a, b) + r(t, u) + s(v, w)$$

will cover every cell of the fundamental square if $tw - uv$
is prime to m, and the resulting square will be at least

semimagic if t, u, v, w are all prime to m. The square will be magic if the origin is chosen so that the central cell of the fundamental square becomes the central cell of the new square, and it will be panmagic if $t + v$, $t - v$, $u + w$, and $u - w$ are all prime to m.

Thus we can have a panmagic square of order 35 generated by $(x, y) = (1, 1) + r(2, 1) + s(1, 2)$. The square is panmagic because its diagonals are generated by $(3, 3)$ and $(1, -1)$.

If the square is not panmagic the situation may be more complicated than when the order is prime. Whereas pre-

73	74	75	76	77	78	79	80	81
64	65	66	67	68	69	70	71	72
55	56	57	58	59	60	61	62	63
46	47	48	49	50	51	52	53	54
37	38	39	40	41	42	43	44	45
28	29	30	31	32	33	34	35	36
19	20	21	22	23	24	25	26	27
10	11	12	13	14	15	16	17	18
1	2	3	4	5	6	7	8	9

81	10	29	48	67	5	24	43	62
71	9	19	38	57	76	14	33	52
61	80	18	28	47	66	4	23	42
51	70	8	27	37	56	75	13	32
41	60	79	17	36	46	65	3	22
31	50	69	7	26	45	55	74	12
21	40	59	78	16	35	54	64	2
11	30	49	68	6	25	44	63	73
1	20	39	58	77	15	34	53	72

FIGURE 39.

viously the diagonals that caused the trouble were always rows or columns in the fundamental-square, this is no longer the case. Suppose a set of diagonals is generated by (T, U). If one of the direction numbers is divisible by m the corresponding diagonals will be rows or columns of the fundamental square, as before. But if one of the direction numbers, though not divisible by m, has a factor in common with m, then the corresponding diagonals of the new square are neither rows nor columns of the fundamental square, but they form in it a set of one- or two-dimensional lattices with sides parallel to the axes. For example, if $m = 9$ and we generate a semimagic square by the lattice $(x, y) = (1, 1) + r(1, 2) + s(1, 1)$, the set of upward diagonals is generated by $(2, 3)$, and the set of downward diagonals is generated by (0, 1). (The fundamental square and the corresponding semimagic square generated by this lattice are shown in Figure 39.) It will be seen that the downward diagonals, generated by (0, 1), are columns of the fundamental square. As in the case of prime order, only the diagonal corresponding to the central column of the fundamental square will be a magic

68	76	3	**11**	19	36	**44**	52	60		
54	62	70	78	5	13	21	29	37		
31	39	47	55	72	80	7	15	23	31	39
17	25	33	**41**	49	57	**65**	73	9	17	25
75	2	10	27	35	43	51	59	67	75	2
61	69	77	4	12	20	28	45	53	61	69
38	46	63	**71**	79	6	**14**	22	30	38	46
24	32	40	48	56	64	81	8	16	24	32
1	18	26	34	42	50	58	66	74	1	18
		3	11	19	36	44	52	60	68	76
		70	78	5	13	21	29	37	54	62

FIGURE 40.

series. But the upward diagonals, generated by (2, 3), are very different in appearance. For example, the diagonal generated by $(x, y) = (3, 2) + r(2, 3)$ is composed of three one-dimensional lattices in three of the rows of the fundamental square: 12, 15, 18 in the second row; 38, 41, 44 in the fifth row; and 64, 67, 70 in the eighth row.

If we form the sums of the upward diagonals we find that there are three magic series among them, and that these intersect the only downward magic diagonal at the numbers **68**,

41, and 14.   Hence if any of these numbers be made the center of the square by cyclically permuting the rows and columns of the semimagic square, the resulting square will be magic.

Consider the square of order 9 generated by the lattice

```
167 186 205 224   3  22  41  60  64  83 102 106 125 144 163
108 127 146 165 169 188 207 211   5  24  43  47  66  85 104
 49  68  87  91 110 129 148 152 171 190 209 213   7  26  45
215   9  28  32  51  70  89  93 112 131 150 154 173 192 196
156 175 194│198 217  11  30  34  53  72  76  95 114 133 137│156 175 194
 97 116 135│139 158 177 181 200 219  13  17  36  55  74  78│ 97 116 135
 38  57  61│ 80  99 118 122 141 160 179 183 202 221  15  19│ 38  57  61
204 223   2│ 21  40  59  63  82 101 120 124 143 162 166 185│204 223   2
145 164 168│187 206 225   4  23  42  46  65  84 103 107 126│145 164 168
 86 105 109│128 147 151 170 189 208 212   6  25  44  48  67│ 86 105 109
 27  31  50│ 69  88  92 111 130 149 153 172 191 210 214   8│ 27  31  50
193 197 216│ 10  29  33  52  71  90  94 113 132 136 155 174│193 197 216
134 138 157│176 195 199 218  12  16  35  54  73  77  96 115│134 138 157
 75  79  98│117 121 140 159 178 182 201 220  14  18  37  56│ 75  79  98
  1  20  39│ 58  62  81 100 119 123 142 161 180 184 203 222│  1  20  39
           224   3  22  41  60  64  83 102 106 125 144 163 167 186 205
           165 169 188 207 211   5  24  43  47  66  85 104 108 127 146
            91 110 129 148 152 171 190 209 213   7  26  45  49  68  87
            32  51  70  89  93 112 131 150 154 173 192 196 215   9  28
```

FIGURE 41.

$(x, y) = (1, 1) + r(8, 1) + s(5, 2)$, whose diagonals are generated by the motions $(4, 3)$ and $(3, -1)$ (Figure 40).   In this case there are just three magic diagonals in each direction, as can be determined by forming the sums for all the diagonals.   We then find that these two sets of diagonals intersect in the cells occupied by the nine numbers, 68, 14, 41, 65, 11, 38, 71, 17, 44. The square will be magic if and only if one of these numbers is at the center.

If a set of diagonals is generated by a motion (T, U), the three numbers m, T, U cannot have a common divisor other than 1. For it is easily shown that if they have, then the determinant of the generating lattice, $tw - uv$, is not prime to m. But it may happen that each of the numbers T, U has a

1	34	33	32	9	2
29	11	18	20	25	8
30	22	23	13	16	7
6	17	12	26	19	31
10	24	21	15	14	27
35	3	4	5	28	36

1	8	10	15
12	13	3	6
7	2	16	9
14	11	5	4

FIGURE 42.

different factor in common with m. For example, take the semimagic square of order 15 generated by

$$(x, y) = (1, 1) + r(4, 1) + s(-1, 4),$$

whose diagonals are generated by $(3, 5)$ and $(5, -3)$ (Figure 41). The main upward diagonal, generated by

$$(x, y) = (1, 1) + r(3, 5),$$

forms in the fundamental square a rectangular lattice lying at the points of intersection of columns 1, 4, 7, 10, 13, and rows 1, 6, 11. All the other diagonals, of both kinds, follow a similar pattern. In this particular case only those diagonals which contain the number in the central cell of the fundamental square, 113, are magic series, so the square can be made magic in just one way.

There are no regular panmagic squares of order $3k$. For if a square be generated by motions (t, u), (v, w), its diagonals will be generated by $(t + v, u + w)$. Since t, u, v, w must all be prime to 3, one number in each of the arithmetic progres-

1	142	141	140	139	138	129	11	10	9	8	2
12	23	120	119	118	117	112	29	31	32	24	133
15	39	41	102	101	100	99	47	48	42	106	130
18	36	49	55	88	87	86	63	56	96	109	127
19	40	52	83	65	72	74	79	62	93	105	126
22	30	54	84	76	77	67	70	61	91	115	123
132	110	95	60	71	66	80	73	85	50	35	13
131	107	94	64	78	75	69	68	81	51	38	14
128	111	92	89	57	58	59	82	90	53	34	17
125	108	103	43	44	45	46	98	97	104	37	20
124	121	25	26	27	28	33	116	114	113	122	21
143	3	4	5	6	7	16	134	135	136	137	144

FIGURE 43.

sion $(t - v, t, t + v)$, $(u - w, u, u + w)$ must be divisible by 3, so neither set of diagonals is completely magic.

7. BORDER SQUARES

A border square is a magic square that remains magic when its border (that is, its top and bottom rows and its left- and right-hand columns) have been removed. We shall obtain one by reversing the procedure — starting with a given magic square and bordering it.

Let us begin with a square of order 4 (Figure 42) using the numbers 1 to 16. We must supply $6^2 - 4^2 = 20$ numbers. First increase each number in the original square by $20 \div 2 = 10$. Then we must try to insert the numbers 1 to 10 and

7	32	6	18	35	13
1	29	10	9	26	36
34	20	15	16	23	3
33	14	21	22	17	4
12	11	28	27	8	25
24	5	31	19	2	30

7	36	8	11	31	18
9	2	33	34	5	28
27	17	22	21	14	10
25	23	16	15	20	12
24	32	3	4	35	13
19	1	29	26	6	30

FIGURE 44.   FIGURE 45.

27 to 36 into the border. Arrange these numbers in complementary pairs:

1	2	3	4	5	6	7	8	9	10
36	35	34	33	32	31	30	29	28	27

We take care of the diagonals by inserting two complementary pairs at the diagonal corners. Then we select numbers to fill in the top row and right-hand column so as to give the magic constant, and set their complements orthogonally opposite them.

By repeating this procedure we can form magic squares of order 8, 10, 12, $\cdots$. Figure 43 represents a magic square of order 12 obtained from the square of Figure 42 in this way.

The squares we have formed consisted of consecutive numbers, but that is not necessary. In Figures 44 and 45 we give two border squares whose interior squares do not have consecutive numbers.

One can also border squares of odd order. Figure 46 shows a square of order 9 obtained by successively bordering a square of order 3.

According to Frolow all possible ways of bordering the normal magic square of order 3 are obtained from the 10 borders given in Figure 47 by (a) permuting the middle three rows, (b) permuting the middle three columns, and (c) sub-

16	81	79	78	77	13	12	11	2
76	28	65	62	61	26	27	18	6
75	23	36	53	51	35	30	59	7
74	24	50	40	45	38	32	58	8
9	25	33	39	41	43	49	57	73
10	60	34	44	37	42	48	22	72
14	63	52	29	31	47	46	19	68
15	64	17	20	21	56	55	54	67
80	1	3	4	5	69	70	71	66

FIGURE 46.

jecting each border to the 8 transformations described on page 144. Since there is just one square of order 3, we get

$$10 \cdot (3!)^2 \cdot 8 = 2,880$$

nonequivalent normal border squares of order 5.

These are not all, however, since these include only those border squares of order 5 formed from a magic square of order 3 composed of the numbers 9 to 17, the middle nine of the first 25 numbers. Violle has completed the study of the question by showing that there are 26 different magic squares that can be formed with 9 of the first 25 numbers, and by finding for each case the total number of possible borders. He finds $594 \cdot 288 = 171{,}072$ squares in all,

8. COMPOSITE MAGIC SQUARES

A composite $m \times n$ magic square is a magic square of order mn which can be decomposed into m^2 magic squares, each of

3	22	21	18	1
7				19
24				2
6				20
25	4	5	8	23

3	22	20	19	1
8				18
24				2
5				21
25	4	6	7	23

6	24	23	8	4
25				1
7				19
5				21
22	2	3	18	20

6	25	23	7	4
24				2
5				21
8				18
22	1	3	19	20

7	25	24	6	3
22				4
8				18
5				21
23	1	2	20	19

7	22	25	8	3
6				20
5				21
24				2
23	4	1	18	19

7	6	23	24	5
25				1
8				18
4				22
21	20	3	2	19

7	25	24	4	5
23				3
8				18
6				20
21	1	2	22	19

8	25	23	7	2
22				4
5				21
6				20
24	1	3	19	18

8	24	23	4	6
25				1
5				21
7				19
20	2	3	22	18

FIGURE 47.

order n. A general method of constructing such squares is shown in the following examples.

We begin with the normal magic square of order 3 (Figure 48). In this square we shall replace each element by a square of order 3 as follows: Replace 1 by the square itself. Replace 2 by the square obtained by adding 9 to each element of the given square. Replace 3 by the square obtained by adding 18 to each element of the given square. In general, replace each number k in the given square by the square obtained from the given square by adding $(k - 1)n^2$ to each element of the given square. The result is the 3×3 composite magic square in Figure 48.

Mr. Royal V. Heath has shown that this square may be made panmagic by suitably orienting the squares of order 3.

Figures 49 and 50 show the 4×3 and 3×4 composite squares that can be formed in this way from given squares of orders 3 and 4.

Here is another method, one which does not require that the smaller squares be composed of consecutive integers.

8	1	6
3	5	7
4	9	2

71	64	69	8	1	6	53	46	51
66	68	70	3	5	7	48	50	52
67	72	65	4	9	2	49	54	47
26	19	24	44	37	42	62	55	60
21	23	25	39	41	43	57	59	61
22	27	20	40	45	38	58	63	56
35	28	33	80	73	78	17	10	15
30	32	34	75	77	79	12	14	16
31	36	29	76	81	74	13	18	11

FIGURE 48.

Arrange the numbers from 1 to $(mn)^2$ in fundamental position. (By way of illustration we shall take $m = n = 3$.) Decompose the fundamental square into m^2 squares of order n. For each of the smaller squares determine the magic constant for a magic square formed from the numbers it contains — that is, the nth part of the sum of the numbers — and form a magic square with these magic constants (Figure 51). In this magic square replace each number by a magic square formed from the numbers in the fundamental square from which that magic constant was derived. The result is an $m \times n$ composite square (Figure 51).

The same procedure can be applied to the fundamental square of order 15. It is to be noted that the magic constants

8	1	6
3	5	7
4	9	2

1	12	7	14
8	13	2	11
10	3	16	5
15	6	9	4

8	1	6	107	100	105	62	55	60	125	118	123
3	5	7	102	104	106	57	59	61	120	122	124
4	9	2	103	108	101	58	63	56	121	126	119
71	64	69	116	109	114	17	10	15	98	91	96
66	68	70	111	113	115	12	14	16	93	95	97
67	72	65	112	117	110	13	18	11	94	99	92
89	82	87	26	19	24	143	136	141	44	37	42
84	86	88	21	23	25	138	140	142	39	41	43
85	90	83	22	27	20	139	144	137	40	45	38
134	127	132	53	46	51	80	73	78	35	28	33
129	131	133	48	50	52	75	77	79	30	32	34
130	135	128	49	54	47	76	81	74	31	36	29

FIGURE 49.

determined by the squares of order 5 into which the fundamental square is decomposed form three arithmetic progressions with the same common difference and having their first terms in arithmetic progression, so that a magic square of order 3 can be formed from them. These progressions are: 165, 190, 215; 540, 565, 590; 915, 940, 965. When this magic

113	124	119	126	1	12	7	14	81	92	87	94
120	125	114	123	8	13	2	11	88	93	82	91
122	115	128	117	10	3	16	5	90	83	96	85
127	118	121	116	15	6	9	4	95	86	89	84
33	44	39	46	65	76	71	78	97	108	103	110
40	45	34	43	72	77	66	75	104	109	98	107
42	35	48	37	74	67	80	69	106	99	112	101
47	38	41	36	79	70	73	68	111	102	105	100
49	60	55	62	129	140	135	142	17	28	23	30
56	61	50	59	136	141	130	139	24	29	18	27
58	51	64	53	138	131	144	133	26	19	32	21
63	54	57	52	143	134	137	132	31	22	25	20

FIGURE 50.

204	33	132
51	123	195
114	213	42

20	1	12
3	11	19
10	21	2

73								
64								
55								
46								
37								
28								
19								
10								
1	2	3	4	5	6	7	8	9

77	58	69	20	1	12	53	34	45
60	68	76	3	11	19	36	44	52
67	78	59	10	21	2	43	54	35
26	7	18	50	31	42	74	55	66
9	17	25	33	41	49	57	65	73
16	27	8	40	51	32	64	75	56
47	28	39	80	61	72	23	4	15
30	38	46	63	71	79	6	14	22
37	48	29	70	81	62	13	24	5

FIGURE 51.

square of order 3 has been formed, and the corresponding squares of order 5 have been formed and inserted in the correct positions, the 5 × 3 square of Figure 52 results.

940	165	590
215	565	915
540	965	190

202	219	156	173	190	47	64	1	18	35	132	149	86	103	120
218	160	172	189	201	63	5	17	34	46	148	90	102	119	131
159	171	188	205	217	4	16	33	50	62	89	101	118	135	147
175	187	204	216	158	20	32	49	61	3	105	117	134	146	88
186	203	220	157	174	31	48	65	2	19	116	133	150	87	104
57	74	11	28	45	127	144	81	98	115	197	214	151	168	185
73	15	27	44	56	143	85	97	114	126	213	155	167	184	196
14	26	43	60	72	84	96	113	130	142	154	166	183	200	212
30	42	59	71	13	100	112	129	141	83	170	182	199	211	153
41	58	75	12	29	111	128	145	82	99	181	198	215	152	169
122	139	76	93	110	207	224	161	178	195	52	69	6	23	40
138	80	92	109	121	223	165	177	194	206	68	10	22	39	51
79	91	108	125	137	164	176	193	210	222	9	21	38	55	67
95	107	124	136	78	180	192	209	221	163	25	37	54	66	8
106	123	140	77	94	191	208	225	162	179	36	53	70	7	24

FIGURE 52.

9. PANMAGIC SQUARES

We have seen already that it is impossible to form panmagic squares of order 3, or regular panmagic squares of order divisible by 3. Mr. Raynor has proved that it is not possible to form a panmagic square of order $4k + 2$. There are 3 essentially distinct panmagic squares of order 4, 16 regular panmagic squares of order 5, and 54 of order 7.

Any set of n numbers of a magic square of order n that form a magic series will be called a constellation. In a regular panmagic square of order 5 there are the following constellations of five numbers:

> In a straight line — orthogonal or diagonal.
>
> Forming a cross — orthogonal, large or small;
> or diagonal, large or small.

Each of the first constellations is found 10 times — in the 5 rows and in the 5 columns. In the same manner each of the second constellations is found 10 times — in the 5 ascending and 5 descending diagonals. Each of the four crosses is found 25 times, once for each of the 25 cells of the square. The total number of constellations of order 5 is

$$(2 \cdot 10) + (4 \cdot 25) = 120 = 5!.$$

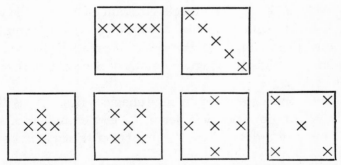

FIGURE 53*a*. *Constellations in a Panmagic Square of Order 5.*

Cyclic permutation of the orthogonals of a constellation may change its form so that it is scarcely recognizable. Figure 53*b* shows some examples.

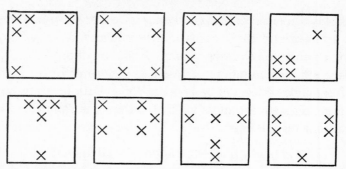

FIGURE 53*b*. *Variations of the Constellations of Figure 53a.*

10. MULTIMAGIC SQUARES

A magic square is multimagic of degree p if the square formed by replacing each element by its kth power is magic, for every k from 1 to p. Similarly we may define multimagic series. The magic constant of degree 1 is the nth part of the sum of the first n^2 integers, $\frac{1}{2}n(n^2 + 1)$. The magic constant of degree 2 is the nth part of the sum of the first n^2 squares, $\frac{1}{6}n(n^2 + 1)(2n^2 + 1)$. The magic constant of degree 3 is the nth part of the sum of the first n^2 cubes, $\frac{1}{4}n^3(n^2 + 1)^2$; and so on. n numbers form a magic series of degree p if the sum of their kth powers is the magic constant of degree k, for every k from 1 to p.

Here are some statistics on multimagic series. N_1 is the number of magic series of order n, N_2 is the number of bimagic series of order n, N_3 is the number of trimagic series of order n.

n	2	3	4	5	6	7	8	9	10	11
N_1	2	8	86	1,394	—	—	—	—	—	—
N_2			2	8	98	1,844	38,039	—	—	—
N_3			2	2	—	—	115	41	—	961

Tarry was the first to give a method of forming a trimagic

square of order 128. His method was improved by Cazalas, who formed trimagic squares of orders 64 and 81. Mr. Royal V. Heath has formed many bimagic squares, and a trimagic square of order 64 different from Cazalas' square.

Here is a very simple method (due to Aubry) for the formation of a bimagic square of order 8.

Let a, b, c, d represent the numbers 0, 3, 5, 6 in some order, and let A, B, C, D be numbers determined by the relations $A + a = B + b = C + c = D + d = 7$. These eight numbers form a multigrade of second order (see p. 79), since

$$a + b + c + d = A + B + C + D$$

and $$a^2 + b^2 + c^2 + d^2 = A^2 + B^2 + C^2 + D^2.$$

Symbolic expressions such as the following will be called bimagic lines of 8:

I	$0a$	$1b$	$2c$	$3d$	$4d$	$5c$	$6b$	$7a$
II	$0a$	$1b$	$2c$	$3d$	$4A$	$5B$	$6C$	$7D$
III	$0a$	$1c$	$2A$	$3C$	$4b$	$5d$	$6B$	$7D$
IV	$0a$	$1A$	$2b$	$3B$	$4c$	$5C$	$6d$	$7D$

If we interpret each term ($0a$, $1b$, $2c$, and so on) as a product, then the sum of the terms in each line is the same. If we interpret each term as a two-digit number in the scale of notation with base 8, then their sum, and the sum of their squares, is constant. These results follow from the given relations connecting a, b, $\cdots$, D, and are true no matter how the values of a, b, c, d are chosen from among the numbers 0, 3, 5, 6.

Other magic lines of 8 can be formed from these by permuting the letters among themselves and the digits among themselves. For example, if we interchange the numbers of the pairs (0, 1), (2, 3), (4, 5), (6, 7) in II we get $1a$, $0b$, $3c$, $2d$, $5A$, $4B$, $7C$, $6D$. Such a permutation will be denoted: (01), (23), (45), (67). We shall use the following permutations of this sort:

I:	(the identity)				I′:	(the identity)			
P:	(01)	(23)	(45)	(67)	P′:	(aD)	(bC)	(cB)	(dA)
Q:	(02)	(13)	(46)	(57)	Q′:	(aC)	(bD)	(cA)	(dB)
R:	(03)	(12)	(47)	(56)	R′:	(ab)	(cd)	(AB)	(CD)
S:	(04)	(15)	(26)	(37)	S′:	(aB)	(bA)	(cD)	(dC)
T:	(05)	(14)	(27)	(36)	T′:	(ac)	(bd)	(AC)	(BD)
U:	(06)	(17)	(24)	(35)	U′:	(ad)	(bc)	(AD)	(BC)
V:	(07)	(16)	(25)	(34)	V′:	(aA)	(bB)	(cC)	(dD)

For the first column of our square we use the magic line of 8:

$$0a \quad 2A \quad 4b \quad 6B \quad 1c \quad 3C \quad 5d \quad 7D.$$

For the downward main diagonal we use

$$0a \quad 3B \quad 6d \quad 5C \quad 5b \quad 6A \quad 3c \quad 0D.$$

We form the other columns of the square by applying to the first column the substitution on the digits and the substitution on the letters that will give the correct element in the main diagonal.

11. LATIN SQUARES

A Latin square is formed with n sets of the numbers 1 to n arranged in the cells of a square of order n in such a way that

1	2	3	4	5
2	3	4	5	1
3	4	5	1	2
4	5	1	2	3
5	1	2	3	4

1	2	3	4	5
3	4	5	1	2
5	1	2	3	4
2	3	4	5	1
4	5	1	2	3

Figure 54.

no orthogonal contains the same two numbers. A diagonal Latin square is one in which the main diagonals are also without repetitions. The squares in Figure 54 are Latin squares, of which the second is diagonal.

12. EULER (GRAECO–LATIN) SQUARES

From n objects $(\alpha, \beta, \cdots, \nu)$ and n objects $(a, b, \cdots, n)$ form the n^2 pairs $\alpha a, \alpha b, \cdots, \alpha n, \beta a, \cdots, \nu n$. An arrangement of these n^2 pairs in the cells of a square of order n in such a way that the array formed of the first elements of the pairs is a Latin square and the array formed of the second elements of the pairs is also a Latin square is called a Graeco-Latin or Euler square of order n. If the two Latin squares are both diagonal, the Euler square is called diagonal. Figure 55 shows two diagonal Euler squares of order 4.

11	22	33	44
43	34	21	12
24	13	42	31
32	41	14	23

11	22	33	44
34	43	12	21
42	31	24	13
23	14	41	32

FIGURE 55.

These squares originated in a problem that Euler states as follows: "A very curious question is the following: A meeting of 36 officers of 6 different ranks and from 6 different regiments must be arranged in a square in such a manner that each orthogonal contains 6 officers from different regiments and of different ranks."

This problem is impossible of solution, as Tarry has shown that no Euler squares of order 6 exist.

If we take as the fundamental position of the n^2 pairs of numbers the arrangement (Figure 56, p. 180), in which the first number of the pair gives the row and the second number the column in which the pair lies, we may apply to this fundamental square the method of lattices used for forming magic squares, provided the order of the square is a composite odd number. Since we are not concerned with the diagonals we need only require that $tw - uv, t, u, v, w$ all be prime to n. If we make the further requirement that the coefficients of the motions generating the diagonals also be prime to m, we obtain Euler squares that are not only diagonal, but pandiagonal. These can be obtained for every odd order n except those that are divisible by 3.

The fact that "regular" Euler squares can be formed subject to fewer restrictions than are applied to the formation of regular magic squares of the corresponding orders might

$n1$	$n2$	$n3$	$n4$	$n5$	$\cdots$	nn
$\cdots$	$\cdots$	$\cdots$	$\cdots$	$\cdots$	$\cdots$	$\cdots$
$\cdots$	$\cdots$	$\cdots$	$\cdots$	$\cdots$	$\cdots$	$\cdots$
31	32	33	34	35	$\cdots$	$3n$
21	22	23	24	25	$\cdots$	$2n$
11	12	13	14	15	$\cdots$	$1n$

FIGURE 56.

lead one to suppose that there are more Euler squares than magic squares. The contrary is actually the case. Every Euler square gives rise to a semimagic square, but many irregular magic squares cannot be translated into Euler squares.

Except for the condition that the elements of a magic square be distinct numbers, the requirements on the elements in a magic square are purely quantitative. The conditions on the elements of an Euler square, on the other hand, may be expressed purely qualitatively. As in the case of the problem of the 36 officers, the objects to be arranged may be any objects at all that are capable of being described in terms of two qualities, each of which has n categories. The objects themselves must then form a set containing just one representative of every combination of a category of one quality with a category of the other.

For example, we may classify playing cards by suit and rank, selecting the 4 suits and any 4 ranks, say ace, king, queen, jack. Then either square in Figure 55 gives a solution of the problem of arranging the 16 cards — ace, king, queen, and jack of each suit — in a square so that no two cards in the same row or column belong to the same suit or

♠A	♡K	♢Q	♣J
♢J	♣Q	♠K	♡A
♣K	♢A	♡J	♠Q
♡Q	♠J	♣A	♢K

FIGURE 57.

have the same rank. Figure 57 gives the translation of the first of these squares into these terms.

Euler squares may be generalized to include squares formed with respect to any k qualities. Let k be any number greater than one and let $(a_1^1, \cdots, a_n^1), \cdots, (a_1^k, \cdots, a_n^k)$ be any k sets of n distinct objects each. From these form the n^k possible ordered sets $(a_{i_1}^1 a_{i_2}^2 \cdots a_{i_k}^k)$, each of which contains an element of the first set in the first position, an element of the second set in the second position, and so on. An nth order square array of n^2 of these ordered sets, so arranged that the array of first elements forms a Latin square, the array of second elements forms a Latin square, $\cdots$, and the array of kth elements forms a Latin square, is called an Euler square of order n and rank k. Such squares have been investigated by Lehmann, Fleisher, and others.

13. MAGIC SQUARES OF ORDER 4

1. The theory of magic squares of even order is much more difficult than that of squares of odd order. For example, the methods we employed for construction of regular squares of odd order cannot be employed for squares of even order with-

	a	b	c	d
A	$A+a$	$A+b$	$A+c$	$A+d$
B	$B+a$	$B+b$	$B+c$	$B+d$
C	$C+a$	$C+b$	$C+c$	$C+d$
D	$D+a$	$D+b$	$D+c$	$D+d$

FIGURE 58.

out modification, since the coefficients of the motions generating the square and of those generating the diagonals cannot all be odd. In fact, the situation is even worse, since the one-dimensional lattices generated by any two independent motions will always intersect at least twice.

It is possible, however, to treat the squares of order 4 completely. Since the theory of these squares is simple and the results are rather interesting, we shall give an account of them.

2. ADDITION TABLES. One method of obtaining magic squares of order 4 is by means of what we shall call an addition table. Starting with 8 numbers, a, b, c, d, A, B, C, D, we write the first four as headings of the columns and the other four as headings of the rows of a table in which each entry is the sum of the numbers heading the row and column in which it lies. In terms of the letters we get the table of

Figure 58. If (Figure 59) we form from this a new array by interchanging each sum (not on a main diagonal) and the sum symmetric to it with respect to the center, we get a square that is magic if $A + D = B + C$ and $a + d = b + c$. If in this new array we interchange the upper right and lower left quadrants (corner squares of order 2), there results a square that is magic for all values of the letters.

$A + a$	$D + c$	$D + b$	$A + d$	$A + a$	$D + c$	$B + d$	$C + b$
$C + d$	$B + b$	$B + c$	$C + a$	$C + d$	$B + b$	$D + a$	$A + c$
$B + d$	$C + b$	$C + c$	$B + a$	$D + b$	$A + d$	$C + c$	$B + a$
$D + a$	$A + c$	$A + b$	$D + d$	$B + c$	$C + a$	$A + b$	$D + d$

FIGURE 59.

It is easy to verify that if we arrange the numbers in order of size so that $a < b < c < d$ and $A < B < C < D$, and if we take $A = 0$, then there are just three choices of sets of values for the letters so that the entries in the addition table will use the numbers from 1 to 16 without repetition or omission. These three choices yield the three tables in Figure 60. Permuting the rows and columns of these three tables gives us $\dfrac{3 \cdot 2(4!)^2}{8} = 432$ nonequivalent magic squares; 48 of these are panmagic.

3. MAGIC SERIES. There are 86 magic series of order 4. These are of three kinds, which we shall call algebraic, symmetric, and arithmetical.

Algebraic magic series are those formed by taking an ele-

1	2	3	4
5	6	7	8
9	10	11	12
13	14	15	16

1	2	5	6
3	4	7	8
9	10	13	14
11	12	15	16

1	3	5	7
2	4	6	8
9	11	13	15
10	12	14	16

FIGURE 60.

ment from each orthogonal of an addition table. This can be done in $3 \cdot 4! = 72$ ways; but each series appears twice, so there are only 36 different series. They are:

```
1  4 13 16*   2  3 13 16    3  5 10 16    4  5 11 14
     14 15          14 15*       12 14*         6  9 15
   6 11 16*      5 11 16        6  9 16          11 13*
     12 15          12 15*       10 15      7  9 14
   7 10 16*      7  9 16        12 13          10 13*
     12 14          11 14     8  9 14*    5  8  9 12*
   8 10 15          12 13        10 13          10 11
     11 14      8  9 15*   4  5  9 16     6  7  9 12
     12 13          11 13        10 15          10 11*
```

Two of these, 2, 8, 9, 15 and 3, 5, 12, 14, are not only magic but bimagic and trimagic as well.

Here is a very beautiful recreation based on the fact that any four numbers selected from an addition table so that one is taken from each orthogonal will always add up to 34. Write the numbers from 1 to 16 on 16 like cards and arrange them in the form of an addition table, but face downwards. Ask a person to pick up any one of the cards without showing you the number written on it. When he has done so, gather up the cards remaining in the two orthogonals in which the selected card lay. Then let him choose another card. Again remove the remaining cards in its orthogonals. When this has been done once more there is only one card left, which he

* These series are symmetric; see discussion below.

must take. You can then tell him that the sum of the numbers selected is 34.

Symmetric magic series are those that contain only pairs of complementary numbers. (Two numbers are complementary if their sum is $n^2 + 1$, in this case 17.) All possible symmetric magic series of order 4 will be formed by taking all possible pairs of numbers not greater than 8, together with their complements. Hence there are $\dfrac{8 \cdot 7}{2} = 28$ distinct symmetric magic series, of which 12 are also algebraic, and so have already been listed. They are marked in the preceding table with an asterisk. The other 16 are:

```
1   2 15 16      2   4 13 15      3   6 11 14      5   6 11 12
    3 14             6 11             7 10             7 10
    5 12             7 10         4   5 12 13      6   8  9 11
    8  9         3   4 13 14          8  9         7   8  9 10
```

The remaining magic series, which are neither algebraic nor symmetric, we shall call arithmetic. They are due merely to the chance of arithmetical combinations and contain many anomalies. There are the following 34:

```
1   5 13 15(o)      2   9 10 13(l)      4   7  8 15(s)
    6 13 14             11 12(l)            11 12
    7 11 15(o)      3   4 11 16             8 10 12(e)
    9 10 14(l)          12 15               9 10 11(l)
      11 13(lo)         5 11 15(o)      5   6  7 16(s)
   10 11 12(l)          7  8 16(s)            8 15(s)
2   4 12 16(e)            9 15(o)             9 14
    5 13 14              7 11 13(o)          10 13
    6 10 16(e)           8 11 12         7   8 14(s)
    6 12 14(e)           9 10 12(l)            9 13(o)
    8 10 14(e)       4   6  8 16(se)     6   7  8 13(s)
                        10 14(e)
```

Every magic series (of order 4) contains two large numbers (> 8) and two small (< 9), except those arithmetic series marked (l) or (s) respectively. Likewise each magic series contains two even numbers and two odd, except those arithmetic series marked with (e) and (o) respectively.

Except for the symmetric series, magic series occur in complementary pairs, the numbers of one series of such a pair being the complements of the numbers of the other series.

a	b	c	d
e	f	g	h
i	j	k	l
m	n	p	q

FIGURE 61.

4. LITERAL MAGIC SQUARES. Let us determine what relations the elements of every magic square of order 4 (not necessarily normal) must satisfy. For this purpose we shall

a	b	c	$S-(a+b+c)$
e	f	g	$S-(e+f+g)$
i	$2a+b+c+e-g+i-S$	$2S-2a-b-c-e-f-i$	$f+g-i$
$S-(a+e+i)$	$2S-2a-2b-c-e-f+g-i$	$2a+b+e+f-g+i-S$	$a+b+c+e+i-S$

FIGURE 62.

write the square with letters, as in Figure 61. By definition the values of 10 sums (the sums of the 4 rows, of the 4 columns and of the 2 diagonals) are fixed. But the sum of the sums of the rows is identical with the sum of the sums of the columns, so that only 9 of the 10 relations are independent. There are thus $16 - 9 = 7$ independent elements (and the magic constant, S). We find that the square may be written as in Figure 62.

From this one can readily verify that every magic square contains 4 magic series in addition to the 10 prescribed. In the notation of Figure 61 these are:

$$a + d + m + q = f + g + j + k$$
$$= b + c + n + p = e + i + h + l = S.$$

There are many other relationships connecting the elements of a magic square of order 4. The following relations are typical:

$$a + d = n + p, \qquad e + h = j + k, \qquad a + q = g + j,$$
$$a + b + e + f = c + d + g + h$$
$$i + j + m + n = k + l + p + q.$$

a	b	c	$S - (a + b + c)$
e	$S - (a + b + e)$	$a - c + e$	$b + c - e$
$\dfrac{S}{2} - c$	$(a + b + c) - \dfrac{S}{2}$	$\dfrac{S}{2} - a$	$\dfrac{S}{2} - b$
$\dfrac{S}{2} - (a - c + e)$	$\dfrac{S}{2} - (b + c - e)$	$\dfrac{S}{2} - e$	$(a + b + e) - \dfrac{S}{2}$

FIGURE 63.

If we want the square to be panmagic, apparently six more conditions are added, corresponding to the sums of the two sets of three diagonals. Actually only three of these are independent, so there are four independent constants left, and the square may be written as in Figure 63.

5. ALGEBRAIC SQUARES. One of the above sets of relations holding for every magic square of order 4 states that the sum of the numbers in opposite quadrants of the square is the same. If this sum is also the magic constant, we shall call the square algebraic. This adds one further condition on the constants of the square, so one of the constants disappears. Such a square may be written as in Figure 64.

An algebraic magic square contains 6 magic series in addition to the 18 already noted:

$$a + c + i + k = b + d + j + l = e + g + m + p$$
$$= f + h + n + q = c + h + i + n = b + e + l + p = S.$$

All 24 magic series are algebraic.

It is easily shown that an algebraic magic square may be formed from an addition table by the methods given on page 183. If $A + D = B + C$ and $a + d = b + c$, only the first

a	b	c	$S - (a + b + c)$
e	$S - (a + b + e)$	g	$a + b - g$
i	$2a + b + c + e$ $- g + i - S$	$S - (a + c + i)$	$\bullet S - a - b - e$ $+ g - i$
$S - (a + e + i)$	$S - a - b - c$ $+ g - i$	$a - g + i$	$a + b + c + e$ $+ i - S$

FIGURE 64.

transformation is necessary. If not, the second form is certainly magic. Both forms are clearly algebraic.

In addition to the transformations (pp. 144–145) to which every magic square may be subjected, an algebraic magic square remains both algebraic and magic if we interchange the first two orthogonals with the last two. For example, columns 1, 2, 3, 4 may be put in the order 3, 4, 1, 2.

6. THE NUMBER OF NORMAL ALGEBRAIC SQUARES. Normal algebraic squares are all derivable from the addition tables in Figures 58 and 59. In forming squares from these tables we may use any of the 24 permutations of its rows with any of the 24 permutations of its columns, and we may interchange rows and columns. This gives $3 \cdot 2 \cdot 24 \cdot 24 = 3,456$ magic squares derivable from the tables. But these contain all 8 equivalents of any one of them, so that the total number of distinct nonequivalent algebraic magic squares is $3,456 \div 8 = 432$.

7. CLASSIFICATION OF NORMAL ALGEBRAIC SQUARES. The distribution of the pairs of complementary numbers forms the basis of a complete classification of algebraic squares. Six types may be discerned, in the first three of which the pairs of complements lie on diagonals, while in the others they lie on orthogonals.

(1) *Central.* The complementary numbers are symmetrically placed with respect to the center.

1	2	3	4
5	6	7	8
8	7	6	5
4	3	2	1

1	2	3	4
2	1	4	3
5	6	7	8
6	5	8	7

1	2	3	4
5	6	7	8
3	4	1	2
7	8	5	6

1	1	2	2
3	3	4	4
5	5	6	6
7	7	8	8

1	2	1	2
3	4	3	4
5	6	5	6
7	8	7	8

1	2	2	1
3	4	4	3
5	6	6	5
7	8	8	7

FIGURE 65.

(2) *Diagonal.* The complementary numbers form the diagonals of the quadrants.

(3) *Panmagic.* A panmagic algebraic magic square is characterized by the fact that the complementary numbers lie on the diagonals in pairs whose elements separate each other.

(4) and (5) *Orthogonal (Adjacent and Alternating).* The complementary numbers lie in two columns, adjacent or alternating.

(6) *Symmetric.* The complementary numbers are symmetric to the vertical median.

If we designate a number and its complement by the same digit, the six types may be represented as in Figure 65.

It is interesting that an algebraic magic square can have
no other distribution of the complementary numbers.

The distribution of the squares in the various classes is:

Central	48
Diagonal	48
Panmagic	48
Adjacent orthogonal	96
Alternating orthogonal......	96
Symmetric	96
Total algebraic magic squares	432

Figure 66 is a list of the basic squares of the various types.
Since a panmagic square is converted into a diagonal square
by interchanging the two central orthogonals, the diagonal
squares have not been listed separately. Neither have the
alternating orthogonal squares, since they may be similarly
derived from the adjacent orthogonal squares.

8. These 432 are the full set of normal algebraic squares.
However, if one interchanges the middle numbers of the end
columns of a normal symmetric algebraic square it remains
symmetric magic but not algebraic. In literal form it becomes
as shown in Figure 67. Such a square will be called derivative symmetric. There are 96 of them, one for each symmetric algebraic square.

In addition to these there are 112 arithmetic symmetric
squares, 224 semiorthogonal and 16 irregular squares. Thus
the total number of normal magic squares of order 4 is 880.

Algebraic.....................	432
Derivative symmetric	96
Arithmetic symmetric..........	112
Semiorthogonal	224
Irregular	16
Total	880

We may remark in passing that the three kinds of symmetric squares are very similar, and Frénicle put them into a single class. There are 304 of them in all.

<table>
<tr><td>Central:</td><td>

1   8 12 13
14 11 7   2
15 10 6   3
 4   5   9 16

</td><td>

1   8 14 11
12 13 7   2
15 10 4   5
 6   3   9 16

</td><td>

1   8 15 10
12 13 6   3
14 11 4   5
 7   2   9 16

</td></tr>
</table>

Central:

1	8	12	13
14	11	7	2
15	10	6	3
4	5	9	16

1	8	14	11
12	13	7	2
15	10	4	5
6	3	9	16

1	8	15	10
12	13	6	3
14	11	4	5
7	2	9	16

Panmagic:

1	8	10	15
12	13	3	6
7	2	16	9
14	11	5	4

1	8	11	14
12	13	2	7
6	3	16	9
15	10	5	4

1	8	13	12
14	11	2	7
4	5	16	9
15	10	3	6

Adjacent Orthogonal:

1	4	16	13
14	15	3	2
7	6	10	11
12	9	5	8

1	6	16	11
12	15	5	2
7	4	10	13
14	9	3	8

1	7	16	10
12	14	5	3
6	4	11	13
15	9	2	8

Symmetric:

1	4	13	16
14	15	2	3
8	5	12	9
11	10	7	6

1	6	11	16
12	15	2	5
8	3	14	9
13	10	7	4

1	7	10	16
12	14	3	5
8	2	15	9
13	11	6	4

FIGURE 66.

9. If the magic squares are not normal there are three cases to consider.

First, if the given 16 numbers can be arranged so as to form an addition table whose components satisfy the relations $A + D = B + C$, $a + d = b + c$, then the 528 algebraic and derivative symmetric squares can be formed, but in general no arithmetic squares exist.

Second, if the given numbers form an addition table whose components do not satisfy the above relations, algebraic and derivative symmetric magic squares can be formed, but from only one table, so there are only $144 + 32 = 176$ such squares.

Finally, if the given numbers do not form an addition table, no algebraic magic squares can be formed from them.

a	b	$17 - b$	$17 - a$
d	$34 - a - b - c$	$a + b + c - 17$	$17 - d$
c	$a - b + d$	$17 - a + b - d$	$17 - c$
$34 - a - c - d$	$b + c - d$	$17 - b - c + d$	$a + c + d - 17$

FIGURE 67.

10. The literal form of a magic square may be used to make an arithmetical magic square with four given numbers that form a famous date — for example, the date of the first Independence Day, 7/4/17–76. These four numbers determine the magic constant 104. We may now take four more rather arbitrarily selected numbers to fill out the square, but avoiding repetitions and negative numbers.

7	4	17	76
51	50	1	2
33	14	39	18
13	36	47	8

FIGURE 68.

CHAPTER EIGHT

GEOMETRIC RECREATIONS

1. DISSECTION OF PLANE FIGURES

OUR first problems are applications of a remarkable theorem proved by Hilbert: *If two polygons are equivalent* (that is, have the same area) *then it is possible to transform either poly-*

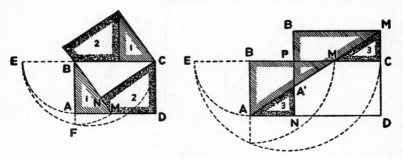

FIGURE 69. *Two Dissections of a Rectangle to Form a Square in Three Pieces.*

gon into the other by cutting it into a finite number of polygons and rearranging the pieces.

To save cumbrous locutions we shall state applications of this procedure as follows: Suppose it is desired to transform one figure into another by making a certain number of straight cuts (as with shears) in the first figure and rearranging the resulting polygons so that the assembled pieces form the second. Then we shall say, "Dissect the first figure into (so many) pieces by (so many) cuts so as to form the second figure."

1. Dissect a given rectangle into three pieces by two cuts so as to form a square.

Solution: It is clear that such a construction is not possible for every rectangle. For as the ratio of length to width increases the number of cuts necessary will also increase. However, Figure 69 shows two distinct constructions, the first applicable when the length does not exceed twice the width, the second when the length is not greater than four times the width.

Let the rectangle be *ABCD* (Figure 69, left). Find the

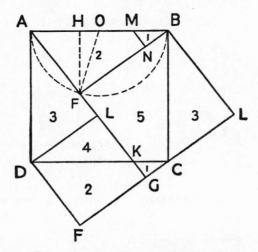

FIGURE 70. *Dissection of a Square into Two Squares, One Twice the Area of the Other.*

mean proportional *BF* between the lengths of the sides. Locate the point *M* on *AD* which makes *BM* = *BF*, and draw through *C* a perpendicular to *BM* meeting *BM* at *N*. The rectangle is cut along the lines *BM* and *CN*. The three pieces are then rearranged as in the figure to form the square.

In the second solution (Figure 69, right), *BM* = *DN* = *CP* = the mean proportional between the sides. *AM* meets *NP* at *A'*. The cuts are made along *AM* and *NA'*, and the pieces are reassembled as shown.

2. Dissect a square into five pieces so as to form two squares, one with twice the area of the other.

Solution: Let the square be *ABCD* (Figure 70). With the mid point *O* of *AB* as center and *OA* as radius draw a semi-

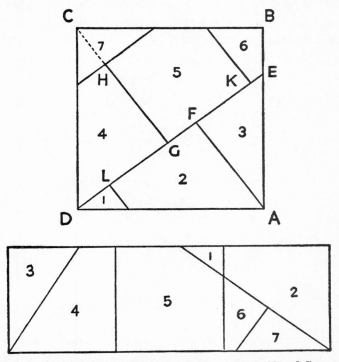

FIGURE 71. *A Square Dissected to Form Three Equal Squares.*

circle in the square. Locate the point *H* on *AB* so that *AH* = $\frac{1}{3}AB$. At *H* erect a perpendicular to *AB* meeting the semicircle at *F*. Draw *BF* and draw *AF* produced to meet *DC* at *K*. Through *D* draw a perpendicular to *AK* meeting *AK* at *L*. On *BA* lay off *BM* = *CK* and through *M* draw a perpendicular to *BF* meeting *BF* in *N*. The cuts are made along *AK*, *DL*, *BF*, and *MN*. The rearrangement of the resulting five pieces is shown in the figure.

3. Dissect a square into seven polygonal pieces so as to form three equal squares.

Solution: In the square *ABCD* (Figure 71), *AE* is half the diagonal, and *AF* and *CG* are perpendiculars to *DE*; *GH* = *GK* = *FL* = *AF*; and the remaining lines are perpendiculars to the lines they intersect at *H*, *K*, and *L* respectively. The desired rearrangement is shown.

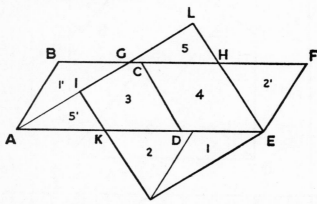

FIGURE 72. *A Hexagon Dissected to Form a Square of the Same Area.*

4. Dissect a regular hexagon into five polygonal pieces so as to form a square.

Solution: First cut the hexagon in half along a diameter and rearrange the two pieces to form a parallelogram *ABFE* as in Figure 72. Locate *G* on *BF* so that *AG* is the mean proportional between the base *AE* and the corresponding altitude of the parallelogram. Through *E* draw a perpendicular to *AG* meeting *BF* at *H* and *AG* produced at *L*.

On *LA* lay off *LI* = *LE*, and through *I* draw a perpendicular to *AG* meeting *AE* at *K*. Make the cuts along *AG*, *EH*, and *IK*, and rearrange the pieces as shown.

5. Dissect a regular pentagon into seven polygonal pieces so as to form a square.

Solution: Let the pentagon be *ABCDE* (Figure 73). Cut off the triangle *CDE* along *CE* and place it beside the piece *ABCE* so that *C* falls on *A*, and *D* on *E*. *DE* will then form the continuation *EF* of *CE*, so that *ABCFA* is a trapezoid equivalent to the pentagon. Through the mid point *G* of *AF* draw a parallel to *BC* meeting *CF* at *K*, and *BA* produced

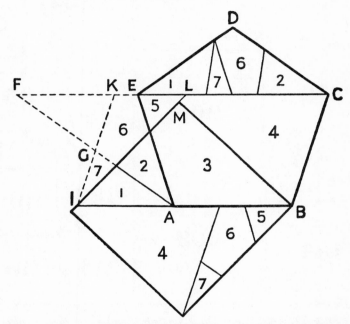

FIGURE 73. *A Pentagon Dissected to Form an Equivalent Square.*

at *I*. *IBCK* is then a parallelogram equivalent to the trapezoid and to the pentagon, and it may be formed by cutting along *GK* and placing the triangle *FGK* with *F* at *A*, *K* at *I* and *G* at *G*. From *I* as center draw an arc of a circle with radius equal to the mean proportional between the base *IB* and corresponding altitude of the parallelogram, and let the arc cut *CK* at *L*. Draw *IL*, and through *B* draw a perpendicular to *IL* meeting *IL* at *M*. When the parallelogram has been cut along *IL* and *BM* the resulting pieces may be rearranged to form an equivalent square as shown.

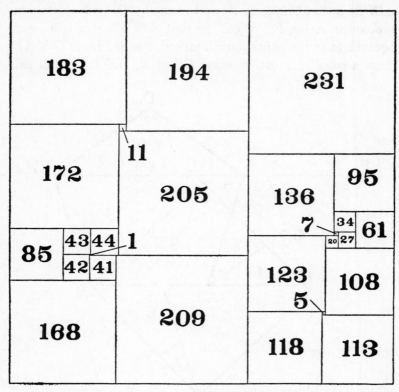

FIGURE 74. *A Square Dissected into Smaller Squares, No Two Being Equivalent.*

6. Divide a square into a number of smaller squares, no two of them equivalent.

A solution of this problem, long thought to be impossible, is given by Brooks, Smith, Stone, and Tutte in *Duke Mathematical Journal*, vol. 7, December, 1940 (see Figure 74).

2. MOSAICS

1. The fundamental problem of mosaics is to cover the plane completely with regular polygons of a single kind. First consider the case where no vertex of one polygon lies on an edge of another. Let n be the number of sides of each

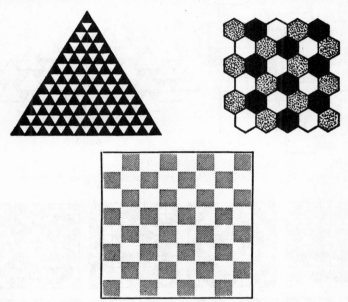

Figure 75. *Mosaics of Triangles, Squares, and Hexagons.*

polygon. The interior angle at each vertex of such a polygon is $\frac{n-2}{n} \cdot 180°$. At each vertex we shall have

$$\frac{360}{\frac{n-2}{n} \cdot 180} = \frac{2n}{n-2} = 2 + \frac{4}{n-2}$$

such polygons. In order that this number be an integer for $n > 2$ we must have $n = 3, 4$, or 6. In each case the desired covering of the whole plane can be made. These give us the mosaic of Figure 75.

Now suppose that a vertex of one polygon lies on a side of another. Since the edge of the second polygon occupies half the perigon about such a vertex, for the remaining polygons at the vertex we must have $\frac{1}{2} \cdot \frac{2n}{n-2} = 1 + \frac{2}{n-2}$ an integer,

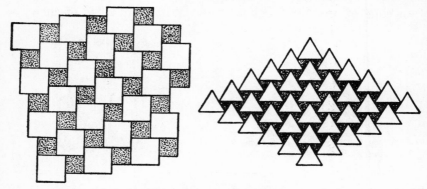

FIGURE 76. *Mosaic of Polygons Not Meeting at Vertices.*

FIGURE 77. *Patterns from Diagonally Divided Squares.*

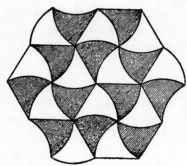

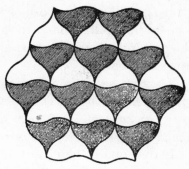

FIGURE 78. *Mosaic of Modified Triangles.*

FIGURE 79. *Mosaic of Modified Triangles.*

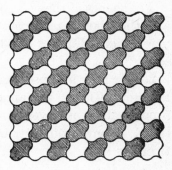

FIGURE 80. *Mosaic of Modified Squares.*

FIGURE 81. *Mosaic of Modified Squares.*

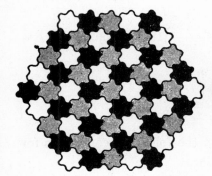

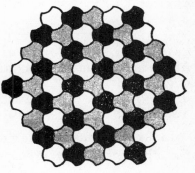

FIGURE 82. *Mosaic of Modified Hexagons.*

FIGURE 83. *Mosaic of Modified Hexagons.*

that is, $n = 3$ or 4. Both of these cases can be realized, say by sliding the horizontal rows of black and white triangles in Figure 75 past each other, and similarly for the horizontal rows of squares.

Thus we have the following theorem: *If the plane is completely covered by a set of congruent regular polygons, these polygons can have only 3, 4, or 6 sides. Only in the last case must the polygons meet solely at vertices.*

If the squares be given different colors in the regions determined by a diagonal they may be arranged so as to give very beautiful mosaics, as in Figure 77.

The shapes of the polygons may be altered in various ways and then put together as before to form many interesting new designs (Figures 78-83).

2. One may also use regular polygons of different kinds at a vertex. Clearly we cannot have fewer than 3 or more than 6 polygons at any vertex. The resulting arrangements are called ternary, quarternary, quinary, and senary, respectively.

Since the sum of the angles around any vertex must be 360° a ternary arrangement of polygons of n_1, n_2, and n_3 sides respectively will be possible only if

$$\left(\frac{n_1 - 2}{n_1} + \frac{n_2 - 2}{n_2} + \frac{n_3 - 2}{n_3}\right)180° = 360°,$$

from which we find the condition

$$\frac{1}{n_1} + \frac{1}{n_2} + \frac{1}{n_3} = \frac{1}{2}.$$

In the same manner we find the following conditions for the other possible arrangements:

$$\frac{1}{n_1} + \frac{1}{n_2} + \frac{1}{n_3} + \frac{1}{n_4} = 1.$$

$$\frac{1}{n_1} + \frac{1}{n_2} + \frac{1}{n_3} + \frac{1}{n_4} + \frac{1}{n_5} = \frac{3}{2}.$$

$$\frac{1}{n_1} + \frac{1}{n_2} + \frac{1}{n_3} + \frac{1}{n_4} + \frac{1}{n_5} + \frac{1}{n_6} = 2.$$

Following are the seventeen possible solutions in integers of these equations:

No.	n_1	n_2	n_3	No.	n_1	n_2	n_3	n_4	n_5	n_6
1	3	7	42	10	6	6	6			
2	3	8	24	11	3	3	4	12		
3	3	9	18	12	3	3	6	6		
4	3	10	15	13	3	4	4	6		
5	3	12	12	14	4	4	4	4		
6	4	5	20	15	3	3	3	4	4	
7	4	6	12	16	3	3	3	3	6	
8	4	8	8	17	3	3	3	3	3	3
9	5	5	10							

Solutions 10, 14, and 17 have already been examined. Solutions 1, 2, 3, 4, 6, and 9 are possible at a single vertex, but cannot be extended to cover the whole plane. Thus there remain only the following cases to consider:

No.	n_1	n_2	n_3	n_4	No.	n_1	n_2	n_3	n_4	n_5
5	3	12	12		11	3	3	4	12	
7	4	6	12		13	3	4	4	6	
8	4	8	8		15	3	3	3	4	4
12	3	3	6	6	16	3	3	3	3	6

Any of these except No. 11 can be used as the sole type of arrangement in a design covering the whole plane. No. 11 must be used in conjunction with others, as Nos. 5, 15, or 17.

In No. 5 two dodecagons and a triangle meet at a vertex. The extended figure may be formed by juxtaposing dodecagons as in Figure 84. The remaining spaces form the triangles.

No. 7 gives a more complicated pattern composed of do-

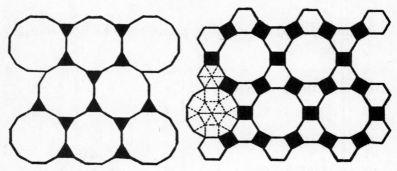

FIGURE 84.   FIGURE 85.

FIGURE 86.

decagons, hexagons and squares, one each at each vertex (Figure 85). No. 8 is formed by the juxtaposition of octagons. The empty spaces form the needed squares.

Two different forms of mosaic can be obtained from No. 12 by the juxtaposition of hexagons, according as the hexagons have edges in common or only vertices. The empty spaces form triangles, or lozenges composed of pairs of triangles (Figures 87–88).

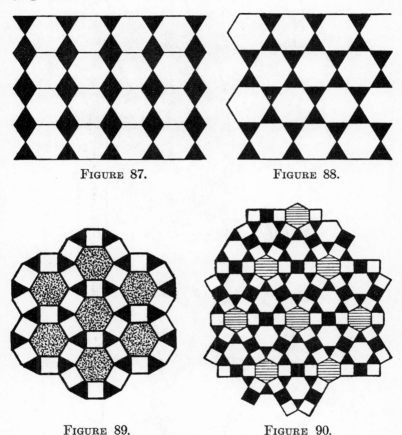

FIGURE 87.   FIGURE 88.

FIGURE 89.   FIGURE 90.

Nos. 13 and 15 yield great varieties of designs, some of which are shown in Figures 89 and 90.

Figures 91, 92, and 93 give mosaics involving No. 11 in combination with Nos. 15, 17, and 5, respectively.

No. 16 results in hexagons surrounded by triangles, as in Figure 94.

Let S_n be the area of a regular n-gon with side 1 unit long. Then $S_3 = \frac{1}{4}\sqrt{3}$, $S_4 = 1$, $S_6 = \frac{3}{2}\sqrt{3}$, and $S_{12} = 6 + 3\sqrt{3}$,

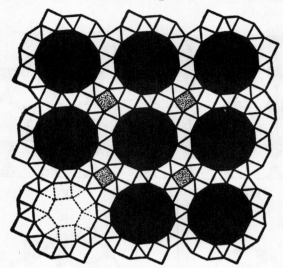

FIGURE 91.

FIGURE 92.

so that $S_6 = 6S_3$ and $S_{12} = 12S_3 + 6S_4$. Actually a hexagon can be decomposed into 6 triangles with the same side, and a dodecagon into 12 triangles and 6 squares, as shown in Figure 95. Hence we may replace a 6 by 3, 3 in the table of solutions, transforming Nos. 7, 12, 13, and 16 into Nos. 11 16, 15, and 17; and conversely. Similarly, since the angle of the dodecagon, 150°, is the sum of the angles of the square and triangle, we may replace a 12 in the tables by 3, 4, transforming No. 5 into No. 11 or No. 15, and No. 7 into No. 13; and conversely.

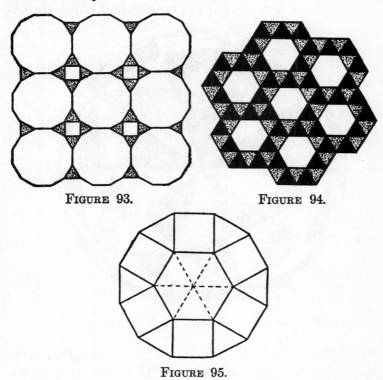

FIGURE 93.   FIGURE 94.

FIGURE 95.

The forming of mosaics with cardboard polygons can be a beautiful and fascinating game, interesting to people of all ages. It is also useful to architects in the designing of decorative patterns.

3. A MOSAIC ON THE SPHERE

Mr. H. M. S. Coxeter has described (*Scripta Mathematica*, 1936, p. 156) a dissection of the surface of a sphere into triangles by the 15 planes of symmetry passing through the opposite edges of an icosahedron (Figure 96).

The sphere is divided into 120 spherical triangles, the an-

FIGURE 96. *Mosaic on a Sphere Surface.*

gles of which are 90°, 60°, and 36°. The vertices of all these triangles together give 62 points — 12 where 10 triangles meet, 20 where 6 meet, and 30 where 4 meet. The 12 points can be regarded as either the vertices of an icosahedron or as the centers of the faces of a dodecahedron; the 20 points can be regarded as either the vertices of a dodecahedron or as the centers of the faces of an icosahedron; and the 30 points can be regarded as the centers of the edges of either polyhedron. Each of the 15 great circles contains 4 of the 12 points, 4 of the 20, and 4 of the 30 — in all, 12 of the 62. This dissection of the spherical surface was considered by Felix Klein.

Mr. Royal V. Heath has placed the numbers from 1 to 62 on the 62 points in such a way that the sum of the 12 numbers on each of the 15 great circles, as well as the sum of the numbers at each of the 12 points where 10 triangles meet (i.e. the vertices of the icosahedron), add up to 378 (Figure 97).

FIGURE 97. *Spherical Mosaic with Magic Features.*

4. TOPOLOGY

There are certain geometric questions in which the specific size and shape of the objects under consideration are of no importance — only their relative position matters. One may bend, stretch or tear the figure (provided the edges are sewn up again as they were) without altering the essential nature of the problem. Such questions are called topological.

1. The problem of the Königsberg bridges provided the occasion for the first researches in topology. The problem was proposed and solved by Euler. It consists in determining whether one can pass just once over all the bridges over the river Preger at Königsberg. The arrangement of the bridges is given in Figure 98. If we shrink each piece of land to a point and each bridge to a line, we transform the geographic map into what is called a linear graph, shown in Figure 99. This particular graph has four odd vertices — vertices at which an odd number of lines come together. It can be shown that it is impossible to pass just once over every arc of a linear graph without jumping if the graph has more than two odd vertices. Hence it is impossible to fulfill the prescription of the Königsberg bridges problem.

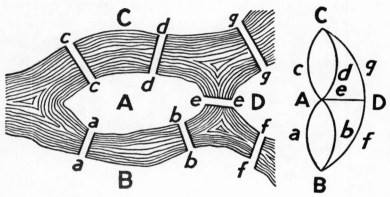

FIGURE 98. *Geographic Map:*
The Königsberg Bridges.

FIGURE 99.
Linear Graph.

The problem is sometimes stated in the following form: A smuggler wishes to cross just once every frontier of each of the various countries of a certain continent. What is his route? If we represent the various countries by points and join by simple arcs every pair of points representing countries with a common frontier, the problem is seen to be of the same type. If the continent is that of Europe no solution is possible, since several countries, Denmark and Portugal for example, have an odd number of frontiers.

Every linear graph has an even number of odd vertices. If there are no odd vertices the graph is unicursal and closed — that is, it can be traversed completely just once without jumping, and the path stops where it started. In this case the path may be started at any point of the graph. If the graph has two odd vertices it is still unicursal, but the path starts at one odd vertex and ends at the other.

The square with its diagonals is not unicursal, but the heptagon with its transversals is unicursal and closed. The square with one diagonal is unicursal, but the path must start at one extremity of the diagonal and end at the other.

2. Probably the most famous unsolved problem after Fermat's last theorem, and certainly the most deceptively simple in appearance, is the map-coloring problem. Suppose that we wish to print a map of certain countries, and we want to be sure that no two countries which have a common boundary line have the same color. We suppose that every country is in one piece and has no holes in it. No harm will be done if two countries which have no common boundary have the same color. What is the least number of colors which will suffice for every such map?

Two colors suffice to color the squares of a chessboard, and three for the hexagons in Figure 75. But if one wishes to color the "ocean" around the hexagons, four colors are needed. Thus a printer of maps must have at least four colors at his disposal.

Heawood has shown that five colors are sufficient for every map on the plane or on the sphere, but no one has ever produced a map which needs that many colors, nor has it ever been shown that four colors will always suffice.

One of the most tantalizing aspects of the problem is the fact that the problem has been solved for surfaces more complicated than the surface of the sphere. For example, seven colors are necessary and sufficient to color every map drawn on the surface of a torus. Only in the apparently simplest case has the problem remained unsolved.

3. One-sided Surfaces. A very interesting geometrical fact of a topological nature is the existence of one-sided surfaces. A one-sided surface is one which a fly, for example, could traverse in such a way as to come back to his starting point, but upside down, without crossing an edge. Although closed surfaces of this sort exist ideally in four-dimensional space, none can be formed in three dimensions which does not either cut itself or have an edge. The simplest surface of the latter type is the Möbius band, named after the dis-

Figure 100. *The Möbius Band.*

coverer of its properties. This may easily be formed by cutting a long and relatively narrow strip of paper, and giving the paper one twist before pasting the ends together as in Figure 100.

It is clear from the figure that if one starts in the middle of the colored surface and pursues a lengthwise course along the middle of the strip, after one trip around the band one will return to the original point of departure, but on the uncolored side. The surface also has just one edge, as one will discover if he traces out its course.

This surface has many other interesting properties. For

example, suppose one cuts it lengthwise through the middle.
When the cut has been completed and the pieces apparently
fall apart, it will be found that there are not really two pieces
at all — only one, but twice twisted instead of once. It is
now an ordinary two-sided band. If the operation be repeated, the strip will now really fall into two pieces which are
interlaced. If the first cut had been made parallel to the
edge and one third of the way from one side of the strip to the
other, the result would have been two interlaced strips, one
like the original, the other twice as long and twice twisted.

CHAPTER NINE

PERMUTATIONAL PROBLEMS

1. DIFFICULT CROSSINGS

THERE are many problems of this sort. We shall treat a number of characteristic cases, approximately in the order of their difficulty.

1. THE WOLF, THE CABBAGE, AND THE GOAT. A boatman must carry a wolf, a goat, and a cabbage across a river in a boat so small that he can take only one at a time. Furthermore, he must be on hand to keep the wolf from eating the goat, and the goat from eating the cabbage. How shall he do it?

The key to the solution is the goat — the only one that cannot be left unguarded in the presence of either of the other two. One solution is: The boatman (1) takes the goat over, (2) comes back alone, (3) takes the cabbage over, (4) brings back the goat, (5) takes the wolf over, (6) comes back alone, (7) takes the goat over. Another solution is found by interchanging the wolf and the cabbage.

This problem suggested to Aubry the following question: How shall we place in line 3 hunters, 3 wolves, 3 goats, and 3 cabbages without disturbing the peace by having a hunter next to a wolf, a wolf next to a goat, or a goat next to a cabbage, and without creating rivalry by having 2 hunters, 2 wolves, 2 goats or 2 cabbages side by side? The solutions are:

$$w\,c\,w\,c\,w\,c\,h\,g\,h\,g\,h\,g \qquad \text{and} \qquad g\,h\,g\,h\,g\,h\,c\,w\,c\,w\,c\,w.$$

A similar problem, also due to Aubry, is the following: Four families, each consisting of a man, his wife and their child, are to be seated at the 12 places of a round table in such a way that each man is between a woman and a child, each woman is between a child and a man, and each child is between a man and a woman, yet no two members of any family are seated side by side.

If we denote the families by the subscripts 1, 2, 3, 4, and the members of a family by M, W, C, one solution is:

$$M_1C_3W_2M_4C_1W_3M_2C_4W_1M_3C_2W_4.$$

Poulet proved that there are 5,040 solutions.

2. Transporting the Regiment. How shall a regiment cross a river when the only available means of transportation is a boat containing two small boys? Either boy can operate the boat, but the boat is so small that it can carry at most one soldier or the two boys.

Solution: (1) Two boys go over, (2) one boy comes back, (3) one soldier goes over, (4) the other boy comes back, (5) the first four steps are repeated for every remaining soldier of the regiment.

3. The Jealous Husbands. Two jealous husbands and their wives must cross a river in a boat that holds only two persons. How can this be done so that a wife is never left with the other woman's husband unless her own husband is present?

Solution: (1) A couple crosses over, (2) the husband returns, (3) the men cross over, (4) the other husband returns, (5) the second couple crosses over. Another type of solution can be obtained by having (1) the two women cross over and (2) one of them return. A similar change may be made in steps (4) and (5). The first solution seems the most just, since the men are penalized for their jealousy by having to do the rowing.

There are many generalizations of this problem. The most direct would seem to be that in which the number of couples is n (> 1) and the capacity of the boat is some number x greater than one and less than the total number of persons. Now, however, the problem is really too general to be interesting, for it is clear that with a relatively large number of places in the boat the solution is too simple. Hence the really significant problem is to determine the least value of x that will serve for a given value of n.

First we notice that $x = 4$ will certainly serve for 3 or more couples. For one of the couples can transport all the other couples, one couple at a time. In this way $n - 2$ round trips and 1 more crossing, $2n - 3$ crossings in all, will suffice. Of course it is not necessary to make one couple do all the work. The rowing may be divided up in various ways, but it is not possible to distribute it evenly.

Another general result is that $x = n - 1$ will serve for $n \geqq 3$. This may be shown as follows: (1) $n - 1$ of the wives cross over, leaving 1 behind, (2) 1 wife returns, (3) the remaining 2 wives cross over, (4) 1 wife returns, (5) she remains with her husband and the other $n - 1$ husbands cross over, (6) 1 couple returns. There are now 2 couples to be transported and the solution depends on the value of n. For $n = 3$ we have: (7) the 2 husbands cross, (8) a wife returns, (9) 2 wives cross, (10) a wife returns, (11) the last 2 wives cross. If $n = 4$, then (7) 2 husbands and a wife cross, (8) a wife returns, (9) the 2 wives cross. When $n \geqq 5$, (7) all cross at once.

If we combine these two theorems we find that we have restricted the possible values of x and n to these combinations:

n	2	3	4	5	> 5
x	2	2	2, 3	2, 3, 4	2, 3, 4

First we can show that a boat holding 2 persons is insufficient to solve the problem for more than 3 couples. To show this we use these two facts: (1) If there are both men and women on one side of the river, the women must be in the minority, since otherwise some wife would be in the presence of other men without her husband. (2) If h is any number between 1 and $2n$, at some time there must be just h persons and the boat on the far side of the river. For after the first crossing the number of persons on the far side of the river is never increased by more than one at a time.

Suppose n is even and that $n + 1$ persons and the boat are on the far side of the river, $n - 1$ persons are on the near side. Since both numbers are odd there must be more women than men on one side, which is only possible if there are no men on that side. Hence all the men and one woman are on the far side. But on the last crossing either one or two men must have been taken from the near side, where they were in the minority, which is not permitted.

If n is odd, let there be n people on each side, with the boat on the far side. As before, all the men must be on one side. If the men are on the far side, none of them may take the boat back to get the women. If the men are on the near side, they cannot get across, since the first man or men to cross will be in a minority.

Almost the same arguments show that a boat holding 3 persons will not serve to transport more than 5 couples. The only problem left is to determine whether $x = 3$ will serve for 5 couples. This is settled by showing that there is a solution when $n = 5$ and $x = 3$: (1) 3 wives cross over, (2) 1 wife returns, (3) 2 wives cross, (4) 1 wife returns, (5) the 3 wives who have crossed are joined by their husbands, (6) a couple returns, (7) the 3 husbands cross, (8) a wife returns, (9) 3 wives cross, (10) a wife returns, (11) the last 2 wives cross.

Thus we have the following results (N being the least number of crossings required for the given values of n and x):

n	2	3	4	5	> 5
x	2	2	3	3	4
N	5	11	9	11	$2n - 3$

A boat holding only two persons will suffice to transport any number of these unhappy couples if there is an island in the river. First one couple is brought to the farther bank and one couple and the boat are established on the island by the following sequence of nine trips:

1	Two wives go to the island.	$ABCcDd\cdots$	ab	—
2, 3	One of them fetches a third.	$ABCDd\cdots$	abc	—
4, 5	One of the three women rejoins her husband and the other two are joined by their husbands.	$CcDd\cdots$	$AaBb$	—
6, 7	One of the women on the island takes the other to the farther shore and returns to the island.	$CcDd\cdots$	ABb	a
8, 9	Her husband transports the other man to the farther shore and returns.	$CcDd\cdots$	Bb	Aa

Next, one couple is taken from the near shore to the island and one couple is taken from the island to the far shore by the following sequence of eight trips (the boat is returned to the island):

1, 2	The man on the island returns to the near bank and two wives go to the island.	$BCDEe\cdots$	bcd	Aa
3, 4	One wife returns to the near bank and the husbands of the two wives on the island rejoin their wives.	$DdEe\cdots$	$BbCc$	Aa

5, 6	The two husbands on the island cross to the far shore and the wife then returns to the island.	$DdEe\cdots$	abc	ABC
7, 8	Two of the women on the island cross to the far shore and the husband of the third returns to the island.	$DdEe\cdots$	Cc	$AaBb$

Since the boat is still at the island these last operations may be repeated until just one couple is left on the near shore and one on the island. These two couples may then be carried to the farther shore by a final sequence of nine trips:

1, 2	The husband on the island fetches the husband on the near shore to the island.	n	MmN	$Aa\cdots$
3, 4	The two husbands on the island go to the far shore and one wife there returns to the island.	n	lm	$LMNAa\cdots$
5, 6	A wife on the island fetches the wife on the near shore to the island.	—	lmn	$LMNAa\cdots$
7, 8	A wife on the island takes another to the far shore and returns.	—	mn	$NAa\cdots$
9	The two wives on the island go to the far shore.	—	—	$Aa\cdots$

Thus $9 + 8(n - 3) + 9 = 8(n - 1) + 2 = 8n - 6$ trips are required to transport the n couples.

There is a certain ambiguity in the problem owing to differing interpretations of what constitutes a trip. The solution above assumes that a trip is a crossing between the island and either bank of the river. If a crossing from one bank to the other is a single trip, the number of trips is reduced, though the distance traveled is the same.

Tarry has complicated the problem still further by supposing the wives unable to manage the boat. In the solution of this problem we assume that a trip includes a crossing from bank to bank. Our first endeavor is to free two men from their wives. This may be accomplished as follows:

Trip	Bank	Island	Bank	Trip	Bank	Island	Bank
—	$AaBb\cdots$	—	—	6	$ACcDd$	Bb	a
1	$BbCc\cdots$	—	Aa	7	$ADd\cdots$	$BbCc$	a
2	$ABbCc\cdots$	—	a	8	$ABCDd\cdots$	bc	a
3	$ACcDc\cdots$	Bb	a	9	$CDd\cdots$	bc	AaB
4	$ABCcDd\cdots$	b	a	10	$BCDd\cdots$	bc	Aa
5	$CcDd\cdots$	ABb	a				

Now B and C are free to row the other couples across. This they can do in four trips for each couple. First B takes C to the other bank and returns; then the couple rows over and C brings back the boat. At the end of $10 + 4(n - 4)$ trips just one couple are on the first bank with B and C and the boat, b and c are on the island, and the others are on the second bank. The crossing can now be completed in the following 11 trips:

Trip	Bank	Island	Bank	Trip	Bank	Island	Bank
1	Dd	bc	$AaBCEe\cdots$	7	d	c	$AaBbCDEe\cdots$
2	CDd	bc	$AaBEe\cdots$	8	d	Cc	$AaBbDEe\cdots$
3	d	bc	$AaBCDEe\cdots$	9	d	—	$AaBbCcDEe\cdots$
4	d	$BbCc$	$AaDEe\cdots$	10	Dd	—	$AaBbCcEe\cdots$
5	d	Cc	$AaBbDEe\cdots$	11	—	—	$Aa\cdots$
6	d	CcD	$AaBbEe\cdots$				

Thus it takes $10 + 4(n - 4) + 11 = 4n + 5$ trips to complete the operation.

Tarry proposed a still further complication by adding to the requirements made so far the assumption that one of the husbands was a bigamist traveling with both his wives. The problem can still be solved, but no fewer than 43 trips are required for the transportation of 4 families.

4. THE THIEVES AND THE LOOT. Saint-Laguë gave an amusing problem of this sort:

Three robbers, old Babylas, his nephew Hilary, and Hilary's son Sosthenes, stole a treasure chest from an old castle. The treasure was hidden at the top of a tower overlooking a river. To avoid pursuit they have had to destroy the ladders by which they climbed up inside the tower, and their only means of escape is to go down the outside of the tower by means of a crude tackle they have with them. This consists of a long rope with a basket at each end and a single pulley. If the difference in weight of the contents of the two baskets is greater than 20 pounds, the heavier basket descends too rapidly for the safety of the robbers, though the box will stand it. Babylas weighs 170 pounds, Hilary 100 pounds, Sosthenes 80 pounds, and the treasure 60 pounds. But this is not their only problem. When they reach the bottom they divide the treasure into three unequal parts, the largest for Babylas, and each puts his portion into a separate bag. They must then cross the river in a boat so small that it will hold only two men or one man and a bag. There is no honor among them, and none of them wishes to leave his bag with one of the others. However, they decide that the man who is managing the boat will be too busy to tamper with the bags. How did they make good their escape?

Solution: First they let the box down in one basket. When that has reached the bottom Sosthenes climbs into the basket at the top and goes down, bringing the treasure up. The box is taken out, Hilary climbs in and descends, bringing up Sosthenes. Both men get out and the box is sent down a second time. Hilary gets in at the bottom, and Babylas descends, bringing up both Hilary and the box. Hilary and Babylas get out and the box is sent down a third time. This time Sosthenes goes down as the box comes up. The box is lowered a fourth time and Hilary goes down bringing Sosthenes up. Sosthenes goes down bringing the box up, and the box is lowered for the fifth and last time.

To get across the river, Sosthenes crosses first with his bag. He leaves it and returns to bring Hilary's bag. On his return from this trip Sosthenes is taken across by Hilary, who returns with his own bag. Hilary then takes Babylas over, and makes two more round trips to get the two bags.

Perhaps it is easier to be honest.

Here is another variation of the fundamental problem. Three citizens and three robbers are to get across a river in a boat holding only two persons. How shall it be done so that there are never more robbers than citizens together at any time?

This problem differs from that of the jealous husbands only in that no citizen shows any preference for any robber. For we showed in the former case that it was necessary that the women should not outnumber the men whenever they were together. Hence any solution of the corresponding problem of the jealous husbands yields a solution of this problem; and all solutions of this problem can be obtained by permuting the various robbers in the solutions obtained from the first problem.

2. SHUNTING PROBLEMS

1. A railroad track and two spurs form a triangle as in Figure 101. The portion of the track at C is just long enough to accommodate one caboose, but it will not take a locomotive.

Initially there is a locomotive on the open track, a caboose *P* at 1 and a caboose *Q* at 2. How can the positions of the cabooses be interchanged?

Solution: The engine (1) pushes *P* to *C* and uncouples, (2) goes to spur 2 and couples to *Q* and couples *Q* to *P*, (3) pulls both *P* and *Q* onto the open track and pushes them to the left of the switch to spur 1, (4) uncouples *P*, pulls *Q* clear of the switch to spur 2 and pushes *Q* to *C*, (5) uncouples, goes to spur 1 and pulls *Q* to 1, (6) picks up *P*, pulls it clear of the switch to spur 2, and pushes *P* to 2.

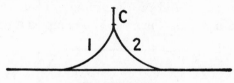

FIGURE 101.

2. Boats *A*, *B*, *C* meet boats *D*, *E*, *F* in a river too narrow to allow them to pass. There is a small basin at *G* (Figure 102) which will admit any one of the boats. How shall the two sets of boats pass?

Solution: Boat *D* enters *G*, boats *A*, *B*, *C* pass *G*, boat *D*

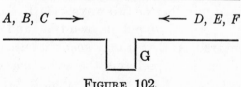

FIGURE 102.

goes on its way, boats *A*, *B*, *C* return to the other side of *G*, and the same operations are repeated for boats *E* and *F*.

3. Trains *A* and *B*, going in opposite directions on a single-track line, meet at a station at which there is a siding too short to take all of either train. The siding leads into the main track at each end (Figure 103). How can the trains pass?

Solution: Train *A* pulls onto the siding, leaves as many of its rear cars as the siding will take, pulls onto the main track and backs away well clear of the siding. Train *B* pulls past the siding, backs onto the siding, couples on the part of train *A* that is there, backs through the siding well clear of the switch. Train *A* pulls onto the siding. If not all of what is left will go on the siding, the operation is repeated. If the operation is repeated, train *B* leaves the first part of train *A* on the main track while it switches the second part. This continues until enough of train *A* has been taken off so that the remainder can stand on the siding. Then train *B* pulls the rest of train *A* past the switch, uncouples it and goes on.

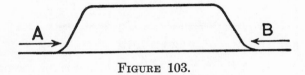

FIGURE 103.

The part of train *A* on the siding pulls off and goes back to pick up the rest.

If train *A* is split into more than two parts, this procedure reverses the order of the sections taken off. This reversal may be avoided in either of two ways: (1) If the engine of train *B* is strong enough to pull its own train and all the cars detached from train *A*, then it may keep the successive parts of *A* coupled on as it performs the switching operations. (2) In any case, train *A* can use the siding to bring the sections back into their normal order.

4. Deal with the same problem, but with a dead-end siding (Figure 104).

Solution: Train *B* leaves some cars on the siding, pulls out of the siding, and backs up out of the way. Train *A* pulls up onto the siding, couples on the cars and backs out of the way. The operations are repeated until what is left of train *B* can get onto the siding. Train A passes the siding and allows train B to pull out of the way. Train A comes back and leaves some cars of train B on the siding, backs past the switch and pulls out of the way. Train B recaptures the cars on the siding and pulls off the siding out of the way. These operations are continued until train A has dropped all the cars of train B that it had picked up. Train A then goes on its way, train B picks up the last installment of cars, and goes on its way.

If the locomotive of train A is not sufficiently strong, the

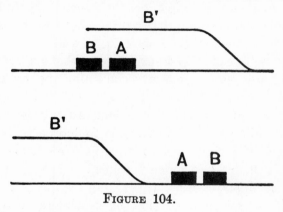

FIGURE 104.

switching may be modified as follows: When train A is to the right of the switch preparatory to picking up the first installment of B's cars, it leaves all of its cars on the main track, until it has finished switching B's cars. B behaves as before. When the portion of train B containing the engine is on the siding, the engine of train A first pushes B's cars out of the way beyond the siding, then goes back and pulls its cars out of the way before the part of B containing the engine pulls off the siding. Then every time train A leaves an installment of B's cars on the siding its engine must first leave its own cars to the right of the switch, go back to pick up B's cars to leave some on the siding, push the rest of B's cars that

it has not yet delivered out of the way to the left of the siding,
and then pull its own cars to the left of the siding. Then B
can pick up its cars and get out of the way. This procedure
is repeated until train B is all assembled.

3. DISTRIBUTIONS

1. THE DAILY PROMENADE. Years ago, when girls were
called young ladies and were never permitted more violent
exercise than walking, the headmistress of a boarding school
wished to arrange matters so that her pupils would derive the
maximum amount of companionship in their daily walks without forming boisterous groups. She therefore ordered the
young ladies, of whom there were $2n$, to walk in pairs, but to
form new pairs each day in such a way that no young lady
had the same companion a second time before she had
walked with every other young lady. This worked well for
a day or two, but presently the young ladies began to spend
more and more time each day trying to find partners. They
would be nearly ready when it was discovered that the last
two young ladies had already walked together. Can you
help the headmistress?

Here is one solution. Divide the circumference of a circle
into $2n - 1$ equal parts by successive points a_1, a_2, $\cdots$, a_{2n-1}.
To simplify, let us say $2n - 1 = 11$, and letter the points
from A to K. Mark the center a_{2n} with an L, draw the diameter through A, and draw the $n - 1$ chords perpendicular to
this diameter and through the remaining $2n - 2$ points,
which are symmetrically placed with respect to this diameter. The result is Figure 105. The pairs of points located
on the diameter and on the chords give an arrangement of
the promenade for one day. For the following days the diameter and the chords are rotated so that the diameter passes
successively through B, C, $\cdots$, K, and the pairs of points
determined by the new positions of the chords and the diam-

eter give $2n - 1$ arrangements satisfying the requirements of the headmistress.

Another method of solution uses an arrangement such as that shown in Figure 106. (Here also we take $n = 6$.) Twelve lettered cubes fit easily into a box, forming two rows as

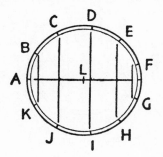

FIGURE 105.

shown. A vertical fin between the two rows keeps the rows separated, except at the ends. The pairs in the vertical columns of the given figure form the arrangement for one day. To find another, remove the cube marked L, slip A into its

A	B	C	D	E	F
L	K	J	I	H	G

FIGURE 106.

place, slide the rest of the cubes in the top row to the left, move G up to the top row, slide the lower row to the right, and replace L. The vertical pairs give the new arrangement. Successive arrangements are found by repeating this procedure, always removing L and sliding the other cubes around in the counterclockwise direction before replacing L.

2. ROUND DANCES. Children are dancing in a circle. Can successive arrangements be determined by which each child has every other child just once as neighbor, on one side or on the other?

Solution: Since each child has 2 neighbors at a time, the total number of children must be odd, say $2n + 1$. (In Fig-

FIGURE 107.

ure 107 is shown the case where $n = 5$.) Mark the circumference of the circle with $2n$ equally spaced points and letter them in the order $a_1 a_2 a_4 \cdots a_{2n} a_{2n-1} a_{2n-3} \cdots a_3$. Letter the center a_0 and join the points $a_0 a_1 a_2 a_3 \cdots a_{2n} a_0$ by a zigzag line. Each successive rotation of the zigzag line through a $(2n)$th part of a revolution yields a new circular permutation of the

A	C	E	G	I	K
B	D	F	H	J	A

FIGURE 108.

$2n + 1$ letters. The full set satisfies all the requirements.

We can also use the two-rowed rectangular box. For this problem one of the letters is repeated, and the arrangement corresponding to the circular permutation *ABCDEFGHIJK* is given in Figure 108. To obtain a new permutation the two cubes *A* are removed, the two rows are slid in opposite directions, and the end cubes are moved so that the cubes *A* can go back to their original positions. The first such operation yields the permutations $ACEBGDIFKHJA$. The others are found similarly.

If the number of children is even we may modify the problem by requiring that every child have every other child but one as his neighbor. Circular permutations satisfying this requirement can be found from Figure 107 by marking an extra point on the other diameter of the figure.

Here is a variation of the problem. n boys and n girls are

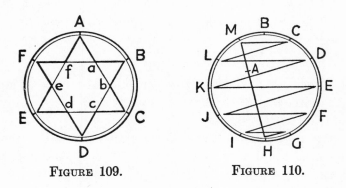

FIGURE 109. FIGURE 110.

dancing in a circle, a boy between each two girls. Can one make successive permutations in their order so that every boy has every girl as neighbor just once?

In all there are n^2 pairs to be formed. In any one round there are $2n$ such pairs. If there are to be no repetitions or omissions, $\dfrac{n^2}{2n} = \dfrac{n}{2}$ arrangements must form the n^2 desired pairs, so n must be even, say $n = 2p$. Join the alternate vertices of an inscribed regular n-gon, so as to form two inscribed regular p-gons (as in Figure 109). Denote the boys by capital letters and the girls by corresponding small letters. Letter the points on the circle with the capital letters in order, and letter the points of intersection of the two p-gons correspondingly, as in the figure. The successive arrangements are found by keeping the outer points fixed and rotating the inner figure.

In another variation children dance about one of their number, and we are asked to determine a set of arrangements so that each child shall be in the center just once and have every other child as neighbor just twice.

If the number of children is odd, the solution is given by a diagram such as that of Figure 110. Here A is placed in the center in the first arrangement and the other letters are taken in their natural order. For the later arrangements the letter not touched by the zigzag line represents the person to be put in the center, and the others are taken in the order given by the zigzag.

3. THE NINE MUSES. How can nine Muses be grouped in successive sets of three triads so that each Muse is in the same triad with every other Muse just once?

There are many solutions of this problem. It is a generalization of the first problem in this section. Kirkman suggested the same problem for the promenades of 15 girls in sets of three.

4. MATCHES AND TOURNAMENTS

One of the commonest situations in which problems of distribution arise is in arranging the schedules of sporting matches and tournaments. Bridge offers a great variety of such problems because of the different types of contest that may be arranged, depending on whether the unit in the competition is a team of four, a team of two, or the individual player. We shall give here the solutions of some of these problems.

The most equitable form of bridge match is the team-of-four duplicate match. Here each team of four players, say A, B, C, D, divides into two minor teams, A–B and C–D.

When two teams of four meet, each minor team of one of them engages a minor team of the other. Both sets of four players play with the same cards, but one minor team of each side plays North and South while the other plays East and West. (For example, A and B play the North and South hands at one table, while C and D play the East and West hands at another.) In this way each team of four plays exactly the same hands as its opponent, and the element of chance is reduced to a minimum. The contests may be arranged among the teams of four in the pattern of the elimination tournament or of the round-robin tournament.

1	7–2	6–3	5–4
5	4–6	3–7	2–1
2	1–3	7–4	6–5
6	5–7	4–1	3–2
3	2–4	1–5	7–6
7	6–1	5–2	4–3
4	3–5	2–6	1–7

FIGURE 111. *Round-robin.*

In a round-robin tournament among teams of four or two we must arrange a schedule by which every team meets every other just once. This is precisely equivalent to the problem of arranging the daily promenade of the school girls (p. 226), and may be solved by the same methods. Here is another procedure.

If there are $2n - 1$ teams write the numbers of the teams in order n times in $2n - 1$ lines and n columns. Then in the last $n - 1$ columns write the remaining numbers in reverse order beside the previous entries. (In Figure 111, $n = 4$. The first entries are in ordinary type and the second in bold face.) Each row gives a round of play, the last $n - 1$ columns give the pairs that meet in each round, and the first column tells which team is idle. If there are $2n$ teams, a table for $2n - 1$ teams is first made up. Then in each round the $2n$th team has to play the idle team given in the first column.

The most difficult and common case is that in which the competition is between individual players. Here we would like to satisfy the following conditions:

(1) Each player must play the same number of rubbers.

(2) Each player must have every other player as partner the same number of times.

(3) Each player must play against as many teams as can be formed from the remaining $n - 1$ players, and must play each of them the same number of times.

Let us denote by R_n the total number of rubbers that must be played to satisfy these conditions, and by $_nC_r$ the combinations of n things r at a time (that is, the number of ways of selecting r things from a set of n things). We must form every possible set of four players, and each such set must play 3 rubbers so that each one of the four has each of the others as partner. Then

$$R_n = 3 \ _nC_4 = \frac{n(n - 1)(n - 2)(n - 3)}{8}.$$

This may also be found by finding the number of all possible matches between pairs of players,

$$\frac{_nC_2 \cdot \ _{n-2}C_2}{2}.$$

Here is a table of values of R_n.

n	4	5	6	7	8	9	10
R_n	3	15	45	105	210	378	630

It will be seen that the number of rubbers increases very rapidly. For $n = 40$, $R_n = 274,170$. Such a tournament is obviously impracticable.

However, if we neglect the third condition the number can be radically reduced. When n is of the form $4k$ or $4k + 1$,

$$R_n = \frac{{}_nC_2}{2} = \frac{n(n-1)}{4};$$

while in all other cases

$$R_n = {}_nC_2 = \frac{n(n-1)}{2}.$$

First we shall give a set of tables giving the arrangement of matches under the less restrictive conditions, for $n = 4$, 5, 8, 9, 12, 13, 16, 17. These tables were formed by the procedure suggested for a round-robin tournament for teams of two, except that here each number represents an individual player and the columns have been grouped by pairs to form the sets of four players participating in each game.

$n = 4$	$n = 5$		$n = 8$	
1,3–2,4	1,5–2,4	3	1,7–2,6	3,5–4,8
2,1–3,4	3,2–4,1	5	2,1–3,7	4,6–5,8
3,2–1,4	2,1–3,5	4	3,2–4,1	5,7–6,8
	4,3–5,2	1	4,3–5,2	6,1–7,8
	5,4–1,3	2	5,4–6,3	7,2–1,8
			6,5–7,4	1,3–2,8
			7,6–1,5	2,4–3,8

$n = 9$			$n = 12$		
1,9–2,8	3,7–4,6	5	1,11– 2,10	3, 9– 4, 8	5, 7– 6,12
2,1–3,9	4,8–5,7	6	2, 1– 3,11	4,10– 5, 9	6, 8– 7,12
3,2–4,1	5,9–6,8	7	3, 2– 4, 1	5,11– 6,10	7, 9– 8,12
4,3–5,2	6,1–7,9	8	4, 3– 5, 2	6, 1– 7,11	8,10– 9,12
5,4–6,3	7,2–8,1	9	5, 4– 6, 3	7, 2– 8, 1	9,11–10,12
6,5–7,4	8,3–9,2	1	6, 5– 7, 4	8, 3– 9, 2	10, 1–11,12
7,6–8,5	9,4–1,3	2	7, 6– 8, 5	9, 4–10, 3	11, 2– 1,12
8,7–9,6	1,5–2,4	3	8, 7– 9, 6	10, 5–11, 4	1, 3– 2,12
9,8–1,7	2,6–3,5	4	9, 8–10, 7	11, 6– 1, 5	2, 4– 3,12
			10, 9–11, 8	1, 7– 2, 6	3, 5– 4,12
			11,10– 1, 9	2, 8– 3, 7	4, 6– 5,12

n = 13

1,13– 2,12	3,11– 4,10	5, 9– 6, 8	7
2, 1– 3,13	4,12– 5,11	6,10– 7, 9	8
3, 2– 4, 1	5,13– 6,12	7,11– 8,10	9
4, 3– 5, 2	6, 1– 7,13	8,12– 9,11	10
5, 4– 6, 3	7, 2– 8, 1	9,13–10,12	11
6, 5– 7, 4	8, 3– 9, 2	10, 1–11,13	12
7, 6– 8, 5	9, 4–10, 3	11, 2–12, 1	13
8, 7– 9, 6	10, 5–11, 4	12, 3–13, 2	1
9, 8–10, 7	11, 6–12, 5	13, 4– 1, 3	2
10, 9–11, 8	12, 7–13, 6	1, 5– 2, 4	3
11,10–12, 9	13, 8– 1, 7	2, 6– 3, 5	4
12,11–13,10	1, 9– 2, 8	3, 7– 4, 6	5
13,12– 1,11	2,10– 3, 9	4, 8– 5, 7	6

n = 16

1,15– 2,14	3,13– 4,12	5,11– 6,10	7, 9– 8,16
2, 1– 3,15	4,14– 5,13	6,12– 7,11	8,10– 9,16
3, 2– 4, 1	5,15– 6,14	7,13– 8,12	9,11–10,16
4, 3– 5, 2	6, 1– 7,15	8,14– 9,13	10,12–11,16
5, 4– 6, 3	7, 2– 8, 1	9,15–10,14	11,13–12,16
6, 5– 7, 4	8, 3– 9, 2	10, 1–11,15	12,14–13,16
7, 6– 8, 5	9, 4–10, 3	11, 2–12, 1	13,15–14,16
8, 7– 9, 6	10, 5–11, 4	12, 3–13, 2	14, 1–15,16
9, 8–10, 7	11, 6–12, 5	13, 4–14, 3	15, 2– 1,16
10, 9–11, 8	12, 7–13, 6	14, 5–15, 4	1, 3– 2,16
11,10–12, 9	13, 8–14, 7	15, 6– 1, 5	2, 4– 3,16
12,11–13,10	14, 9–15, 8	1, 7– 2, 6	3, 5– 4,16
13,12–14,11	15,10– 1, 9	2, 8– 3, 7	4, 6– 5,16
14,13–15,12	1,11– 2,10	3, 9– 4, 8	5, 7– 6,16
15,14– 1,13	2,12– 3,11	4,10– 5, 9	6, 8– 7,16

$n = 17$

1,17– 2,16	3,15– 4,14	5,13– 6,12	7,11– 8,10	9
2, 1– 3,17	4,16– 5,15	6,14– 7,13	8,12– 9,11	10
3, 2– 4, 1	5,17– 6,16	7,15– 8,14	9,13–10,12	11
4, 3– 5, 2	6, 1– 7,17	8,16– 9,15	10,14–11,13	12
5, 4– 6, 3	7, 2– 8, 1	9,17–10,16	11,15–12,14	13
6, 5– 7, 4	8, 3– 9, 2	10, 1–11,17	12,16–13,15	14
7, 6– 8, 5	9, 4–10, 3	11, 2–12, 1	13,17–14,16	15
8, 7– 9, 6	10, 5–11, 4	12, 3–13, 2	14, 1–15,17	16
9, 8–10, 7	11, 6–12, 5	13, 4–14, 3	15, 2–16, 1	17
10, 9–11, 8	12, 7–13, 6	14, 5–15, 4	16, 3–17, 2	1
11,10–12, 9	13, 8–14, 7	15, 6–16, 5	17, 4– 1, 3	2
12,11–13,10	14, 9–15, 8	16, 7–17, 6	1, 5– 2, 4	3
13,12–14,11	15,10–16, 9	17, 8– 1, 7	2, 6– 3, 5	4
14,13–15,12	16,11–17,10	1, 9– 2, 8	3, 7– 4, 6	5
15,14–16,13	17,12– 1,11	2,10– 3, 9	4, 8– 5, 7	6
16,15–17,14	1,13– 2,12	3,11– 4,10	5, 9– 6, 8	7
17,16– 1,15	2,14– 3,13	4,12– 5,11	6,10– 7, 9	8

These tables are not as satisfactory as they might be since a particular player does not have the other players as opponents the same number of times. For example, when $n = 8$ the first player meets the second 4 times, the third twice and the fourth not at all. A more equitable arrangement would be obtained if we could replace conditions (2) and (3) by the following:

(2′) Each player has every other player as partner just once.

(3′) Each player has every other player as opponent just twice.

These conditions can be realized when n is of the form $4k$ or $4k + 1$, but not otherwise.

For $n = 4$ and $n = 5$ the schedule is the same as in the preceding table.

$n = 8$		$n = 9$		
1,2–3,4	5,6–7,8	1,2–6,9	4,8–5,7	3
1,4–5,8	2,3–6,7	1,5–2,4	3,6–7,8	9
1,6–4,7	2,5–3,8	1,8–2,7	3,9–4,5	6
1,8–2,7	3,6–4,5	1,3–5,8	6,7–4,9	2
1,3–6,8	2,4–5,7	1,6–3,4	2,5–7,9	8
1,5–2,6	3,7–4,8	1,9–3,7	2,8–4,6	5
1,7–3,5	2,8–4,6	1,4–8,9	2,6–3,5	7
		1,7–5,6	2,9–3,8	4
		2,3–4,7	5,9–6,8	1

For $n = 12$ there are 33 games:

1,12– 5, 6	2,11– 3, 9	4, 8– 7,10
2,12– 6, 7	3, 1– 4,10	5, 9– 8,11
3,12– 7, 8	4, 2– 5,11	6,10– 9, 1
4,12– 8, 9	5, 3– 6, 1	7,11–10, 2
5,12– 9,10	6, 4– 7, 2	8, 1–11, 3
6,12–10,11	7, 5– 8, 3	9, 2– 1, 4
7,12–11, 1	8, 6– 9, 4	10, 3– 2, 5
8,12– 1, 2	9, 7–10, 5	11, 4– 3, 6
9,12– 2, 3	10, 8–11, 6	1, 5– 4, 7
10,12– 3, 4	11, 9– 1, 7	2, 6– 5, 8
11,12– 4, 5	1,10– 2, 8	3, 7– 6, 9

From $n = 13$ on the players may be assigned to various groups of 4 or 5 players. Then each of these groups play a tournament among themselves. Thus for $n = 13$ there are 39 games resulting from the following 13 tournaments of 4 players each: 1,2,3,4; 1,5,6,7; 1,8,9,10; 1,11,12,13; 2,5,8,11; 2,6,9,12; 2,7,10,13; 3,5,10,12; 3,7,9,11; 3,6,8,13; 4,5,9,13; 4,6,10,11; 4,7,8,12.

For $n = 16$ we have 60 games, or 20 tournaments of 4 players each:

1,2, 3, 4	5,6, 7, 8	9,10,11,12	13,14,15,16
1,5, 9,13	2,6,10,14	3, 7,11,15	4, 8,12,16
1,6,11,16	2,5,12,15	3, 8, 9,14	4, 7,10,13
1,7,12,14	2,8,11,13	3, 5,10,16	4, 6, 9,15
1,8,10,15	2,7, 9,16	3, 6,12,13	4, 5,11,14

For $n = 17$ there are 68 games. We can put the 17th player in the first four tournaments of the table for 16 players, making them tournaments for 5 players. The other tournaments in the table remain unchanged.

If the number of players is $4k + 2$ or $4k + 3$ this method cannot be used, and the number of games becomes very large. We shall give tables for $n = 6, 7, 10,$ and 11.

For $n = 6$ we have 15 isolated games: 1,2–3,4; 1,3–4,6; 1,5–2,4; 1,6–4,5; 2,5–3,6; 1,2–5,6; 1,4–2,6; 1,5–3,6; 2,3–4,6; 2,6–4,5; 1,3–2,5; 1,4–3,5; 1,6–2,3; 2,4–3,5; 3,4–5,6.

For $n = 7$ there are 21 games, or 7 tournaments of 4 players each: 1,2,3,4; 1,2,5,6; 1,3,5,7; 1,4,6,7; 3,4,5,6; 2,4,5,7; 2,3,6,7.

For $n = 10$ there are 45 games, or 15 tournaments of 4 players each: 1,3,5,6; 4,6,7,8; 1,2,6,8; 1,2,4,7; 5,7,8,9; 2,3,7,9; 2,3,5,8; 1,8,9,10; 3,4,8,10; 1,3,4,9; 2,6,9,10; 4,5,6,9; 2,4,5,10; 3,6,7,10; 1,5,7,10.

For $n = 11$ there are 55 games, or 11 tournaments of 5 players each: 1,2,4,7,11; 1,2,3,5,8; 2,6,7,8,10; 2,3,4,6,9; 3,7,8,9,11; 3,4,5,7,10; 1,4,8,9,10; 4,5,6,8,11; 2,5,9,10,11; 1,5,6,7,9; 1,3,6,10,11.

CHAPTER TEN

THE PROBLEM OF THE QUEENS

MATHEMATICS owes many interesting problems to the game of chess. Indeed the game itself is a single enormously complicated mathematical problem that has never been — and probably never will be — completely solved. In this chapter and the next we shall deal with certain problems suggested by the game, but we hasten to assure any of our readers who do not play chess that each of these problems will be restated in nontechnical language, and that no knowledge of chess is involved in their solution.

The problem from which this chapter derives its name is that of placing eight queens on a chessboard so that no one of them can take any other in a single move. This is a particular case of the more general problem: On a square array of n^2 cells place n objects, one on each of n different cells, in such a way that no two of them lie on the same row, column, or diagonal.

Since the problem is again one of arranging objects on the cells of a square array, as was the problem of magic squares, we shall use much of the terminology and many of the ideas of Chapter Seven. In particular, n is the order of the problem, and rows and columns will be referred to indifferently as orthogonals. However, the term diagonal will usually be restricted to mean a main diagonal or one of the two connected pieces of a broken diagonal. The diagonals which go upward from left to right will be called upward diagonals, the others downward diagonals. The array of cells on which the objects are to be placed will be called a chessboard of order n.

1. THE LINEAR PERMUTATIONS OF n DIFFERENT THINGS

There are $n! = 1 \cdot 2 \cdot 3 \cdots n$ distinct permutations of (that is, ways of arranging) n different objects in a row. This almost trite fact of elementary mathematics might seem to have little freshness or novelty left after performing its innumerable services in the solution of problems of combinations, circular permutations, and the like. But if we give it a certain simple graphical interpretation we shall find that

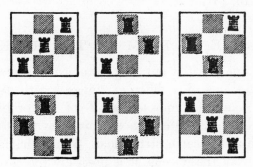

FIGURE 112. *Permutations of Three.*

it opens up a whole new field in terms of which we may find the solutions of many new problems, including the problem of the queens. The graphical representation we have in mind is as follows:

Denote the n objects to be permuted by the numbers

$$x = 1, 2, \cdots, n,$$

and n positions each may occupy by

$$y = 1, 2, \cdots, n.$$

Then a single permutation is equivalent to n pairs of values of x and y, $(x, y) = (1, y_1), (2, y_2), \cdots, (n, y_n)$, just one for each value of x and one for each value of y. If we number the columns of a chessboard of order n from left to right, and its rows from bottom to top, every cell will correspond to just one pair of numbers (x, y), the one which gives the number x of the column and the number y of the row in which it lies. Thus each permutation of n objects corresponds to a set of n cells of our chessboard, so selected that no two cells lie in the same orthogonal. The graphical representation may be completed by marking the selected cells on a set of chessboards, one for each permutation. Figure 112 gives the representation of all permutations of three things, namely 123, 132, 213, 231, 312, 321.

2. THE PROBLEM OF THE ROOKS

As we have pointed out, the graphical representation of the permutations of n different things constitutes a set of solutions — and the complete set — of the problem of arranging n objects on a chessboard of order n so that no two of them lie in the same orthogonal. While this is not quite the problem of the queens, it is precisely the corresponding problem for rooks — to place n rooks on an nth-order chessboard so that no one of them can take any other in a single move. Before going on to the problem of the queens let us examine the solutions of this problem in more detail, particularly in respect to their geometric properties.

In dealing with magic squares we agreed (p. 144) to consider as *equivalent* any solutions which could be derived from each other by certain simple geometrical transformations of the square — namely, rotation in its own plane through a right angle in the counterclockwise direction, reflection in a mirror, and repetitions and combinations of these operations. We make the same agreement here. By means of these transformations and their effect on the solutions we are able to make a very simple and useful classification of the solutions. First let us examine the transformations themselves more closely.

Denote a rotation through 90° by R, a reflection by S, and the result of performing two transformations in succession by the product (discussed below) of their symbols in the same order. Then RR represents a rotation through 180° and may be denoted by R^2. Both R^2R and RR^2 correspond to a rotation through 270°, so they may be denoted by R^3. In the same way $R^{h-1}R$ and RR^{h-1} both represent rotations through h right angles, so we shall denote them by R^h. However, R^4, rotation through 4 right angles, has no effect on the chessboard, so we shall denote it by I, representing the identical transformation; and higher powers may consequently be reduced modulo 4. S may also be thought of as being the result of a rotation through 180° in a plane vertical to that of the board and about the middle vertical line of the board as axis. SR, SR^2, and SR^3 are then seen to be the results of similar rotations or reflections, with the upward main diagonal, the middle horizontal and the downward main diagonal as axes, respectively. One can readily verify that $SR = R^3S$, $SR^2 = R^2S$, and $SR^3 = RS$; and that each of these reflections yields I when repeated. From the three relations $R^4 = I$, $S^2 = I$, $SR = R^3S$ one can easily show that even unlimited repetitions and combinations of R and S yield only the 8 distinct transformations: $I, R, R^2, R^3, S, SR, SR^2, SR^3$.

The symbols of these transformations have been combined as by multiplication, and we shall call the combinations (both of the symbols and the transformations they denote) products. This multiplication is just like ordinary multiplication except in one important respect: a product *may not be independent* of the order of the factors. Thus $R^2R = RR^2$, but $RS \neq SR$. The set has the further important property that the product of any two members of it lies in the set. Such a set is called in mathematics a group — a concept which has had a profound influence on all branches of mathematics. It will be worth our while to see what it can contribute to our present problem.

Following is the multiplication table of the group — a table which gives in each row and column the product of the element at the left of the row by the element at the head of the column.

I	R	R^2	R^3	S	SR	SR^2	SR^3
R	R^2	R^3	I	SR^3	S	SR	SR^2
R^2	R^3	I	R	SR^2	SR^3	S	SR
R^3	I	R	R^2	SR	SR^2	SR^3	S
S	SR	SR^2	SR^3	I	R	R^2	R^3
SR	SR^2	SR^3	S	R^3	I	R	R^2
SR^2	SR^3	S	SR	R^2	R^3	I	R
SR^3	S	SR	SR^2	R	R^2	R^3	I

From it we can see that the group contains other groups — called subgroups. There are in fact just these 10 subgroups, including the group itself as a subgroup:

(1) The identity: I.
(2) Rotations through 2 right angles: I, R^2.
(3) Reflections about the middle vertical line: I, S.
(4) Reflections about the middle horizontal line: I, SR^2.
(5) Reflections about the downward diagonal: I, SR.
(6) Reflections about the upward diagonal: I, SR^3.
(7) Rotations through one right angle: I, R, R^2, R^3.
(8) Reflections about either middle orthogonal line: I, R^2, S, SR^2.
(9) Reflections about either main diagonal: I, SR, SR^3, R^2.
(10) The whole group.

Every solution of the problem of the rooks has its corresponding group — the largest subgroup of the given group which leaves it invariant (that is, unchanged). In this way we can classify the various solutions. It will be found that no solution is left invariant by any of the subgroups (3),(4), (5), (8), or (10). With one exception the group of a given solution is also the group of every solution equivalent to it. In the exceptional case, noted below, half of the solutions of a set of equivalent solutions are invariant under one group and the other half under another. We shall put the full set of these equivalent solutions in a single class. We denote these classes as O, C, D, Q, and R. Here is the classification:

(*O*) *Ordinary solutions*, invariant only under the identity.

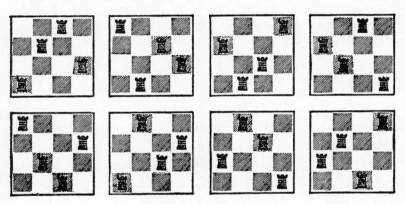

FIGURE 113. *Rook Problem.*

Each such solution is therefore one of 8 distinct equivalent solutions, and each of them is ordinary. We shall denote by O_n the number of complete sets of equivalent ordinary solutions of order n. There are none for $n < 4$. For $n = 4$ there is just one set: 1342, 4132, 3124, 3241, 4213, 1423, 2431, 2314. They are illustrated in Figure 113.

(*C*) *Centrosymmetric solutions*, invariant under subgroup (2), but under no larger subgroup. Each belongs to a complete set of 4 equivalent solutions, all centrosymmetric. Each is symmetric with respect to the center, but has no other symmetry. The number of complete sets of equivalent centrosymmetric solutions of order n will be denoted by C_n.

$C_n = 0$ for $n = 2, \cdots, 5$; $C_6 = 7$. One of these sets of order 6 is 246135, 362514, 415263, 531642 (Figure 114).

(D) *Diagonally symmetric solutions*, invariant under either (5) or (6), but not both, nor under any larger group. Each belongs to a complete set of 4 equivalent solutions, half of them invariant under (5), the other half under (6). The cor-

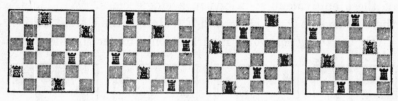

FIGURE 114. *Rook Problem.*

responding solutions are symmetric with respect to the downward or upward diagonal, respectively, but have no other symmetry. D_n denotes the number of complete sets of diagonally symmetric solutions of order n. $D_2 = 0$, $D_3 = 1$. This set of order 3 is 132, 312, 213, 231 (Figure 115).

FIGURE 115. *Rook Problem.*

(Q) *Doubly centrosymmetric solutions*, invariant under (7), but not under the whole group. Each belongs to a complete set of 2 equivalent solutions, both doubly centrosymmetric. The board must be of order $4k$ or $4k + 1$. Q_n is the number of complete sets of equivalent solutions of this type. For $n = 4$ there is one such set: 2413, 3142 (Figure 116).

(R) *Doubly diagonally symmetric solutions*, invariant under (9), but not under the whole group. Each belongs to a set of 2 equivalent solutions, both doubly diagonally symmetric.

Such a solution is symmetric with respect to each of the main diagonals. R_n denotes the number of complete sets of equivalent solutions of this type. The simplest set occurs when $n = 2$, and is 12, 21 (Figure 117).

The following table gives the number of complete sets of equivalent solutions of different types for small values of n.

FIGURE 116.

FIGURE 117.

n	O	C	D	Q	R	Total	Permutation
1							1
2				1	1		2
3			1		1	2	6
4	1		2	1	3	7	24
5	9		10	1	3	23	120
6	70	7	28		10	115	720
7	571	7	106		10	694	5,040
8		74		6	38		40,320
9		74		6	38		362,880
10							3,628,800

Since the total number of solutions is $n!$ we have

$$8O_n + 4C_n + 4D_n + 2Q_n + 2R_n = n!$$

The following relations can also be shown:

$$4C_n + 2Q_n + 2R_n = 2 \cdot 4 \cdot 6 \cdots 2k = 2^k \cdot k!,$$

where $n = 2k$ or $2k + 1$;

$$2Q_n = 2 \cdot 6 \cdot 10 \cdot 14 \cdots (4k - 2) = \frac{(2k)!}{k!}$$

for $n = 4k$ or $n = 4k + 1$;

$$2Q_n = 0$$

for $$n = 4k + 2 \text{ or } n = 4k + 3.$$

The whole set of solutions may be separated into $(n - 1)!$ sets of n solutions each in such a way that each set of n solutions just fills the board. If each solution in the set is assigned a different color, each such set is a solution of the problem of coloring the cells of the board with n colors in such a way that no color appears twice in the same orthogonal. If the numbers from 1 to n are used instead of colors

FIGURE 118.

FIGURE 119.

we have a Latin square. Since, however, these may not all be independent, this does not give the total number of independent Latin squares.

In analogy with magic squares we may call a solution regular if it is generated by a motion (u, v). In order to fulfill the requirements of the problem such a motion cannot have a factor of n as a factor of either u or v, since then more than one element would be found in certain orthogonals. All solutions for $n = 2$ and $n = 3$ are regular, and are generated by $(1, 1)$ or by $(1, -1)$. For $n = 4$ the solutions 1234, 4321, 2143, 3412, 2341, 1432, 4123, 3214 are regular.

A solution is called composite if the board can be broken

up into a set of smaller boards of higher order than 1, together with empty square or rectangular boards, in such a way that each board which is occupied contains a solution for its order. A composite so-

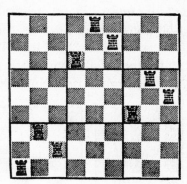

lution may be called proper or improper, according as the pieces into which the board is broken are equal squares or not. Figure 118 shows an improper composite solution of order 8, and Figure 119 shows a proper composite solution of order 9. In a proper composite solution the occupied and unoccupied squares themselves

FIGURE 120.

form a solution, so that if the solutions in the smaller squares are identical the composite solution may be regarded as the product of the two solutions. Figure 120 is the square of the solution in any occupied small square.

3. THE PROBLEM OF THE QUEENS

The solutions of the problem of the queens are now seen to consist of those solutions of the problem of the rooks which have no two queens on any diagonal (in the sense explained on p. 238). If we classify these solutions as we did in the previous section we find that there are no simply or doubly diagonally symmetric solutions. Thus only the classes O, C, and Q remain, and not all members of those classes. (For example, the ordinary solutions of the problem of the rooks for $n = 4$ are not solutions of the problem of the queens.) But it is still true that all solutions of a set of equivalent solutions belong to the same class.

There are no ordinary solutions for $n < 5$, and there is just one complete set of ordinary solutions for $n = 5$, namely

13524, 52413, 24135, 35241, 53142, 14253, 42531, 31425 (Figure 121).

We shall call centrosymmetric solutions of the problem of the queens symmetric merely. There are no symmetric solutions for $n < 6$, and there is just one complete set for $n = 6$: 135246, 362514, 415263, 531642 (Figure 122).

Doubly centrosymmetric solutions will be called merely doubly symmetric. None exist for $n < 4$. In Figure 123 are

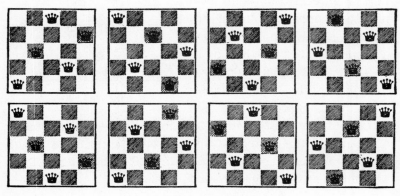

FIGURE 121.

shown the only complete sets for $n = 4$ (2413, 3142,) and for $n = 5$ (25314, 41352).

In a symmetric solution the position of a queen not at the center determines the position of another queen, symmetrically placed with respect to the center. Hence if the order is odd there must be a queen at the center.

In a doubly symmetric solution the position of a queen not at the center determines the positions of 3 other queens so placed that the four queens are at the four vertices of a square. Clearly there must be just one such set of four queens on each such square. From this we may conclude that the order of the square must be $4k$ or $4k + 1$, ac-

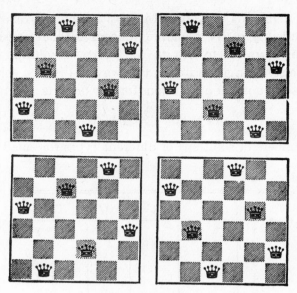

FIGURE 122.

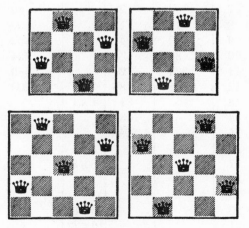

FIGURE 123.

cording as n is even or odd. From these facts one can also conclude that the number of doubly symmetric solutions is always divisible by 2^k, since the four queens in any one of the k squares may be altered in position by the reflection S independently of the remaining queens without causing the total configuration to lose its character as a solution. Thus any one solution generates in this way 2^k distinct solutions.

The total number of solutions for any order is

$$T_n = 8O_n + 4C_n + 2Q_n.$$

The numbers of solutions of different types for small values of n are:

n	O	C	Q	Total
1			1	1
2				
3				
4			1	2
5	1		1	10
6		1		4
7	4	2		40
8	11	1		92
9	42	4		352
10	89	3		724
11	329	12		2,680
12	1,765	18	4 x 1	14,200
13		31	4 x 1	
14		103		
15		298		
16			8 x 4	
17			8 x 8	
18				
19				
20			16 x 14	
21			16 x 22	
22				
23				
24			32 x 51	
25			32 x 51	

On the ordinary chessboard of 8^2 cells there are 92 solutions, consisting of 11 sets of equivalent ordinary solutions and one set of equivalent symmetric solutions. There are no doubly symmetric solutions in this case. Following is a list containing one ordinary solution from each set of equivalents: 15863724, 16837425, 24683175, 25713864, 25741863, 26174835, 26831475, 27368514, 27581463, 35841726, 36258174. The set of symmetric solutions may be generated by 35281746.

REGULAR SOLUTIONS. These are defined as before, namely as solutions generated by a motion (u, v). Now, however, not only must both u and v be prime to n, we must also avoid having two queens on the same diagonal. What restriction this places on the choice of the generating motion can be seen by the following observation:

Any two-dimensional lattice $(a, b) + r(u, v)$, modulo n, in which both u and v are prime to n may be obtained by replacing (u, v) by (ru, rv) for any r prime to n. In particular we may choose r so that $ru = +1$. When this has been done it turns out that two elements of the original lattice will be on the same diagonal if and only if $rv \equiv \pm 1$, modulo n. Hence in order to get a regular solution of the problem of the queens it is necessary and sufficient that the solution be generated by a motion $(1, v)$ having v, $v + 1$, and $v - 1$ all prime to n. Since these three numbers are consecutive, and one of any two consecutive numbers is divisible by 2, and one of any three consecutive numbers is divisible by 3, it results that no regular solutions exist when n is divisible by 2 or 3.

It is clear that if any regular solutions exist they will occur in sets of n obtained from each other by changing the origin of the lattice. None of these n solutions can intersect, so they may be superimposed on the same board without overlapping, forming a solution of the problem of coloring each of the cells of the board with one of n colors in such a way that no color appears twice in the same orthogonal or diagonal. Such a juxtaposition of the 11 regular solutions for $n = 11$ is shown in Figure 124.

FIGURE 124. *Eleven Colors without Repetition in Any Row or Column.*

A regular solution will be symmetric if the central cell is occupied. This requires that in the lattice $(a, b) + r(1, v)$ we have

$$a + r \equiv \frac{n+1}{2} \text{ and } b + rv \equiv \frac{n+1}{2}, \text{ modulo } n.$$

If we take the origin in the first column by setting $a = 1$, we have $r \equiv \dfrac{n-1}{2}$ and $b + \dfrac{n-1}{2}v \equiv \dfrac{n+1}{2}$, modulo n, whence

$2b \equiv v + 1$, modulo n. The converse also holds.

Let a symmetric solution be given by the lattice $(1, b) +$
$r(1, v)$, $2b \equiv v + 1$, modulo n. In
order that the solution be also
doubly symmetric it is necessary
and sufficient to require that a
queen be in the cell resulting from
$(1, b)$ by a rotation through $90°$,
that is that the cell (b, n) be a
part of the solution. This is
equivalent to requiring that

$n \equiv b + (b - 1)v = b + (b - 1)$,
$\quad (2b - 1) = b^2 + (b - 1)^2$.

FIGURE 125.

It is evident from their method of formation that the reg-

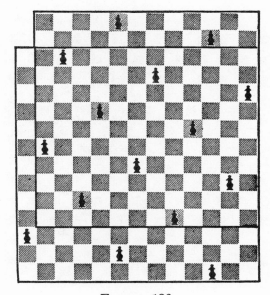

FIGURE 126.

FIGURE 127.

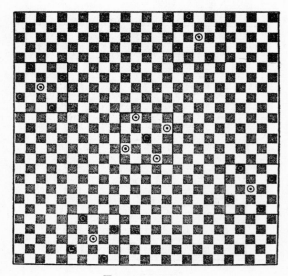

FIGURE 128.

ular solutions are cyclic; that is, their rows and columns may
be permuted cyclically without destroying their character as
solutions, though the individual solutions may be changed.
This procedure may be used to obtain what may be called
quasiregular solutions for cer-
tain boards which have no regular solutions. For example,
no regular solutions exist for
$n = 6$. However, if we take
a regular solution for $n = 7$
which has a queen in the lower
left corner and suppress the
two orthogonals which contain
it, we have left a quasiregular
solution for $n = 6$ (Figure 125).

FIGURE 129.

A doubly symmetric solu-
tion for $n = 13$ may be obtained from the relations $13 = b^2 +
(b - 1)^2$, $2b = v + 1$. The first gives $b = 3$, and the second,
$v = 5$. The corresponding solution is given in Figure 126. If
the two bottom rows are carried to the top and the orthogonals containing the lower left cell in the resulting solution be
suppressed, a quasiregular solution of order 12 is obtained.

COMPOSITE SOLUTIONS. These are defined as for magic
squares. It is not always possible, however, to form them
by replacing every queen of one solution by a board containing another solution, as is the case in the problem of the
rooks. Figures 127 and 128 show two composite solutions.

4. DOMINATION OF THE CHESSBOARD

A different sort of problem is that of determining how
many queens are needed, and in what position, so that every
unoccupied square of the chessboard is under direct attack
from (on the same orthogonal or diagonal as) some queen.
The queens are then said to dominate the board. For the

usual chessboard 5 queens are sufficient; 5 are also sufficient for boards of orders 9, 10, and 11 (Figures 129 and 130).

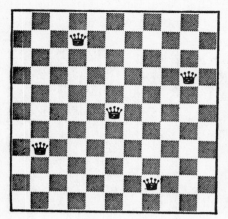

FIGURE 130.

FIGURE 131.

For rooks the problem is the same as the earlier one. In Figure 131 is given a solution of the problem for knights on the ordinary chessboard; 12 are required.

CHAPTER ELEVEN

THE PROBLEM OF THE KNIGHT

THE strange move of the knight in chess makes his operations particularly fascinating. He is allowed to occupy any unoccupied space on the board which is two columns and one row or two rows and one column away from the cell he is in, regardless of whether or not the intervening cells are occupied. Almost the first question one would be likely to ask on learning of this irregular move is whether he can reach every cell on the board. When this has been answered in the affirmative, one might well ask what strange sort of journey he would make in going just once to every cell, if that is possible. It *is* possible, and the investigation of these "grand tours" is the subject of this chapter. (If the reader finds any of our notations or terminology unfamiliar, he is advised to glance through Chapter Ten on the Problem of the Queens.)

1. A solution is called re-entrant or closed if the knight can be brought back to his initial position by one more move; otherwise the solution is open.

A solution is usually described by placing in each cell the number indicating the order in which that cell was reached, the initial cell being denoted by 1. Since the color of the cell on which the knight lands changes at each move, all odd-numbered cells are of one color, all even-numbered cells of the other.

It follows that if a board of a particular shape has one more cell of one color than of the other, a solution (if it exists) must be open. Hence all solutions on boards of odd order are open. But if the difference in the numbers of cells of the two colors is greater than 1, then no solution is possible. (For example, it is not possible to visit all the cells of the board in Figure 132, which contains 32 black and 25 white cells.) If the squares are not colored it is often more difficult to tell whether a tour is possible.

FIGURE 132.

A solution will be called symmetric to the center if the sum or difference of the numbers of each pair of cells symmetric to the center is constant, using the sum or difference according as the order of the board is odd or even.

A solution is symmetric to a median (central horizontal or vertical line) if the difference of the numbers of each pair of cells symmetric with respect to the median is constant. Two cells symmetric with respect to a median are of different colors, so the difference of their numbers must be odd, say $2k + 1$. Hence the total number of cells is $2(2k + 1)$, which shows that such solutions are not possible on ordinary chessboards, but only on those having $4k + 2$ cells and having a median of symmetry.

Solutions may also be represented geometrically by drawing on the surface of the board a broken line joining the centers of the successive squares visited by the knight. A solution represented in this manner is called doubly symmetric if it is not changed by a rotation through one or more right angles. Such a solution is not possible on the ordinary chessboard, but may be realized on certain boards having $4k$ cells and a center of symmetry.

A symmetric solution represented in this geometric manner is not changed by a rotation through two right angles.

2. WARNSDORF'S RULE. Among the many methods for obtaining knight's tours, perhaps the best is by Warnsdorf's rule: At every move place the knight in the cell from which there are the fewest exits to unoccupied cells.

In applying Warnsdorf's rule we find many cases where the knight has a choice of two cells, each having the same minimum number of exits. Each choice offers two alternative solutions. However, the total number of solutions obtainable by this method is not very great, and we may even be able to find all the solutions corresponding to a given initial cell. Warnsdorf's method gives only a few particular solutions.

Although it is laborious to compute every time the number of possible exits, this inconvenience is counterbalanced by the advantage of a surprising property that is very difficult to analyze, namely: the many mistakes that it is difficult to avoid do not prevent one from finishing the tour, except in certain cases.

The rule is a rule of common sense, and is applicable to all chessboards. It is also good if the move of the knight is changed.

3. In this and the succeeding paragraph we consider possible routes on small rectangular boards. Here we assume that neither dimension is 4.

If one dimension is < 3 no tour is possible.

If one dimension is 3 the other must be ≥ 7. If the second dimension is even and ≥ 10, closed solutions exist.

If one dimension is 5 the other must be as great; and if the second dimension is even, there are closed tours.

If one dimension is 6 the other must be ≥ 5. Closed tours will then exist.

If one dimension is 7 or more, a tour can always be found.

Closed routes are possible in general when the total number of cells is even and neither dimension is 4.

4. Consider a rectangular chessboard of dimensions 4 and k. Divide the set of cells into two domains, α and β. Domain α contains the cells marked A or a in Figure 133, do-

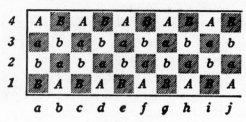

FIGURE 133.

main β contains those marked B or b. The cells on the outer rows will be called exterior, those on the other two rows, interior. Thus the board contains k cells of each of the follow-

	a4	b1	c4	d1	e4	f1	g4	h1	
a3	22	8	8	16	13	8	10	33	118
b2	8	4	3	5	3	3	6	10	42
c3	8	3	2	2	3	3	3	8	32
d2	16	5	2	6	6	3	3	13	54
e3	13	3	3	6	6	2	5	16	54
f2	8	3	3	3	2	2	3	8	32
g3	10	6	3	3	5	3	4	8	42
h2	33	10	8	13	16	8	8	22	118
	118	42	32	54	54	32	42	118	492

FIGURE 134.

ing four classes: exterior cells A, interior cells a, exterior cells B, interior cells b. Each column contains one cell of each class. The cells A and b have one color, B and a the other.

The routes on this board are based on the theorem that a

tour is possible only if one first visits all the cells of one domain before going to any cell of the other.

In Figure 134 are listed all the solutions for a board
of 4×8 cells, half the usual chessboard. (The letters on the
margin of the table denote the columns, and the numbers
indicate the rows.) According to Figure 134 there are 22
routes from $a4$ to $a3$, 8 routes from $b1$ to $a3$, and so on.

We suppose that every route begins on an outside cell A
or B and ends on an inside cell b or a. The route may, of
course, be reversed.

Every route has three others symmetric to it:

    (1) With respect to the horizontal median.
    (2) With respect to the vertical median.
    (3) With respect to the center.

For example, for $k = 5$ the fundamental route and those
symmetric to it are:

1	·	3	·	7
10	·	6	·	4
·	2	·	8	·
·	9	·	5	·

·	9	·	5	·
·	2	·	8	·
10	·	6	·	4
1	·	3	·	7

7	·	3	·	1
4	·	6	·	10
·	8	·	2	·
·	5	·	9	·

·	5	·	9	·
·	8	·	2	·
4	·	6	·	10
7	·	3	·	1

FIGURE 135.

The route symmetric with respect to the horizontal median belongs to the domain β and is not given in the table
containing the routes in the domain α.

The route symmetric with respect to the vertical median belongs to the domain α if k is odd, to β if k is even. On the other hand the route symmetric with respect to the center belongs to α if k is even, and to β if k is odd. Hence for every k there is just one route symmetric to a given one and belonging to the same domain.

Every route can be transformed by permuting rows 1 and

1	·	5	·	9
6	·	10	·	4
·	2	·	8	·
·	7	·	3	·

6	·	10	·	4
1	·	5	·	9
·	7	·	3	·
·	2	·	8	·

5	·	1	·	7
10	·	6	·	2
·	4	·	8	·
·	9	·	3	·

9	·	3	·	7	·	13
2	·	8	·	12	·	6
·	10	·	4	·	14	·
·	1	·	11	·	5	·

FIGURE 136.

2, and rows 3 and 4. The new route, called the derivative route, begins on an inside cell and ends on an outside cell, so that we must reverse such a route to get a route from an outside to an inside cell. The derivative route may be identical with the original.

In order to go over every cell we must first cover one domain completely. Suppose that we use the route of Figure 137 to go from $a4$ to $a3$. To complete the tour we need a route in domain β beginning on $c2$. This may be obtained by taking the route symmetric (with respect to the horizontal median) to the route from *c*4 to *c*3, which begins on *c*2 and ends on *c*1. Joining this with our first route we have the complete tour.

It follows from this that every tour begins and ends on an

1	3	5	9
16	14	12	6
2	4	8	10
15	13	11	7

15	1	5	9
2	16	12	6
14	4	8	10
3	13	11	7

14	4	6	10
3	13	9	7
15	1	5	11
2	16	12	8

1	30	3	20	5	22	9	26
16	19	14	29	12	25	6	23
31	2	17	4	21	8	27	10
18	15	32	13	28	11	24	7

FIGURE 137.

outside cell, so no tour on such a chessboard can be closed. Because of its special properties it is easy to count the

FIGURE 138.

number *N* of all possible tours on a board of dimension 4*k*. Thus we have:

k	3	4	5	6	7	8	9	10
N	8	0	82	744	6,378	31,088	189,688	1,213,112.

If we consider the usual chessboard as though formed of two boards of 4×8 cells, we find that it is possible to make 122,802,512 tours which go over one half first and then over

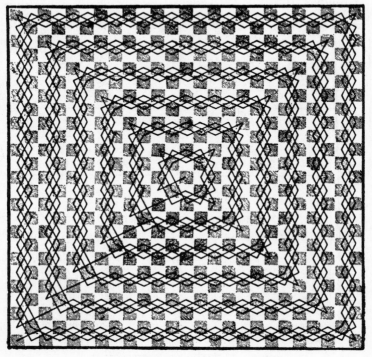

FIGURE 139.

the second. This number includes 7,763,536 closed tours, 3,944 symmetric tours, and 4,064 which have identical halves.

5. SOME MISCELLANEOUS RESULTS. Tours on a 3×7 rectangle are possible only when one of the extremities is on $b2$.

There are 14 tours on the 3×7 rectangle, 2 of which are symmetrical.

There are 376 tours on the 3×8 rectangle, none of them closed.

There are 16 symmetric tours on the 3 × 9 rectangle.

There are 8 closed tours on the 3 × 10 rectangle.

There are 58 symmetric tours on the 3 × 11 rectangle.

FIGURE 140.

There are 28 closed tours on the 3 × 12 rectangle.

There are 5 tours, closed and symmetric with respect to the vertical median, on the 3 × 14 rectangle.

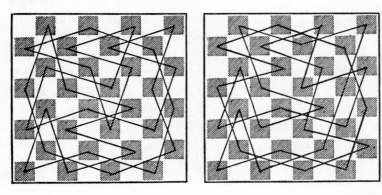

FIGURE 141.

There are 5 doubly symmetric tours on the 6 × 6 square (Figure 138).

There are 1,728 tours on the 5 × 5 square, of which 8 are symmetric.

Figure 139 indicates a general method of making a tour on a board of order $4k + 1$.

6. Many generalizations of the knight's problem have been proposed. Many alterations of the size and shape of the board have already been considered. One may also form a chessboard of unusual shape by covering part of the cells on the usual 8×8 board.

The move of the knight may also be generalized. Instead

of using the components 2 and 1 for his move, other components may be taken. Figure 140 shows three tours of the 24 white cells of the chessboard of order 7, using components 3 and 1. Such a knight cannot move from one color to another. The first tour is closed; the others are symmetric with respect to the center. In Figure 141 are given two such tours on an ordinary board, and in Figure 142 a tour on a board on which no tour can be made by an ordinary knight.

FIGURE 142.

We may also give the knight a double move, using say the components (8, 1) or (4, 7) at will, since $8^2 + 1^2 = 4^2 + 7^2$. Or we may allow him to move with components (4, 3) or (5, 0). This last knight can move from $a1$ to $a6$, to $f1$, to $d3$, or to $c4$. Wherever he may be on the usual chessboard, he has a choice of just 4 cells.

Huber-Stockar proposed another generalization by permitting the knight 8 other moves, according to his position. The components of his move change from place to place. He is not required to change from one color to the other. With this knight, closed routes are possible even when the number of cells is odd.

CHAPTER TWELVE

GAMES

1. POSITIONAL GAMES

1. CHESS AND CHECKERS. The typical positional game is chess. It is not our purpose to give an extended description or discussion of a game so universally known, and con-

FIGURE 143. *Sam Loyd's Shortest Stalemate with No Pieces Lost.*

cerning which there is such a vast literature. We shall confine ourselves to a few remarks, principally touching mathematical aspects of the game.

The shortest possible game, often called the Fool's Mate, is well known:

WHITE	BLACK
1. P–KB3 (or 4)	1. P–K3
2. P–KKt4	2. Q–KR5 (mate).

This checkmate can be accomplished only with the connivance (or incredible folly) of White.

Not so well known is the problem of determining the shortest game in which White obtains a stalemate without any piece being taken by either side. Here is Sam Loyd's solution:

	WHITE		BLACK
1.	P–Q4	1.	P–Q3
2.	Q–Q2	2.	P–K4
3.	P–QR4	3.	P–K5
4.	Q–KB4	4.	P–KB4
5.	P–KR3	5.	B–K2
6.	Q–KR2	6.	B–K3
7.	R–QR3	7.	P–QB4
8.	R–KKt3	8.	Q–QR4(ch)
9.	Kt–Q2	9.	B–KR5
10.	P–KB3	10.	B–QKt6
11.	P–Q5	11.	P–K6
12.	P–QB4	12.	P–KB5
	Stalemate		

Every chess man but the pawn has usually more than one way of getting from one cell to another. This raises the problem of finding the least number of moves required (on an otherwise empty board) to take a given piece from one given cell to another, and of determining how many different shortest routes there are. The problem itself is rather easy, but the method of solution presents a very interesting application of algebra to logic, so it seems worth while to analyze it in some detail.

In order to facilitate reference to the cells of the board we attach a co-ordinate system to it in such a way that the centers of White's first row (from rook to rook) have co-ordinates $(1, 1)$ to $(8, 1)$, and Black's first row goes from $(1, 8)$ to $(8, 8)$. Also, at first we shall allow the pieces to move over the whole plane instead of being limited by the edges of the board. We shall begin with the move of the man in checkers since this is the simplest interesting case.

The checker man moves one step at a time along a diagonal, but always in such a way that he changes rows in the same direction. Hence we need only be concerned with what column he occupies. Let us suppose that he is a White piece and starts at the cell (5, 1), moving up the board. We may mark this cell with a 1 to indicate that there is only one way for him to get there. Similarly we mark with a 1 the two cells that he can reach on his first move, (4, 2) and (6, 2).

1	7	21	35	35	21	7	1	
	1	6	15	20	15	6	1	
		1	5	10	10	5	1	
			1	4	6	4	1	
				1	3	3	1	
					1	2	1	
						1	1	
							1	

FIGURE 144. *Pascal's Triangle in Checker Moves.*

At his second move he can reach the cell (3, 3) only from (4, 2); he can reach (5, 3) either from (4, 2) or (6, 2); and he can reach (7, 3) only from (6, 2). We mark these cells 1, 2, 1, respectively. At his third move he can reach the cells (2, 4) and (8, 4) in only one way. But he can reach (4, 4) either from (3, 5) or from (3, 3). Since there are 2 ways of reaching (3, 5) and 1 of reaching (3, 3), this gives him 3 ways of reaching (4, 4) from (5, 1). Similarly for (4, 6). This is sufficient to show how we may proceed from here on. Suppose we have marked every cell that he can reach in the kth row. Then the number of ways in which he can reach a cell in the next row is always the sum of the numbers in the cells in the kth row from which he can move to the new cell. In this way we get an array of numbers such as that in Figure 144, in which every number is the sum of the two nearest numbers in the row below.

The reader will probably have noticed that the rule for forming this table is just like the rule for forming the binomial coefficients by Pascal's triangle. So it is not surprising that the numbers in the third row from the bottom are the coefficients in the expansion of $(a + b)^2$, those in the fourth row are the coefficients of $(a + b)^3$, and so on. The connection lies deeper than this, however, and it is this deeper meaning that we want to discuss.

Suppose we use the symbol u to mean that the man is 1 column to the right of his original position, and use u^{-1} to mean that he is 1 column to the left. In the same way u^2 will mean 2 to the right, u^{-2} will mean 2 to the left, and so on. Also, $u^0(= 1)$ will indicate no change of column. Now let us use addition to represent the logical notion "or." $x^{-1} + x$ will then mean: "1 column to the left *or* 1 column to the right," which is precisely the statement of the alternatives presented to the man at every move. (We do not need to bother about what row he moves to, since we know that he always moves up one row.) Next we can indicate the fact that he makes more than one move by using multiplication to denote the logical relation "and." Thus, if he makes two moves he makes one move *and* he makes another move, and we can show this by writing $(u^{-1} + u)(u^{-1} + u)$, that is, $(u^{-1} + u)^2$. Expressed without abbreviation this says: "He moves one column to the left *or* right *and* he moves again one column to the left *or* right."

Suppose we multiply this expression out (first without collecting terms) and try to interpret the result in the same logical terms. $(u^{-1} + u)^2 = u^{-2} + u^{-1}u + uu^{-1} + u^2$ then may be interpreted: "Either he moves 2 columns to the left *or* he moves 1 column to the left *and* 1 to the right *or* he moves 1 to the right *and* 1 to the left *or* he moves 2 to the right." But just as $u^{-1}u = uu^{-1} = u^0 = 1$, so "1 to the left *and* 1 to the right" has the same result as "1 to the right *and* 1 to the left," namely "no change." If we collect terms our expression becomes $u^{-2} + 2 + u^2$, which means: "Either he moves 2 to the left in just one way *or* he gets to the original column in either of 2 ways *or* he moves 2 to the right." Similarly, the result of 3 moves may be expressed by $(u^{-1} + u)^3 = u^{-3} + 3u^{-1} + 3u + u^3$, which tells us that he either gets 3 columns to the left (in just one way) or 1 column to the left (in any of 3 ways) or 1 column to the right (in any of 3 ways) **or**

FIGURE 145. *Algebra of the Checkerboard.*

3 columns to the right (in just one way); and any positive power can be interpreted similarly.

If now we wish to take into account the fact that when the man reaches the first or the 8th column he has only one alternative, if he is to stay on the board, we can do so in either procedure. In marking the cells we simply do not mark any cells outside the limits of the board, but continue to mark the cells on the board according to the same rules, using only the cells already marked. If we use the algebraic method we simply drop off as they are formed all terms corresponding to impossible moves. For example the third move gives the term u^3 that takes the man to column 8. No higher power of u may be kept. In forming the fourth power of $(u^{-1} + u)$ we therefore omit the last term and write

$u^{-4} + 4u^{-2} + 6 + 4u^2$. In the fifth power we must also omit negative powers greater than the fourth, so we have $5u^{-3} + 10u^{-1} + 10u + 4u^3$, and so on. The results for the whole board are given in Figure 145.

The king in chess may move one step in any direction, so that he may change either his row or column, or both. However, it is clear that the shortest route to a cell on either diagonal through his initial position must be along the diagonal. These two diagonals divide the rest of the board into four parts such that any shortest route to a cell in one of these parts must consist of moves in which the row or column is always changed in the same direction. Hence we may treat the problem in just one of these quarters of the board and repeat the results in the other three. If we assume that he always moves up one row, the alternatives presented to him at each move are three: either he moves 1 column to the left or he stays in the same column or he moves 1 column to the right. The alternatives may then be represented by $u^{-1} + 1 + u$, and the alternatives resulting from n moves (neglecting the edges of the board) are given by the terms in the expansion of $(u^{-1} + 1 + u)^n$. If we use the method of marking cells we find that each new number is the sum of the three numbers in the line below that lie immediately below or on either side (but not including any numbers beyond those in the diagonals through the initial cell). Figure 146 gives the table for the first few moves in every direction on an unlimited board, and Figure 147 gives the table for the White king on the ordinary board starting from his own cell.

The move of the knight does not permit us to separate the motion in the horizontal direction from that in the vertical. Here we may use u for horizontal motion and v for vertical motion. Then a move 2 columns to the right *and* 1 row upward will be represented by u^2v, and so on. The full set of alternatives for a single move is thus

$$u^{-2}v^{-1} + u^{-2}v + u^{-1}v^{-2} + u^{-1}v^2 + uv^{-2} + uv^2 + u^2v^{-1} + u^2v,$$

and the results of successive moves are found by expanding successively higher powers of this expression. However, in order to be certain that we always get the shortest possi-

1	7	28	77	161	266	357	393	357	266	161	77	28	7	1
7	1	6	21	50	90	126	141	126	90	50	21	6	1	7
28	6	1	5	15	30	45	51	45	30	15	5	1	6	28
77	21	5	1	4	10	16	19	16	10	4	1	5	21	77
161	50	15	4	1	3	6	7	6	3	1	4	15	50	161
266	90	30	10	3	1	2	3	2	1	3	10	30	90	266
357	126	45	16	6	2	1	1	1	2	6	16	45	126	357
393	141	51	19	7	3	1	1	1	3	7	19	51	141	393
357	126	45	16	6	2	1	1	1	2	6	16	45	126	357
266	90	30	10	3	1	2	3	2	1	3	10	30	90	266
161	50	15	4	1	3	6	7	6	3	1	4	15	50	161
77	21	5	1	4	10	16	19	16	10	4	1	5	21	77
28	6	1	5	15	30	45	51	45	30	15	5	1	6	28
7	1	6	21	50	90	126	141	126	90	50	21	6	1	7
1	7	28	77	161	266	357	393	357	266	161	77	28	7	1

FIGURE 146. *Algebra of the King's Move, in Chess: Unlimited Board.*

ble path we must eliminate at each step any term that has already occurred. For example, $uv^2 \cdot u^{-1}v^{-2} = 1$, which means that the knight has gone back to his original position, so this term must be omitted in forming the second power.

While this algebraic procedure may be used for proving general propositions about the knight's moves, it is too cumbersome to be practical for ordinary purposes. Instead it is better to use a modification of the marking procedure. This time we shall have to mark each cell with two numbers — the first, which we shall call the *order* of the cell, to indicate the minimum number of moves required to reach it, and the second, the *multiplicity* of the cell, to tell the number of shortest routes to it. To do this, first mark the initial cell with the order 0, then mark the cells accessible from it in one

70	160	266	357	393	356	259	133
20	50	90	126	141	126	89	44
5	15	30	45	51	45	30	14
1	4	10	16	19	16	10	4
4	1	3	6	7	6	3	1
9	3	1	2	3	2	1	3
12	5	2	1	1	1	2	5
9	4	2	1	1	1	2	4

FIGURE 147.   *Algebra of the King's Move, in Chess:* 8 × 8 *Board.*

move with the order 1, then all cells (not already marked) accessible from cells of order 1 in one move with the order 2, and so on. Then we assign multiplicity 1 to the initial cell and to all the cells of order 1. The multiplicity of a cell of order 2 is then the sum of the multiplicities of the cells of order 1 from which it can be reached in one move. After the multiplicities of the cells of order 2 have been determined we can find the multiplicity of a cell of order 3 by adding the multiplicities of all cells of order 2 from which it is accessible, and so on. Figures 148 and 149 give the results for the first few moves on a   limited   board, and Figure 150 the results for the White knight's moves on the ordinary board starting from his own cell.

How many different chess games can there be?

White can begin with any one of 20 possible first moves

(16 moves for the 8 pawns and 4 moves for the 2 knights). Black can answer in any of 20 different ways for each move of White. Thus there are $20 \cdot 20 = 400$ different ways in which the first moves on each side can be made.

In general the number of possible moves increases after

					a			
	0	**1**	**2**	**3**	**4**	**5**	**6**	**7**
0	0	3_{12}	2_2	3_6	2_2	3_6	4_{24}	5_{100}
1	3_{12}	2_2	1_1	2_2	3_6	4_{28}	3_3	4_{16}
2	2_2	1_1	4_{54}	3_9	2_1	3_6	4_{18}	5_{95}
3	3_6	2_2	3_9	2_2	3_3	4_{24}	3_1	4_{12}
4	2_2	3_6	2_1	3_3	4_{32}	3_3	4_{12}	5_{60}
5	3_6	4_{28}	3_6	4_{24}	3_3	4_8	5_{85}	4_4
6	4_{24}	3_3	4_{18}	3_1	4_{12}	5_{85}	4_6	5_{25}
7	5_{100}	4_{16}	5_{95}	4_{12}	5_{60}	4_4	5_{25}	6_{238}

(The rows are labeled b.)

FIGURE 148. *Knight's Move.*

the first. For example, White's second move can be made in 29 different ways if his first move was P to K4, in 30 ways if it was P to K3. Later in the game the number of possibilities increases enormously. If the queen is on Q5, she alone has 27 possible moves (if the cells where the moves end are free and accessible).

In order to simplify we suppose that we have the choice among

20 moves for White and Black for the first 5 moves,
30 moves for White and Black for the other moves.

We shall also suppose that the average number of moves is

5_{18}	4_7	5_{38}	4_9	5_{36}	4_4	5_{19}	6_{103}
4_7	3_2	4_{10}	3_1	4_9	5_{54}	4_6	5_{19}
3_2	4_8	3_4	4_{14}	3_3	4_6	5_{54}	4_4
2_1	3_3	2_1	3_2	4_{18}	3_3	4_9	5_{36}
3_1	2_1	3_4	2_2	3_2	4_{14}	3_1	4_9
2_1	1_1	4_{16}	3_4	2_1	3_4	4_{10}	5_{33}
3_2	4_{10}	1_1	2_1	3_3	4_8	3_2	4_7
0	3_2	2_1	3_1	2_1	3_2	4_7	5_{18}

FIGURE 149. *Knight's Move.*

40. Under these conditions we find the following number of different chess games:

$$(20 \cdot 20)^5 \cdot (30 \cdot 30)^{35} = 2^{10} \cdot 3^{70} \cdot 10^{80} = 25 \cdot 10^{115}.$$

This is approximate. It is a very big number, in comparison with which the astronomical numbers are miserably dwarfish.

2. FAIRY CHESS. Many variations of chess have been suggested involving changes in the form of the board, the rules of play, or the pieces used. All these we subsume under the name of "fairy" chess.

Former champion Capablanca introduced a board of 12×16 cells, using 32 pieces on each side. Baskerville designed a modified chess game to be played on a rectangular array of 83 hexagonal cells. *Cylindrical* chess results from the or-

4_7	5_{42}	4_{13}	5_{61}	4_{12}	5_{45}	4_4	5_{19}
3_2	4_{13}	3_3	4_{14}	3_1	4_{12}	5_{63}	4_6
4_{10}	3_4	4_{18}	3_6	4_{18}	3_3	4_7	5_{57}
3_3	2_2	3_4	2_1	3_3	4_{24}	3_3	4_9
2_1	3_3	2_2	3_6	2_2	3_2	4_{17}	3_1
1_1	2_1	1_1	4_{24}	3_6	2_1	3_4	4_{10}
2_1	3_4	2_1	1_1	2_1	3_3	4_{11}	3_2
3_2	0	3_3	2_1	3_2	2_1	3_2	4_7

FIGURE 150. *White Queen's Knight's Move.*

dinary game by allowing play to pass from one edge to the opposite edge, as though the board were inscribed on a cylinder. One can even play Möbius chess by treating the board as though it were a Möbius band (see p. 212).

The commonest changes in the rules are those providing a handicap for the stronger player. He may give his opponent the advantage of a move, or a pawn and a move, or a pawn and two moves, or a knight, bishop, rook, queen, or the like. This upsets the initial balance of forces so that the later course of the game is usually different from that of a game begun with balanced forces.

Certain moves may be made obligatory. Some other modifications of the rules are:

The Marseille game, in which each side plays two moves in succession.

The Legal game, in which White uses eight extra pawns instead of the queen.

The marked-pawn game. A pawn, usually the king's knight's, is marked, say with a paper cap. If this pawn is captured its owner loses the game. He can also lose by being checkmated in the usual way, but he may checkmate his adversary only with the marked pawn, which may not be moved to the eighth row and exchanged for another piece. Such odds can only be given to a very much weaker opponent.

We enter the domain of fairy chess proper only by the introduction of new pieces whose moves are defined. The best known pieces of this sort are the following, introduced by Dawson:

The alfil — actually an earlier form of the present bishop. Like the bishop it moves along diagonals in any direction, but must land just two squares away, whether or not the intervening square is occupied. From Q3 it may go to KB1, KB5, QKt1, or QKt5.

The fers, which moves one cell at a time on the diagonals. A fers that results from the promotion of a pawn that has reached the eighth row may also jump one square in any direction, orthogonal or diagonal.

The dabbaba, which moves in the orthogonals as the alfil does in the diagonals.

The chancellor, which combines the moves of the knight and rook.

The *centaur*, which combines the moves of the bishop and knight.

The *grasshopper*, which moves like the queen, except that it must leap over a piece (of either color) and land on the cell beyond.

Neuters, which may be played by either Black or White.

Leapers — generalizations of the knight. Leaper (a, b) may move from a cell (x, y) to any available cell $(x + a, y + b)$, $(x + b, y + a)$. Leaper $(1, 2)$ is the ordinary knight.

The *courser*, which may make as one move as many successive knight's moves as lie in a straight line, provided the intervening landing points are not occupied.

The *half-bishop*, which moves like the bishop, but in one diagonal direction only.

The *great bishop*, which extends the move of the ordinary bishop by being allowed to move along the prolongations of the diagonals — that is, along the broken diagonals.

3. LATRUNCULES. According to M. Becq de Fouquière, the game of latruncules was played by the ancient Romans on a chessboard. Each of the two players had two kinds of pieces, 8 latruncules (pawns) and 8 larrons (pieces). The latruncules were allowed to move straight ahead only, one step at a time; but on reaching the eighth row they became larrons. The larrons moved like our queens in chess.

One man took another as in chess, except that a latruncule, like the king in chess, could take on all adjacent cells.

4. Go. Go was invented in China in the fourteenth century. It is now a favorite game among educated Japanese.

The game is played on a board ruled in squares, and the pieces are placed on the vertices. Each of the two opponents begins with a plentiful supply of pieces, white for one side and black for the other. The opponents play alternately, each placing one piece each time. Every piece or set of pieces that is surrounded by the enemy is captured and removed from the board, provided there is no empty vertex between the pieces that surround and those surrounded, or within the set surrounded. (A set or piece is considered to be surrounded if it cannot escape by moving along the lines of the network. Thus two pieces are sufficient to capture a piece in a corner, three for a piece elsewhere on the border, and four for a piece inside the network.)

The object of the game is to occupy as many vertices as possible. The game ends when both sides agree that neither can place further pieces without being captured. The winner is the one who has the greater number of pieces on the board, and his score is the difference between the total numbers.

Occidentals long resident in the East regard the game as extremely difficult. The Japanese claim that it is a finer game than chess, but we don't have to believe them.

5. Go–Bang (Japanese Checkers). This game is played on a chessboard of 16×16, 18×18 or 20×20 cells. The pieces are all alike, except for difference in color to distinguish the sides. The two players select their colors and take the same number of pieces. They play alternately, placing one piece at a time in the center of a square. The first to get a horizontal or vertical line of five pieces in consecutive squares is the winner. If all pieces have been placed without the game being won, the players move the pieces about, one step at a time, in any orthogonal or diagonal direction (as though moving kings in chess), and the winner is the one who first gets five in a row as before.

There is another game in which each player tries to surround his adversary's pieces (as in Go), and the winner is the one who has thus captured the greater number of pieces. In this game the total number of pieces is just sufficient to cover the board.

6. REVERSI. This is played on a board of 10^2 cells and begins like Go. Whenever one player can surround a set of hostile pieces lying in any orthogonal or diagonal line of consecutive cells by putting a piece of his own at either end, the pieces thus captured are replaced by his own. The winner is the one who has the greater number of pieces on the board at the end.

7. JINX. This game was contributed by Mr. Ling. It is played on a table of thirteen columns of numbers arranged

1	2	3	4	5	6	7	8	9	10	11	12	13
	1	2	3	4	5	6	7	8	9	10	11	12
		1	2	3	4	5	6	7	8	9	10	11
			1	2	3	4	5	6	7	8	9	10
				1	2	3	4	5	6	7	8	9
					1	2	3	4	5	6	7	8
						1	2	3	4	5	6	7
							1	2	3	4	5	6
								1	2	3	4	5
									1	2	3	4

FIGURE 151. *Jinx Board.*

as in Figure 151. Pieces are placed on the 1 and on any other numbers desired in the first (uppermost) line. Pieces are then placed on the same numbers in any other desired lines. (For example, a player may select the numbers 1, 3, 8, 12 and the rows 1, 2, 4. Then the numbers 1, 3, 8, 12 in the first and second rows, and the numbers 1, 3, 8 in the fourth row are covered.)

When the pieces have been placed we play with them as follows: If a column contains an even number of pieces, half of them are removed and the other half are put in the next column to the right. If the column contains an odd number of pieces, one of them is put at the top, half of the remainder are taken away and the other half are moved to the next column. (Hence a single piece in a column is placed, or left, at the head of the column.) This procedure is continued until no further plays can be made.

The object of the game is to obtain a given final distribution of pieces in the top line. For example, to get pieces on 1, 5, 6 we may begin with pieces on 1, 2, 3 in the

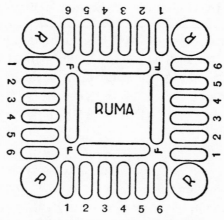

FIGURE 152. *Ruma Board.*

first three rows. If one places pieces so as to have only 1 and 13 in the first line covered at the end, one has achieved the Great Jinx.

8. RUMA. Mr. Punga, the author of this game, describes it as follows:

A playing board, such as that shown in Figure 152, has six oval pockets along each side and a round pocket, called a ruma, in each corner.

Four persons play this game, but two or three may play if some of the players take more than one side of the board. When the game begins a certain number of red balls is distributed among the oval pockets in front of each player, between 2 and 4 balls in each pocket. The object of the game is to clear these balls off the table. The first player chooses one pocket in front of him and distributes the balls from it among the successive pockets to the right of the one chosen, putting one ball in each pocket. He may put the balls in the ruma or in neighboring pockets beyond it, if necessary.

The fundamental rule is that the last ball may not go into an empty pocket.

A ball must be put in the ruma or corner pocket if that is the last one. But the corner pockets may not be emptied.

As the game goes on it will happen that a player cannot play, because the last ball in every one of his pockets would have to be played into an empty pocket. The player then receives a penalty ball, which is put in F.

If a player receives 12 penalty balls he loses. Any player who empties all the pockets on his side wins, however many penalty balls (under 12) he may have.

9. THE NAVAL BATTLE. This is a game for two players in command of opposing fleets. Neither knows the exact location of his opponent's ships, but by firing successive salvos, of whose effect he is kept informed, each tries to determine where each of his opponent's ships lies. The first to "destroy" these ships wins.

The field of battle is the set of cells in a 9×9 square marked off on graph paper. For purposes of reference the cells may be identified by the co-ordinates of their centers. Each player marks off two such squares. On one he records the positions of his own ships and the location of his opponent's shots. On the other he records his own shots. The ships are rectangles of cells, and their locations may be indicated by shading the cells of the battlefield occupied by them. Each fleet consists of 1 battleship (1 cell wide by 4 cells long), two cruisers (each 1×3), 3 destroyers (each 1×2), and 4 submarines (each 1×1).

To begin the game each player locates his own fleet on one of his charts in any manner he chooses, subject to the following restrictions: (1) Each ship must cover a rectangle of cells of the same shape and size as itself. (2) No two ships may touch, even at a vertex. (3) A ship may have at most one side of one cell in common with the border of the field. (Thus a submarine may not be placed in a corner.)

When the fleets have been drawn up in battle array one of the players fires a salvo of 3 shots, by announcing to his opponent the locations of the 3 cells in which they are supposed to land. The opponent must then announce the effect of the shots on his fleet, by indicating how many fell in "open water" and how many hit which types of ships, but without specifying the effect of each individual shot. (For example, he may say, "Two in the water and one on a cruiser," regardless of the order in which these results were obtained.) The second player now fires a salvo and receives the report of its effect. The play alternates in this manner until one of the players disposes of his opponent's entire fleet and announces the fact.

The game raises a number of interesting questions. For example, what disposition of the fleet will require the maximum number of salvos for the determination of its location? Or again, what is the minimum number of salvos that suffice to end a particular game?

10. CHECKERS (DRAUGHTS). As this game is undoubtedly familiar to our readers we shall confine our remarks to comments on variations commonly played in other countries.

In France the game is played on an 8 × 8 board. A piece is called a pawn until it reaches the eighth row, when it becomes a queen. (The game is known as *jeu des dames*, game of the queens.) Unlike our king, the queen may move as far along any diagonal as she wishes, over any number of pieces, taking all over which she passes.

This great power granted the queen has considerable influence on the end game. Curiously enough, it seems to have the effect of weakening her offensive power against other queens. For example, whereas in our game two kings can ordinarily defeat one, in the French game three queens may be insufficient. Here is the theorem and its proof. (We shall denote the cells of the board by the continental notation — the columns lettered from *a* to *h*, counting from

FIGURE 153. *Three Queens Helpless.*

White's left, the rows numbered from 1 to 8 from White's side.)

Three queens can capture an isolated queen unless the queen attacked is on the long diagonal, $a1 — h8$. Four queens are always sufficient.

Consider first the position of Figure 153. If it is White's move he can play $h2 — e5$ and win, since Black must then play $h8 \times d4 \times f2$, and White moves $g1 \times e3$. But if Black has the move he may play $h8 — a1$. If White answers with $e3 — f4$, Black plays $a1 — h8$ (otherwise White wins with $g1 — d4$). If White answers with $h2 — b8$, Black can play $a1 — c3$ (if he returns to $h8$, White wins with $b8 — e5$). Black can always escape this threat by taking refuge in the corner and so preventing White from sacrificing two queens to win.

It is easy to see that four queens are sufficient by placing the fourth queen on $g3$ in Figure 153. Black will then have no refuge.

Now suppose the Black queen is not on the long diagonal and the three White queens are on the strategic triangle, $c3$, $c5$, $f4$ (or $f4$, $f6$, $c5$) (Figure 154). The Black queen must be on

Figure 154. *Strategic Triangle.*

$d8$ or $h4$. In either case she will be easily captured, with or without the move, as the following examples show.

	White	Black	White	Black	White	Black	White	Black
1	c3 — a5	d8 — f6	· · ·	d8 — h4				
2	c5 — e7	×d8	c3 — a5	h4 — f6	· · ·	h4 — d8	· · ·	h4 — e1
3	f4 — c7	×b6	c5 — e7	×d8	f4 — h2	d8— {f6 / h4}	c5 — g1	e1 — h4
4		×c7	f4 — c7	×b6	c5 — e7	×d8	g1 — f2	×e1
5				×c7	h2 — c7	etc.	f4 — d2	etc.

If Black is not on the long diagonal and it is White to play, White can always capture the strategic position.

There is an interesting variation of give-away in the French game. If White starts with all 12 pawns in the usual position, while Black has but one pawn, on $b8$, it can be shown that White can always win, in spite of his apparent enormous handicap.

In Turkey and some other countries each player has 16 pawns on his first two rows, and the pawns move and catch on the columns instead of on the diagonals.

In the Polish game, which is widely played on the Continent, a 10 × 10 board is used, with 20 men to a side. Other-

FIGURE 155. *Give-away in Polish Checkers.*

wise the rules are much like those of the French game. (The Polish game seems to have originated in Paris.)

In the Polish form of the give-away variation described for the French game, White can win with 20 or 30 pawns to 1. To do it he has only to gain the position of Figure 155, in which the Black pawn is taken prisoner until all the White pawns not used in imprisoning Black become queens, Black continuing to oscillate in the double corner. White then plays successively *h4 — g5, h2 — i3, b6 — d8, g1 — i3, a5 — d8, g3 — h4,* and so on, forcing Black to take all of White's pawns and queens.

11. LASCA. Lasca is a very ingenious game invented by Lasker, a former chess champion. It is played on a 7 × 7 checkerboard, using only the cells that lie on the intersections of the odd-numbered rows and columns. For ease of reference we shall assume the cells numbered as in Figure 156.

Although at first there is not more than one piece on a cell, as the game proceeds several pieces may be stacked on one

another, forming what are called *columns*. It will be convenient to refer to the set of pieces on a single cell as a column in every case, even though a particular column may consist of but one piece. The topmost piece of a column is its *guide*, and it is the guide that determines the move-

FIGURE 156. *Lasca Board.*

ment of the column. It is in this that the principal ingenuity of the game consists. For, as we shall see, a column usually contains pieces from both sides in the game, and the guide is constantly changing, so that a column belongs first to one side and then to the other.

There are 22 pieces, 11 to a side. Those of one side are white, and of the other black. (We shall refer to each player by the color of his pieces.) The pieces are flat, to permit stacking. One face of each piece is plain, and the other is marked. When the plain face is up the piece is called a *soldier*. When the marked face is up the piece is called an *officer*.

At the start of the game White's 11 soldiers are placed on cells 1 to 11 and Black's on cells 15 to 25. Hence at first each column has only one member — its guide. White and Black play alternately, White beginning. The manner of executing the moves is described in the next two paragraphs.

Moving without Capturing. A column guided by a soldier may move forward one step along either diagonal to an unoccupied cell. When a column guided by a soldier reaches his seventh row (cells 22–25 if the soldier is White, 1–4 if Black), the *guide alone* is commissioned as an officer (by being turned over), though the whole column moves as he moves as long as he continues to guide it. A column guided by an officer may move forward or backward one step along either diagonal to an unoccupied cell.

Capturing. A column captures only the guide of an opposing column — it never captures more than one piece at a time from a given column. A column *may* capture the guide of an opposing column only when (1) the cell on which the latter rests is one to which (if it were empty) the capturing column could legally move in one step, and (2) there is an empty cell immediately beyond. When a capture is to be made the capturing column is placed on top of the column whose guide is to be captured, the guide is added to the bottom of the capturing column, and the column thus augmented is placed on the cell beyond. If a capture *may* be made it *must* be made, and this applies — with one apparent exception — to a succession of possible captures in a single move. The exception occurs when a column guided by a soldier reaches a cell at which the soldier is to be promoted. In this case the move stops with the promotion of the guide, even though a capture from this cell would have been possible if the guide had been an officer when he reached it. If at any stage two or more alternative captures are possible, the player *may* choose any one of them, and *must* choose some one of them.

The game is won by a side when the opposing side can make no move in its regular turn. This may happen because the first side has captured all the opposing pieces — that is, because every column on the board is guided by his own pieces — or because the opponent is blocked from making any move.

It will be seen that a column consists of at most a set of **pieces of one** color surmounted by a set of pieces of the other color. It is not possible to have an alternation of color such as White-Black-White in a single column. A captured piece in a column is not liberated until every opposing piece above it has been captured. A captured officer keeps his status, but loses his privileges, until such time as he becomes the guide of the column.

To illustrate the method of play we give the first few moves of a sample game. White begins the play and moves a soldier from 9 to 13. Black must take with 17, and does so, so that 13 and 17 are now empty and 9 is occupied by a column of two pieces guided by a Black soldier. White must take the guide of this column, and may do so with either 5 or 6. He chooses the former, so 9 is occupied by a liberated White soldier, and 13 by a column guided by a White soldier. Black plays 21 to 17 and White must play 13 to 21, capturing the Black piece at 17. Black must then play 25 to 17, capturing the White guide at 21 and liberating the two Black captives.

12. HOPSCOTCH. This game (which is not the children's hopping game) is a sort of glorified tick-tack-toe. The

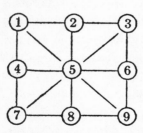

board (illustrated in Figure 157) is essentially the same, though using points instead of cells; the first moves of the game are the same, though the players place black and white pieces at vertices instead of marking ○ or × in cells; and the object of the game is the same — to get three of a kind in a row. The difference lies in the fact that after three

FIGURE 157. *Hopscotch Board.*

pieces have been placed by each player, the players alternate in moving one piece at a time a step at a time along the sides and diagonals of the square. It is still true (as Mr. Sivasankaranarayana Pillai has shown) that when properly played the game must be drawn.

Here are a few games. (*W* stands for White, *B* for Black,
+ indicates that the player wins, 0 denotes a draw, ∞ means
that it makes no difference what the player does.)

W	B	W	B	W	B	W	B	W	B	W	B	W	B	W	B
5	1	5	8	2	5	2	5	1	5	1	5	1	5	1	5
8	2	1	9	8	9	6	7	6	7	2	3	9	8	3	2
3	7	7	4	1	4	3	9	3	2	7	9	2	3	8	7
8–9	∞	1–2	∞	∞	9–6	∞	5–8	∞	7–8	∞	5–6	∞	8–7	1–4	5–6
+		+		+		+		+		+		+		0	

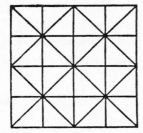

FIGURE 158. *Quadruple Hopscotch Board*

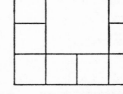

FIGURE 159. *Pettie Board.*

There are many variations of this game. In one, known
in France as "les pendus" (literally, "the hanged"), the
pieces may be moved from any square directly to any other.
The game may still be drawn. Another variation is played
using 5 pieces of each color on the board (Figure 158) obtained by forming a square from 4 ordinary hopscotch
squares. In this game 5 pieces of one color must be aligned.

The ancient Greek game pettie was played like hopscotch,
on a board of the form shown in Figure 159. Each player
had 5 pieces, which he placed on the five vertices on his edge
of the board. The players played alternately, each moving
one piece a step at a turn from vertex to vertex along the
lines of the board, and always toward the opponent's side.
If a player succeeded in surrounding an opponent's piece
with his own pieces, he removed it.

Triple hopscotch is played on the 24 vertices of a board such as that shown in Figure 160. Each player has 9 pieces,

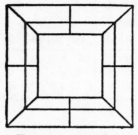

and these, as in simple hopscotch, are placed on the board alternately by the players, and are then moved alternately in the same fashion. Whenever a player gets three pieces in line he may remove any one of his opponent's pieces. The first player to be reduced to two pieces is the loser. In one variation of the game a player who has been reduced to three pieces may move them to any empty vertices without having to follow the lines. In another variation there are no diagonal lines.

FIGURE 160. *Triple Hopscotch Board.*

13. TRICOLOR. This game is a modification of lasca, played on an hexagonal array of hexagonal cells colored white, red, and black so that no two cells which meet along an edge have the same color. (In Figure 161 shading denotes red cells; the black and white cells are obvious. We shall use the numbering of this figure.) As in lasca, the game is played with stacks of one or more pieces, but the stacks are free to move in any one of the three or six directions leading out from a cell.

The *range* of a stack — that is, the maximum number of cells it can traverse in any one direction in a single move — is determined by the number of pieces in the stack: 1 cell for a single piece, 2 cells for a stack of two pieces, and 3 cells for any larger stack.

The *combat strength* of a stack depends upon both the number of pieces in the stack and the color of the cell on which it rests. Taking the strength of a single piece on a white cell as the unit, the strength of a stack of two pieces on a white cell is 2 units, that of any larger stack on a white cell is 3 units. The strength of a stack on a black cell is twice, and of a stack on a red cell is three times, the strength of the same stack on a white cell. Thus the strength of a stack is always represented by one of the numbers 1, 2, 3, 4, 6, 9.

The Game for Two Players. Each player has **18 pieces.**

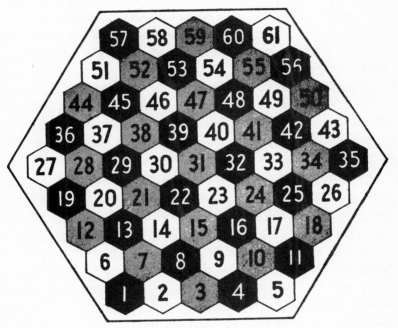

FIGURE 161. *Tricolor Board.*

Those of one player are white, those of the other, black. When the game begins, White has his pieces on cells 1 to 18 (one piece to a cell), and Black has his similarly placed on cells 44 to 61. The players play alternately, each moving a single stack (or piece) as far as he wishes, within the range of the stack, along a straight line in one of the permitted directions. He may move all his stack or only part of it, but the range and strength of the stack is determined by the number of pieces in the part of the stack that is actually moved. He may not jump any occupied cell. He may land on an empty cell, on a cell occupied by a stack of his own or (subject to the rules for attack given in the next paragraph) on a cell occupied by an enemy stack. If the cell to which he moves contains a stack of his own, the two stacks are combined to form a single stack of (possibly) increased strength and range. If the cell to which he moves is occupied by an enemy stack, he has *attacked* the enemy stack, and the disposition of the pieces is made according to the rules in the next paragraph.

A stack may attack an enemy stack if and only if its combat strength is greater than that of the enemy. If it is *more* than twice as strong it is said to *kill* the enemy by removing permanently from play and from the board all hostile pieces in the stack, and adding all friendly pieces to itself. Pieces thus added increase the range and strength of the attacking stack, if that is possible. If the attacking stack is stronger than the enemy without being more than twice as strong, it is said to *capture* the opposing stack, by combining it with itself. In this case only the friendly pieces are counted in determining the range and strength of the resulting stack. If an attack is possible it must be made, though the player attacking is free to choose any one of a set of possible alternative attacks. Not more than one attack may be made in a single turn.

The game ends with the killing or capture of all pieces of one of the players.

The Game for Three Players. Each player has 11 pieces and the pieces of the different players are colored white, black, and red. Initially White's pieces are placed on cells 1 to 11; Black's on cells 19, 27, 28, 36, 37, 44, 45, 51, 52, 57, 58; and Red's on cells 60, 61, 55, 56, 49, 50, 42, 43, 34, 35, 26. The players' turns rotate in the order White, Black, Red. The rules are the same as for the game for two, except at the end of the game. When all the pieces of one player have been killed or captured, he retires from the game, his pieces are removed from the board and the remaining two players continue as in the game for two.

14. THE MOUSE TRAP. n numbered objects are placed in a circle in any order. A player begins at any one of them and counts in order, "1, 2, 3, $\cdots$," until either the number he speaks coincides with the number of the object counted, or until he has exhausted the n numbers. In the former case (called a *success*), he withdraws from the circle the piece on which the success occurred, and starts counting from 1 again, beginning at the next object in the circle. He continues thus until he has either failed to obtain a success or has removed all the pieces from the circle. The player wins only if all the objects are removed.

With four things in the order 3214 the first coincidence will occur on 2, and the second on 1, but no further coincidences can happen. With the order 1423 the player will win, taking the pieces away in the order 1234. Similarly, 5 pieces arranged in the order 13254 can be taken away in the order 12345.

Cayley has shown that there are 9 arrangements of 4 things that give no coincidences, 7 that give only 1, 3 that give 2, and 5 that give 4.

15. THE (FRENCH) POLYTECHNIC SCHOOL'S GAME. Starting with a square array of $(n + 1)^2$ dots the two players alternately draw horizontal or vertical lines joining pairs of adjacent dots. When a player draws the fourth side of one of the n^2 small squares which may be formed in the figure, he initials the square as credited to him. The player who completes the greater number of such squares is the winner. Usually the rule is made that a player who completes a square may draw another line in the same turn, so that a player's turn stops only when he draws a line which fails to complete a square.

16. SQUARES-IN-LINE. The game is played on a square array of n^2 cells, say on graph paper. The players alternate in marking a cell at a time, each using his own distinguishing mark. Whenever a player marks the last cell in a line of cells parallel to a side or diagonal of the big square, he is credited with all the cells in this line, and the player with the higher final total wins. As in the Polytechnic School game, the completion of a line usually is considered to give the player another play.

17. MARKED SQUARES. On a square array of 9^2 square cells two players alternate in marking a cell at a time with a cross (or they may place a counter in the cell). Whenever a player marks the third, sixth, or ninth cell to be marked in a row or column he wins 1, 2, or 3 points, respectively. The player with the higher final total wins.

Variations may be introduced in the rules as follows: Diagonal or broken diagonal alignments may or may not be counted. When a player scores one or more points he may or may not be given another play. If two scores are obtained simultaneously they may or may not both be credited.

In another variation each player has his own mark, say crosses for one and circles for the other. The marks are placed on a board which is unbounded on two sides. The object is then to obtain an orthogonal or diagonal line of five successive marks of the same kind.

18. JOINING POINTS. An arbitrary set of points is marked in an arbitrary manner on a plane. Alternately two players join pairs of points by arbitrary (straight or curved) lines. No point may be the end point of more than one line. No line may pass through any point. No two points may be joined by more than one line. No two lines may cross. The first one to be unable to draw a line satisfying these conditions is the loser.

19. PEG SOLITAIRE. The common property of the many varied forms in which this game appears is that it is played with a set of n objects and a board containing $n + 1$ receptacles into each one of which just one of the objects may be fitted. The objects, their number, the receptacles and the arrangement of the receptacles may vary. We assume that

			37	47	57			
		26	36	46	56	66		
	15	25	35	45	55	65	75	
	14	24	34	44	54	64	74	
	13	23	33	43	53	63	73	
		22	32	42	52	62		
			31	41	51			

FIGURE 162. *Peg Solitaire Board.*

the objects are pegs, that the receptacles are holes in the board, and that there are 37 holes arranged in the board as in Figure 162. We shall use the numbering given in the figure.

If some or all of the pegs are in position, a move is possible only if there is a set of three consecutive holes in the same horizontal or vertical of which two consecutive holes are occupied and the third is vacant. When the move is possible it consists in moving the peg at one end of the three holes to the hole at the other end and removing the peg in the middle. In other words, one takes as in checkers, but along horizontals and verticals, not diagonals.

The game consists in starting with a given distribution of

pegs on the board and removing all but the last by successive moves.

For example, suppose that pegs are in just the six holes 35, 43, 44, 45, 46, 55. One can remove every peg but the center one by the succession of moves: 45–65, 43–45, 35–55, 65–45, 46–44.

The most common problem is to start with all the pegs and remove all but one. This problem is possible if and only if the initially empty hole is one of the following: 24, 42, 46, 64; 34, 43, 45, 54; 13, 15, 31, 37, 51, 57, 73, 75. In case the problem is possible the last peg rests in one of the holes in the list above.

Here is an extract from a letter of January 17, 1716, from Leibnitz to Monmort:

"The game called Solitaire pleases me much. I take it in reverse order. That is to say that instead of making a configuration according to the rules of the game, which is to jump to an empty place and remove the piece over which one has jumped, I thought it was better to reconstruct what had been demolished, by filling an empty hole over which one has leaped. In this way one may set oneself the task of forming a given figure if that is possible, as it certainly is if it can be destroyed. But why all this?, you ask. I reply — to perfect the art of invention. For we must have the means of constructing everything which is found by the exercise of reason."

20. Dominoes. Of all common games dominoes is certainly one of the least standardized. To avoid misunderstanding we give a set of rules which we shall assume determine the basic game.*

There are 28 dominoes, running from 0–0 to 6–6. Two players participate. When the whole set has been shuffled face down on the table each player draws one to determine who shall play first. The one with the higher total wins the

* The selection was quite arbitrary, dear reader. The rules by which you play are doubtless just as good, perhaps better. — M. K.

draw. In case of tie the one with the highest single number wins (for example, 6–4 beats 5–5). When the winner of the draw has been determined, the pieces are returned, the whole set is reshuffled, and each of the players draws seven pieces at random, which he sets up before him so that he and not his opponent can see them. The dominoes not drawn are called the *stock*.

The winner of the draw, A, now places one of his dominoes face up between himself and his opponent. If his opponent B possesses a domino one of whose ends matches an end of the domino played by A, he places such a domino face up on the table with the other so that the two are end to end, with the matching ends together. If B cannot play, A plays again. If B cannot play again, A plays a third time, and so on until B has played or A also can play no farther (which is impossible on the first play). When B has played A has the opportunity. The play continues thus until one of the players has exhausted his hand, or neither can play farther. When play has ceased, the player with fewer total points in his hand wins by the amount of the difference of the totals in the two hands.

Here are some of the commoner variations in the fundamental game. (1) A doublet may or must be placed crosswise instead of end to end. (2) If doublets are permitted or required to be placed crosswise, play may be permitted from the ends as well as the sides. (3) A player who is unable to play may be required to draw one from the stock. If he cannot play after the draw, the other player may play. (4) A player who cannot play may be required to draw one at a time from the stock until he either can play or has exhausted the stock. (5) The range of the dominoes may be greater, say to 9–9 or 12–12, and the number drawn originally may be changed correspondingly.

Returning to the game first described, the same rules may

be used for three or four players, each playing for himself. The winner is the one who first exhausts his hand, or the one with the lowest total in his hand at the end of play. If four persons play partners, two against two, each player draws only six dominoes. If a player exhausts his hand, his side wins. If no player exhausts his hand, the side with the lower remaining total wins. In either case the winners score the total of the points remaining in their opponents' hands.

When four play, each for himself, it is possible for two of the players to be unable to play at all while a third exhausts his hand. Let the players in their order of play be A, B, C, D. Suppose A draws 0–0, 0–1, 0–2, 0–3, 1–4, 1–5, 1–6, and D draws 0–4, 0–5, 0–6, 1–1, 1–2, 1–3, and any other domino. The remaining 14 are divided in any way between B and C. If A and D play alternately in the following order, it will be seen that B and C have no opportunity to play: 0–0, 0–6, 6–1, 1–3, 3–0, 0–5, 5–1, 1–2, 2–0, 0–4, 4–1, 1–1, 1–0. A wins with a total of 120, the maximum possible win. By a different permutation of the numbers $0, 1, \cdots, 6$ the same result can be obtained, except that A's winnings will not be as great.

In a partnership game the maximum score in one game is 105; in a game between two players, 69.

Matador is a variation in which the chain of dominoes is formed by the requirement that the ends which abut must add up to 7. Since no domino could be added to a 0, one is permitted to place a matador (that is a domino totaling 7, and sometimes the 0–0) crosswise against a 0, and play is resumed with a 0 against the other side of the matador. Otherwise the rules are about the same, and the game may be played by two, three, or four individual players, or by partners.

Muggins is another variation, playable by two, three, or four individual players. Play proceeds by the same rules as in the original game, except that doublets must be placed crosswise, and no play is allowed from the end of a doublet. The motives of play are different, however, since a player scores after each play according to whether the totals at the free ends of the chain is exactly divisible by 5. If this total is 0 or is not divisible by 5, the player scores 0. If the total is exactly divisible by 5 the player scores the quotient. (Thus a total of 20 scores 4.)

The 5–5 is the best domino in this game. Suppose A plays it. He scores 2. Unless B has the 5–0 (which would give him 2) he cannot score. Suppose B plays 5–6. If C plays 5–4 he scores 2. If A now plays 4–4 he scores nothing. If B then plays 6–6 he scores 4. And so on.

The number 3 is sometimes used instead of 5.

There are some interesting properties of the dominoes themselves.

If the largest domino is a n-n, there are $\dfrac{(n+1)(n+2)}{2}$ dominoes in the set, each number from 0 to n occurs $n + 2$ times on the faces of the dominoes, and the sum of the numbers of all the dominoes of the set is therefore $(n+2) \cdot \dfrac{n(n+1)}{2}$. Hence also the average value of a domino is n.

Using the rules first laid down, it is always possible to form a chain containing the whole set of dominoes, provided n is 1 or an even number, but it is impossible for any other value of n. When such a chain has been formed for an even value of n, the numbers at the two ends are the same.

There is a simple recreation based on this property. Adroitly conceal any domino except a double, say 3–4, and ask someone to form a proper chain with all the remaining ones. You can promise him that however he does it, one end must have a 3 and the other a 4.

One may construct magic squares with dominoes, although if the order is greater than 3 one must be permitted to repeat numbers with different dominoes having the same sum. Thus the two squares of order 3 in Figure 163 are ordinary

26	01	15
12	14	16
13	36	11

16	00	05
02	04	06
03	26	01

26	12	13	03
14	02	36	11
05	15	01	06
00	25	04	16

35	03	06	22	51
11	32	61	45	40
62	46	00	21	24
01	31	52	63	33
44	41	34	02	05

FIGURE 163. *Domino Magic Squares.*

magic squares, while those of order 4 and order 5 have repetitions such as 1–3 and 0–4, and 3–5, 4–4, and 6–2.

Paillot gives the following arrangement in which the last

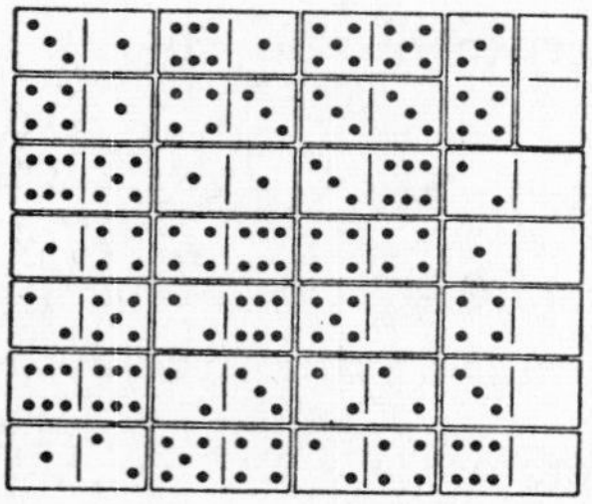

FIGURE 164. *Domino Magic Square with One Border of Blanks.*

column can be omitted, leaving a magic square of order 7 (Figure 164).

Lucas uses the term *quadrille* to describe a certain arrangement of the whole set of dominoes in which the pairs of rows consist of sets of squares composed of four equal half-dominoes. We give four distinct examples, each of which gives rise to many variations by permuting the numbers 0, 1, 2, 3, 4, 5, 6. (Figure 165). Delannoy found three other distinct forms (Figure 166).

2. PERMUTATIONAL GAMES

1. THE 15 PUZZLE. Rather than attempt a detailed description of this familiar puzzle, we shall consider it to be equivalent to a set of 15 equal cubes, numbered from 1 to 15, placed in a shallow box that just holds 16 such cubes. The empty space may be in any of the 16 possible positions, but initially the cubes are set in the box in order, with the empty cell in the lower right corner (Figure 167). The mechanism of the puzzle is such that the cubes may not be removed from the box, but may be slid parallel to the sides of the box. Hence by a series of moves — sliding a cube next to the

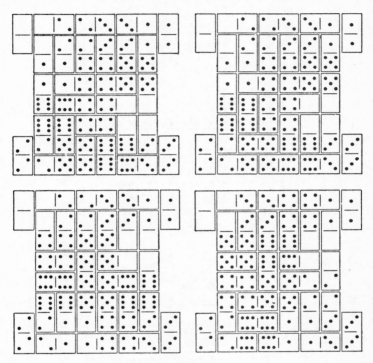

FIGURE 165. *Quadrilles of Lucas.*

empty cell into the empty cell — one may perform various permutations of the sequence of the numbers on the cubes. The problem presented by the puzzle is to determine what permutations can be obtained, and how. It is understood that at the end of any sequence of moves the empty cell is once more at the lower right corner.

The puzzle is most easily understood in terms of certain

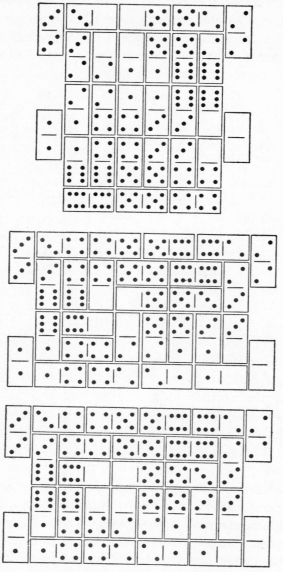

FIGURE 166.   *Quadrilles of Delannoy.*

aspects of the theory of permutations that may be explained
very simply. Suppose we have any set of objects to which
some *normal* order has been assigned. By way of illustration
we may use the numbers from 1 through 5 in the order 12345.

Let them be put in an arbitrary
order, say 25143. Any pair of the
objects that is now not in its normal
relative order is called an *inversion*.
(21 and 53 are inversions in 25143.)

1	2	3	4
5	6	7	8
9	10	11	12
13	14	15	

The total number of inversions in
any permutation of the objects is
most easily found by determining
for each object how many objects
that normally precede it now follow
it. In the permutation 25143, for

FIGURE 167. *The 15
Puzzle; Start.*

example, there are the five inversions 21, 51, 54, 53, 43. According as the number of inversions is even or odd the permutation is called even or odd, and the evenness or oddness
of a permutation is called its *parity*. Thus the parity of a permutation depends solely on the order of the objects permuted,
not on the manner in which the permutation was obtained.

A fundamental property of permutations is the fact that
the parity of a permutation is changed whenever any two of
the objects are transposed. Thus the odd permutation 25143
becomes the even permutation 23145 when 5 and 3 are interchanged. This is obviously true when the objects transposed
are adjacent, since only the relative order of these two objects is affected. If the objects transposed are not adjacent,
one can obtain the result of the transposition by a sequence
of transpositions of adjacent pairs. If object P in position p
is to be interchanged with object Q in position q, ($q - p =
k > 1$), then k successive transpositions of P with the object
next to it on the right will bring P to position q. The last of
these transpositions, however, moves Q one position to the

left, so that only $k - 1$ further transpositions of Q with the object next to it on the left are required to bring Q to the position p. All the other objects are unaffected in the final result. Since each transposition of an adjacent pair produces one change of parity, and since $2k - 1$ is odd, the interchange of P and Q has caused an odd number of changes of parity, that is, has finally changed the parity. (The successive transpositions of adjacent numbers required to change 25143 to 23145 are: 21543, 21453, 21435, 21345, 23145.)

The cyclic interchange of any set of objects in a given permutation will change the parity or not, according as the number of elements affected is even or odd. For if h objects are permuted cyclically the same result can be obtained by $h - 1$ successive transpositions of one of the end elements of the cycle. For example, the cyclic permutation from 253 to 532 can be made by the two transpositions, 523, 532. Hence 53142 is an odd permutation since it results from the odd permutation 25143 by the cyclic interchange of 5 for 2, 3 for 5, 2 for 3.

The crux of the 15 puzzle is the fact that every permutation allowed by the mechanism is an even permutation. This is readily seen. We may think of the empty cell as representing the number 16. Then every permutation obtainable is the result of a succession of transpositions of 16 and some other number, ending in the return of 16 to its original position. In order to return, the 16 must make an even number of moves — one backward for every one forward, though not necessarily in alternation. Hence the sixteen numbers suffer only even permutations. But since there are no inversions involving 16 in its fixed initial and final position, the permutations of the first fifteen numbers are also even.

It is not as easy to show, though it is true, that every even permutation of the fifteen numbers can be gotten. Since it is furthermore true that just half of the permutations of any

n (> 1) objects are even, this means that only half of the possible permutations of the numbers can be obtained.

We shall not prove that one can get every even permutation, but we shall show a systematic procedure by which to get them. If one examines the operations carefully it will be seen that any sequence of moves that returns the empty space to the lower right corner may be expressed as a succession of cyclic interchanges of an odd number of the cubes of the following sort: The cubes permuted form the perimeter of a rectangular block of cubes, except for the cube in the lower right corner of the block (not necessarily the lower right corner of the box); and they are permuted in their order around the perimeter. Thus, for example, we can change $\frac{123}{567}$ into $\frac{512}{637}$ or into $\frac{236}{157}$. If we denote a move by the number of the block moved into the empty place each time, the first permutation can be obtained by the moves 12, 8, 7, 3, 2, 1, 5, 6, 3, 7, 8, 12. Note that at the end only the cells 1, 2, 3, 5, 6 have been left in a different position.

By means of combinations of permutations of this sort, any even permutation of the original order can be derived. Of course it is not necessary to move the empty cell back to the corner every time, since that can be left to the last. As an example, the arrangement shown in Figure 168 is an even permutation, and hence may be gotten. Following is a sequence (quite possibly not the best) that will yield the desired result. The parentheses indicate cyclic interchanges of the type described. 12, 8, (7, 6, 5, 1, 2, 3, 4, 7), (6, 5, 1, 2, 3, 4, 7, 6), (5, 1, 2, 9, 10, 11, 8), (5, 1, 2, 9, 10, 11, 8, 5), 1, (6, 7, 2, 6), 1, (5, 6, 1, 5), 6, (8, 11, 10, 9, 1, 8), (11, 10, 9, 1, 8, 11), 6, 12, 15, (6, 10, 14, 6), 15, (12, 10, 15, 12), (10, 15, 14, 9, 13, 6, 12, 10), (15, 14, 9, 13, 6, 12, 10), (9, 13, 10, 9), 15, (14, 13, 15, 14), (13, 15, 10, 9, 14), (10, 15), (5, 11, 15, 5), (11, 15, 5, 10, 13), (11, 15, 5, 10), (15, 11). In these moves a number of the cycles are truncated because the move that completes one cycle may cancel the move that begins another.

3	4	2	7
1	8	10	5
6	9	15	11
12	14	13	

FIGURE 168. *The 15 Puzzle; One Permutation.*

FIGURE 169.

We have selected the 15 puzzle as characteristic of permutational games and puzzles. There are many, many variations. In some of them variety is gained by a (real or apparent) change in the shape of the path over which the moves may be made, or in the number of cells involved. In others the game may be competitive, with the first moves made according to a pattern like one of those described.

2. Denote the columns of the ordinary chessboard by the letters from a through h and the rows, starting from White's side, by the numbers from 1 through 8.

Place seven white pawns on cells $a1, b1, \cdots, g1$, and seven black pawns on cells $h2, \cdots, h8$. Each pawn may move to a neighboring empty cell in this row and column, and each pawn may leap over (without taking) a pawn of the opposite color in an adjacent cell, provided the following cell is empty. Also, one diagonal move is permitted — that between $g1$ and $h2$ in either direction. The object of the game is to get the two sets of pawns interchanged. One need not play Black and White alternately.

Solution (the : signifies a jump): *g*1–*h*1, *h*2–*g*1, *h*3–*h*2, *h*1 : *h*3, *f*1 : *h*1, *e*1–*f*1, *g*1 : *e*1, *h*2–*g*1, *h*4 : *h*2, *h*5–*h*4, *h*3 : *h*5, *h*1: *h*3, *f*1 : *h*1, *d*1 : *f*1, *c*1–*d*1, *e*1 : *c*1, *g*1 : *e*1, *h*2–*g*1, *h*4 : *h*2, *h*6 : *h*4, *h*7–*h*6, *h*5 : *h*7, *h*3 : *h*5, *h*1 : *h*3, *f*1 : *h*1, *d*1 : *f*1, *b*1 : *d*1, *a*1–*b*1, *c*1 : *a*1, *e*1 : *c*1, *g*1 : *e*1, *h*2–*g*1, *h*4 : *h*2, *h*6 : *h*4, *h*8 : *h*6, *h*7–*h*8, *h*5 : *h*7, *h*3 : *h*5, *h*1 : *h*3, *f*1 : *h*1, *d*1 : *f*1, *b*1 : *d*1, *c*1–*b*1, *e*1 : *c*1, *g*1 : *e*1, *h*2–*g*1, *h*4 : *h*2, *h*6 : *h*4, *h*5–*h*6, *h*3 : *h*5, *h*1 : *h*3, *f*1 : *h*1, *d*1 : *f*1, *e*1–*d*1, *g*1 : *e*1, *h*2–*g*1, *h*4 : *h*2, *h*3–*h*4, *h*1 : *h*3, *f*1 : *h*1, *g*1–*f*1, *h*2–*g*1, *h*1–*h*2.

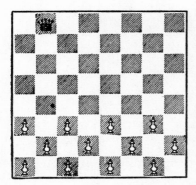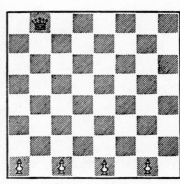

FIGURE 170. *The Wolf and the Goats.*

3. THE WOLF AND THE GOATS. This game is played on an ordinary chessboard. The 12 goats are white pawns placed on the black cells of White's first three rows, and they move like men in checkers, but without being able to take an opposing piece. The wolf is a black king placed on the black queen's knight's square. The wolf moves like a king in checkers, and may take the goats. The wolf tries to reach the opposite side of the board, and the goats try to prevent him by hemming him in on all sides. By keeping together the goats can always win.

There is a variation in which there are only 4 goats, placed initially on the first row, and the wolf is not allowed to take. In this case also the goats can always win.

Another variation, the dogs and the wolf, is played on a 10×10 board between 5 dogs and 1 wolf. The dogs begin on the black cells of the first row, the wolf on any unoccupied black cell. Neither side is allowed to take. In this game the dogs can always win.

4. GRASSHOPPER. Grasshopper is played on a chess-

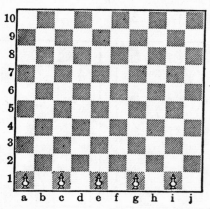

FIGURE 171. *The Dogs and the Wolf.*

board. Each player has 10 pawns, placed initially as in Figure 172, left. Each pawn may move one cell in any direction to an unoccupied cell, and in addition may jump over a pawn of either color that is one cell away (orthogonally or diagonally), provided the cell beyond is empty. Such jumps may be made in succession on a single turn. The object of each side is to occupy the cells originally occupied by his opponent.

A typical situation in this sort of game is shown at the right of Figure 172, where, if it is White's move, White may play in one move: *g1–g3–e3–e5–e7–c7–a7*. If it is Black's move he may play: *d7–f5–d3–f1*.

Grasshopper is a variant of halma, which is played on a 16 × 16 chessboard with 19 men to a side. Another variation is played with 15 men to each side on a 10 × 10 board.

5. THE FOUR-STORY TOWERS. G. Kowalewsky gives the following description of his game: The pieces are little four-story towers, each story represented by a horizontal band painted either red or blue. Every possible arrangement of red and blue bands is represented, so there are $2^4 = 16$ dif-

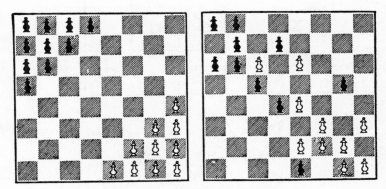

FIGURE 172. *The Grasshopper Game.*

ferent towers. The game is played on a 4 × 4 chessboard.

Two towers are said to be "in domino" if they differ in the color of just one story. The object of the game is to place all 16 towers on the board, one after the other, so that every pair that is separated by a knight's move (1, 2) or by a move (2, 3) shall be in domino (see Figure 173).

Using two boards and two sets of towers, the game may be made competitive. The players play alternately, each on a separate board. The first to be unable to play loses. The other player continues until he can play no further, when he scores as many points as he has towers in position. If he happens to get all 16 towers placed he scores double.

6. TETRACHROME. The inventor of this game, Chican-dard, describes it thus:

The pieces are squares of the same size, each divided into four regions by the two diagonals. Each piece is painted with

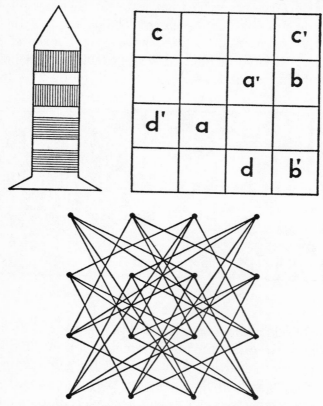

FIGURE 173. *The Four-storied Towers.*

four different colors, and there are 30 pieces in all — one for each of the 30 possible arrangements of four out of five given colors.

The pieces are to be juxtaposed so that two pieces that meet along a common edge have the same color on each side of the common boundary. Taking one piece as a pattern, one tries to construct squares of 4, 9, or 16 pieces whose boundaries will have the same colors as the pattern piece. Some of the many possibilities are illustrated in the sketches of Figure 174.

7. THE 16 BICOLORED PIECES. This game, similar to tetrachrome, is also due to Chicandard. The pieces are painted with two colors chosen from among eight, and the two colored regions are separated by a diagonal line. The

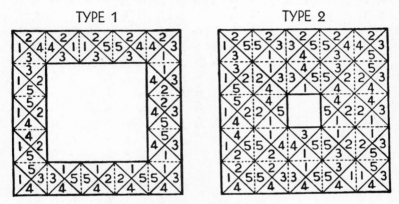

FIGURE 174. *Tetrachrome.*

squares formed from these pieces may be required to satisfy various requirements, such as using a certain number of colors (4, 5, 6, 7, or 8) in each row and column. In Figure 175 are a number of such designs.

8. FROGS AND TOADS. On $2n + 1$ cells in a straight line are placed n frogs and n toads, with one cell between them. A frog may move one cell toward the toads to an empty cell, or may leap over either a frog or a toad to an empty cell; similarly for a toad. The object of the game is to interchange the frogs and toads by such moves. The moves need not alternate. Here are the solutions for $n = 2$, 3, and 4. In general, $n(n + 2)$ steps are needed.

$n = 2$

f_1	f_2	$\cdot$	t_2	t_1
f_1	$\cdot$	f_2	t_2	t_1
f_1	t_2	f_2	$\cdot$	t_1
f_1	t_2	f_2	t_1	$\cdot$
f_1	t_2	$\cdot$	t_1	f_2
$\cdot$	t_2	f_1	t_1	f_2
t_2	$\cdot$	f_1	t_1	f_2
t_2	t_1	f_1	$\cdot$	f_2
t_2	t_1	$\cdot$	f_1	f_2

$n = 3$

f_1	f_2	f_3	$\cdot$	t_3	t_2	t_1
f_1	f_2	$\cdot$	f_3	t_3	t_2	t_1
f_1	f_2	t_3	f_3	$\cdot$	t_2	t_1
f_1	f_2	t_3	f_3	t_2	$\cdot$	t_1
f_1	f_2	t_3	$\cdot$	t_2	f_3	t_1
f_1	$\cdot$	t_3	f_2	t_2	f_3	t_1
$\cdot$	f_1	t_3	f_2	t_2	f_3	t_1
t_3	f_1	$\cdot$	f_2	t_2	f_3	t_1
t_3	f_1	t_2	f_2	$\cdot$	f_3	t_1
t_3	f_1	t_2	f_2	t_1	f_3	$\cdot$
t_3	f_1	t_2	f_2	t_1	$\cdot$	f_3
t_3	f_1	t_2	$\cdot$	t_1	f_2	f_3
t_3	$\cdot$	t_2	f_1	t_1	f_2	f_3
t_3	t_2	$\cdot$	f_1	t_1	f_2	f_3
t_3	t_2	t_1	f_1	$\cdot$	f_2	f_3
t_3	t_2	t_1	$\cdot$	f_1	f_2	f_3

$n = 4$

f_1	f_2	f_3	f_4	$\cdot$	t_4	t_3	t_2	t_1
f_1	f_2	f_3	$\cdot$	f_4	t_4	t_3	t_2	t_1
f_1	f_2	f_3	t_4	f_4	$\cdot$	t_3	t_2	t_1
f_1	f_2	f_3	t_4	f_4	t_3	$\cdot$	t_2	t_1
f_1	f_2	f_3	t_4	$\cdot$	t_3	f_4	t_2	t_1
f_1	f_2	$\cdot$	t_4	f_3	t_3	f_4	t_2	t_1
f_1	$\cdot$	f_2	t_4	f_3	t_3	f_4	t_2	t_1
f_1	t_4	f_2	$\cdot$	f_3	t_3	f_4	t_2	t_1
f_1	t_4	f_2	t_3	f_3	$\cdot$	f_4	t_2	t_1
f_1	t_4	f_2	t_3	f_3	t_2	f_4	$\cdot$	t_1
f_1	t_4	f_2	t_3	f_3	t_2	f_4	t_1	$\cdot$
f_1	t_4	f_2	t_3	f_3	t_2	$\cdot$	t_1	f_4
f_1	t_4	f_2	t_3	$\cdot$	t_2	f_3	t_1	f_4
f_1	t_4	$\cdot$	t_3	f_2	t_2	f_3	t_1	f_4
$\cdot$	t_4	f_1	t_3	f_2	t_2	f_3	t_1	f_4
t_4	$\cdot$	f_1	t_3	f_2	t_2	f_3	t_1	f_4
t_4	t_3	f_1	$\cdot$	f_2	t_2	f_3	t_1	f_4
t_4	t_3	f_1	t_2	f_2	$\cdot$	f_3	t_1	f_4
t_4	t_3	f_1	t_2	f_2	t_1	f_3	$\cdot$	f_4
t_4	t_3	f_1	t_2	f_2	t_1	$\cdot$	f_3	f_4
t_4	t_3	f_1	t_2	$\cdot$	t_1	f_2	f_3	f_4
t_4	t_3	$\cdot$	t_2	f_1	t_1	f_2	f_3	f_4
t_4	t_3	t_2	$\cdot$	f_1	t_1	f_2	f_3	f_4
t_4	t_3	t_2	t_1	f_1	$\cdot$	f_2	f_3	f_4
t_4	t_3	t_2	t_1	$\cdot$	f_1	f_2	f_3	f_4

Another game of the same nature is played on a 7×7 chessboard; 24 white pawns and 24 black pawns are arranged as in Figure 176. The same rules apply for moves in rows or columns as in the game of frogs and toads. Again one must interchange the positions of the two sides. To succeed one interchanges first the pieces in the middle row, then those in the middle column. From the solutions given for the frogs and toads one observes that each position is free at some time. Hence, as one frees a position in the middle column, one takes that opportunity to exchange the pieces in the intersecting row.

9. Eight checkers are placed in a straight line. How can these be reduced to four piles of two each by successive moves

FIGURE 175. *Bicolored Squares.*

in which a checker leaps over two others and lands on a third?

This rearrangement is easily accomplished by jumping the fifth onto the second and the third onto the seventh, and so on.

The problem can be generalized by taking any $2n$ checkers

$(n > 4)$. For one has only to jump the fourth onto the first in each sequence of n to gain the effect of having reduced the number of checkers by two. By repetitions of this move one reduces the case to that of eight checkers.

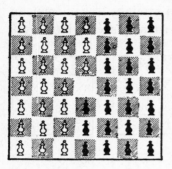

FIGURE 176.

More generally, starting with np checkers $(n > 3)$, one may form n piles of p checkers each by a succession of jumps over p checkers. One first reduces the problem to that of $4p$ checkers by filling up the end piles. For the case of $4p$ checkers we begin by taking checkers from the center to fill the piles next to the end on either side. Then the end piles are filled.

10. n red cards and n black cards are placed alternately in a row. Two empty places are assumed at one end. How can one get the two sets of cards separated from each other by n successive moves, in each of which two adjacent cards are removed and placed in the same order in the two empty places?

The problem is always possible. We give here the solution for $n = 4$.

$$
\begin{array}{ccccccccccc}
\cdot & \cdot & R_1 & B_1 & R_2 & B_2 & R_3 & \underline{B_3} & \underline{R_4} & B_4 \\
B_3 & R_4 & R_1 & B_1 & \underline{R_2} & \underline{B_2} & R_3 & \cdot & \cdot & B_4 \\
B_3 & \underline{R_4} & \underline{R_1} & B_1 & \cdot & \cdot & R_3 & R_2 & B_2 & B_4 \\
B_3 & \cdot & \cdot & B_1 & R_4 & R_1 & R_3 & R_2 & \underline{B_2} & \underline{B_4} \\
B_3 & B_2 & B_4 & B_1 & R_4 & R_1 & R_3 & R_2 & \cdot & \cdot \\
\end{array}
$$

The problem may also be solved, but in $n + 1$ moves, if the order of the two cards is interchanged as they are moved. Here is the solution for $n = 4$.

· · R_1 B_1 R_2 B_2 R_3 $\underline{B_3}$ $\underline{R_4}$ B_4

R_4 B_3 R_1 $\underline{B_1}$ $\underline{R_2}$ B_2 R_3 · · B_4

R_4 $\underline{B_3}$ $\underline{R_1}$ · · B_2 R_3 R_2 B_1 B_4

R_4 · · R_1 B_3 B_2 $\underline{R_3}$ $\underline{R_2}$ B_1 B_4

R_4 R_2 R_3 R_1 B_3 B_2 · · $\underline{B_1}$ $\underline{B_4}$

R_4 R_2 R_3 R_1 B_3 B_2 B_4 B_1 · ·

11. THE THREE PILES. This is a game of guessing a selected card. Someone is asked to choose (in his mind) any one of 27 (or 21) cards in a pack. The person guessing the card then shuffles the pack and deals them into three piles,

1	2	3	4	5
6	7	8	9	10
11	12	13	14	15
16	17	18	19	20

1	6	11	16
2	7	12	17
3	8	13	18
4	9	14	19
5	10	15	20

FIGURE 177.

one card to each pile in turn. The person who has chosen is asked to tell in which pile the card lies. The dealer then places the chosen pile between the other two and deals (without cutting or shuffling) as before. Again he is informed in which pile the chosen card lies. The chosen pile is placed between the other two, the cards are dealt as before, and the pile in which the card lies is pointed out. The dealer can now safely assert that the chosen card is the middle one of that pile.

Martin has given a variation that allows one to guess a card in only two deals. Suppose the whole pack contains ab cards. First deal a rows of b cards each, and ask for the row in which the card lies. Then take the cards up by rows and remember the designated row. Now deal into b rows of a

cards each. This merely permutes the rows and columns of the first distribution, as in Figure 177, so that when you are told in which row the card now lies, you know that it lies in the column whose number was given for the row in the previous distribution.

You can also ask your victim in what order he wishes his card to appear. Suppose he answers that it is to be the sixteenth card. Express $16 - 1 = 15$ in the ternary scale, that is, as 120. When he has indicated the pile after the first deal, pick up the cards so that there are 0 piles above the selected

$$\begin{array}{ccccc}
a_1 & b_1 & a_2 & a_3 & a_4 \\
b_2 & a_5 & b_5 & a_6 & a_7 \\
b_3 & b_6 & a_8 & b_8 & a_9 \\
b_4 & b_7 & b_9 & a_{10} & b_{10}
\end{array}$$

FIGURE 178.

pile. The second time pick up the cards so that there are 2 piles over the selected pile. The third time place 1 pile over the selected pile. On the fourth deal the selected card will be in position $(0 + 2 \cdot 3 + 1 \cdot 9) + 1 = 16$. Goormaghtigh found that a similar method is possible with $45, 52, \cdots$ cards.

Gergonne generalized the game so that one uses m^m cards dealt in m piles of m^{m-1} each. His result is: If $a, b, c, \cdots$ are the numbers of the piles in which the selected card lies, then the position N of the card in the mth deal is given by

$$N = 1 - a + bm - cm^2 + dm^3 \cdots, \quad \text{if } m \text{ is even};$$
$$N = a - bm + cm^2 - dm^3 \cdots, \quad \text{if } m \text{ is odd}.$$

12. To Guess Two Cards. Deal out $n(n + 1)$ cards in pairs and ask someone to select one of the pairs. Collect the cards by pairs in order and deal the individual cards into n rows of $n + 1$ cards each, according to the following scheme: The first two cards in the first row, the third and fourth cards in the first and second rows, the fifth and sixth cards in the first and third rows, $\cdots$, the $(n - 1)$th and nth cards in the first and nth rows, the $(n + 1)$th and $(n + 2)$th cards in the second row, next the second and third rows, and so on. (Figure 178 shows the deal for $4 \cdot 5$ cards, using subscripts to denote the numbers of the pairs.)

1	2	3	7	13	21	31	43
4	5	6	9	15	23	33	45
8	10	11	12	17	25	35	47
14	16	18	19	20	27	37	49
22	24	26	28	29	30	39	51
32	34	36	38	40	41	42	53
44	46	48	50	52	54	55	56

FIGURE 179.

When the victim has indicated the row or rows in which the pair lies, the cards can be found as follows:

(1) If both lie in row h, then the cards occupy positions h and $h + 1$ in that row.

(2) If one lies in row h and the other in row k, then one member of the pair lies in row h, column $k + 1$, and the other lies in row k, column h.

In Figure 179 is given the arrangement for $n = 7$, and the cards have been numbered consecutively from 1 to 56. If the selected pair is in rows 3 and 5 (counting down from the top), one finds 25 in row 3, column 6, and 26 in row 5, column 3.

For ten pairs one may use a verbal memory scheme such

as that shown in Figure 180. If these four five-letter words have no literary merit, at least they have the useful property of containing ten pairs of repeated letters so arranged as to have each pair uniquely determined by the row or rows in which it lies. Hence the pairs of cards may be distributed

```
M   U   T   U   S

D   E   D   I   T

N   O   M   E   N

C   O   C   I   S
```

FIGURE 180.

according to this pattern, and the selected pair determined from memory. This has the advantage of giving a less reg-

```
L   A   N   A   T   A

L   E   V   E   T   E

L   I   V   I   N   I

N   O   V   O   T   O
```

FIGURE 181.

ular distribution than the first scheme, so it is harder for the victim to guess the method.

By using the set of words in Figure 181 one may guess a set of three out of 8 sets of three cards, in a similar manner.

13. From a pack of 32 cards deal four piles face down, one card to each pile in turn. Place the first pile on the second, these on the third, and these on the fourth. Without cutting or shuffling, deal as before. When the cards have been picked

up after the fifth deal in this way, the order of the cards will–
be reversed, and any card whose original order was a multiple of three still has that property. (Marceil)

This table gives the results of the five deals:

1	2	3	4	5
1, 2, 3, 4	29,25,21,17	16,32,15,31	2, 4, 6, 8	25,17, 9, 1
5, 6, 7, 8	13, 9, 5, 1	14,30,13,29	10,12,14,16	26,18,10, 2
9,10,11,12	30,26,22,18	12,28,11,27	18,20,22,24	27,19,11, 3
13,14,15,16	14,10, 6, 2	10,26, 9,25	26,28,30,32	28,20,12, 4
17,18,19,20	31,27,23,19	8,24, 7,23	1, 3, 5, 7	29,21,13, 5
21,22,23,24	15,11, 7, 3	6,22, 5,21	9,11,13,15	30,22,14, 6
25,26,27,28	32,28,24,20	4,20, 3,19	17,19,21,23	31,23,15, 7
29,30,31,32	16,12, 8, 4	2,18, 1,17	25,27,29,31	32,24,16, 8

14. MONGE'S SHUFFLE. Monge investigated the following method of shuffling cards. Form the deck by placing the
second card above the first, the third underneath the pair,
the fourth above the first three, the fifth below the first four,
and so on. With a pack of 52 cards, for example, one gets
the following arrangement: 52, 50, 48, $\cdots$, 6, 4, 2, 1, 3,
5, $\cdots$, 47, 49, 51.

If the pack contains $6k + 4$ cards, the $(2k + 2)$th card occupies the same position after shuffling as before. In a pack
of $10h + 2$ cards the $(2h + 1)$th and the $(6h + 2)$th cards are
interchanged. Hence on the ordinary deck of 52 cards, the
18th remains fixed and the 11th and 32nd are interchanged.

More generally, with a pack of $2p$ cards the final position
x_1 of the card whose initial position was x_0 is

$$x_1 = \tfrac{1}{2}(2p + x_0 + 1) \qquad \text{if } x_0 \text{ is odd,}$$
$$x_1 = \tfrac{1}{2}(2p - x_0 + 2) \qquad \text{if } x_0 \text{ is even.}$$

If the deck be shuffled m times in this way we find the following relation connecting the final position x_m and the initial position x_0 of any card:

$$2^{n+1}x_m = (4p+1)(2^{m-1} \pm 2^{m-2} \pm \cdots \pm 2 \pm 1) \pm 2x_0 + 2^m \pm 1$$

A pack of n cards will regain its original order after a certain number m of such shufflings. This number may be found by substituting x_0 for x_m in the preceding formula and solving for m. The value of m will depend upon the divisibility of $4^m - 1$ by $4p + 1$.

Here is a recreation based on these formulas. Arrange the cards in the order ace to king in spades, then clubs, then diamonds, then hearts. Shuffle the pack n times by Monge's system and then cut them any number of times. (Instead of cutting, one may perform a false shuffling, which consists in appearing to shuffle while actually forming a succession of cuts.) Then the cards are dealt out into 4 rows of 13 cards.

Now we may either guess the position of a given card, or tell what card occupies a certain position. To do this we must cheat a little — just a peek at the bottom card. Suppose that the bottom card is the 7 of diamonds, and that the cards have been shuffled 3 times. The initial position of this card was $2 \cdot 13 + 7 = 33$. As a result of the shufflings its position was successively $(52 + 34) \div 2 = 43$, $(52 + 44) \div 2 = 48$, $(52 - 46) \div 2 = 3$. Since after the cutting the card appeared at the bottom, that is, in the 52nd place, the effect of the cuts has been to shift every card back 49 places, or forward 3 places.

Now we can answer any question of either sort. Suppose we wish to know the location of the jack of hearts. Its initial position was 11. Its successive positions after the shufflings were $(52 + 12) \div 2 = 32$, $(52 - 30) \div 2 = 11$, $(52 + 12) \div 2 = 32$. Raising its position 3 places to take account

of the cuts, we find that it occupies the 29th position, that
is, it lies in the third row and third column.

Suppose we wish to determine which card is the second in
the fourth row. Its final position is then $3 \cdot 13 + 2 = 41$.
Before cutting, its position was $41 + 3 = 44$. Before the
third shuffling its position was $2 \cdot 44 - 52 - 1 = 35$; before
the second shuffling, $2 \cdot 35 - 52 - 1 = 17$, before the first
shuffling, $52 - 2 \cdot 17 + 2 = 20$. Hence it was the 7 of clubs.

15. Offer a pack of n cards to a person and ask him to note
the position x of one of the first m of them. Deal out the
first m cards and pick them up so as to invert their order.
Cut the deck so as to bring y cards from the bottom to the
top. The position of the selected card is now $y + m - x + 1$.
Now deal off the cards, telling the victim to start counting
to himself at the $(x + 1)$th card and to stop you at the $(y + m + 1)$th card. The card dealt out at that moment is the
chosen card.

57. The false coin. The general enunciation of this problem is the following: We have N coins one of which is lighter or heavier than the other, all identical. We are asked to identify the false coin and find its defect by n balancings using an ordinary scale.

We shall use the following notations: The coins are $A, B, C \ldots$ and we write $A > 0$ to say that the coin A is heavier than the other, $A < 0$ is a lighter coin, $A = 0$ is a good coin.

We shall consider the following 3 problems.

1. $N = 4$, and in addition we have 3 good coins. By $n = 2$ balancings we can identify the false coin and find its defect.

Let A, B, C, D be the 4 coins and a, b, c the 3 good coins. We balance ABC and abc and then A and B or A and D. The following events may occur:

$ABC > abc$	,	$A > B$	then	$A > 0$
		$A < B$		$B > 0$
		$A = B$		$C > 0$
$ABC < abc$		$A > B$		$B < 0$
		$A < B$		$A < 0$
		$A = B$		$C < 0$
$ABC = abc$		$A > D$		$D < 0$
		$A < D$		$D > 0$

There are 8 possible cases, each coin may be the false one and lighter or heavier than the other.

2. There are 9 coins one of which is heavier than the other. We can identify it by 2 balancing.

We distribute the 9 coins in 3 groups and we balance 2 groups. If A, B, C are the 3 groups, we balance 2 groups, A and B.

If $A > B$, the group A contains the false coin
    $A < B$ "   " B "   "   "   "
    $A = B$ "   " C "   "   "   "

Hence we can identify the group of 3 coins which contains the false one. If a, b, c are the 3 coins of that group we compare in a second balancing the coins a and b.

If $a>b$, a is the false coin

$\quad a<b$ b " " " "

$\quad a=b$ c " " " "

The solution is similar if the false coin is lighter than the other.

In the case of $N = 3^n$ coins we need n balancings in order to identify the false coin. The same number of balancings is required if $3^{n-1}<N<3^n$.

3. We have 12 coins and we are asked to identify the false coin and find its defect by 3 balancings.

We distribute the 12 coins, $A, B, C \ldots$ in 3 groups: $ABCD, EFGH, IJKL$.

First balancing	Second balancing	Third balancing	Conclusion
$ABCD>EFGH$	$ABE>CDF$	$A>B$	$A>0$
		$A<B$	$B>0$
		$A=B$	$F<0$
	$ABE<CDF$	$C>D$	$C>0$
		$C<D$	$D>0$
		$C=D$	$E<0$
	$ABE=CDF$	$G>H$	$H<0$
		$G<H$	$G<0$
$ABCD<EFGH$	$ABE>CDF$	$C>D$	$D<0$
		$C<D$	$C<0$
		$C=D$	$E>0$
	$ABE<CDF$	$A>B$	$B<0$
		$A<B$	$A<0$
		$A=B$	$F>0$
	$ABE=CDF$	$G>H$	$G>0$
		$G<H$	$H>0$

$ABCD = EFGH$. The false coin is in the third group. That is the problem 1, which we achieve by 2 balancings. With $N = \frac{1}{2}(3^n - 3)$ coins n balancings are needed.

INDEX

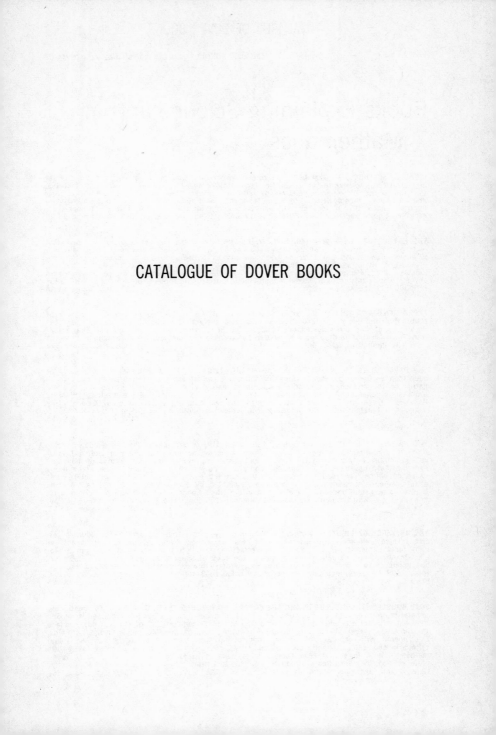

CATALOGUE OF DOVER BOOKS

Books Explaining Science and Mathematics

WHAT IS SCIENCE?, N. Campbell. The role of experiment and measurement, the function of mathematics, the nature of scientific laws, the difference between laws and theories, the limitations of science, and many similarly provocative topics are treated clearly and without technicalities by an eminent scientist. "Still an excellent introduction to scientific philosophy," H. Margenau in PHYSICS TODAY. "A first-rate primer . . . deserves a wide audience," SCIENTIFIC AMERICAN. 192pp. 5⅜ x 8.   S43 Paperbound **$1.25**

THE NATURE OF PHYSICAL THEORY, P. W. Bridgman. A Nobel Laureate's clear, non-technical lectures on difficulties and paradoxes connected with frontier research on the physical sciences. Concerned with such central concepts as thought, logic, mathematics, relativity, probability, wave mechanics, etc. he analyzes the contributions of such men as Newton, Einstein, Bohr, Heisenberg, and many others. "Lucid and entertaining . . . recommended to anyone who wants to get some insight into current philosophies of science," THE NEW PHILOSOPHY. Index. xi + 138pp. 5⅜ x 8.   S33 Paperbound **$1.25**

EXPERIMENT AND THEORY IN PHYSICS, Max Born. A Nobel Laureate examines the nature of experiment and theory in theoretical physics and analyzes the advances made by the great physicists of our day: Heisenberg, Einstein, Bohr, Planck, Dirac, and others. The actual process of creation is detailed step-by-step by one who participated. A fine examination of the scientific method at work. 44pp. 5⅜ x 8.   S308 Paperbound **75¢**

THE PSYCHOLOGY OF INVENTION IN THE MATHEMATICAL FIELD, J. Hadamard. The reports of such men as Descartes, Pascal, Einstein, Poincaré, and others are considered in this investigation of the method of idea-creation in mathematics and other sciences and the thinking process in general. How do ideas originate? What is the role of the unconscious? What is Poincaré's forgetting hypothesis? are some of the fascinating questions treated. A penetrating analysis of Einstein's thought processes concludes the book. xiii + 145pp. 5⅜ x 8.   T107 Paperbound **$1.25**

THE NATURE OF LIGHT AND COLOUR IN THE OPEN AIR, M. Minnaert. Why are shadows sometimes blue, sometimes green, or other colors depending on the light and surroundings? What causes mirages? Why do multiple suns and moons appear in the sky? Professor Minnaert explains these unusual phenomena and hundreds of others in simple, easy-to-understand terms based on optical laws and the properties of light and color. No mathematics is required but artists, scientists, students, and everyone fascinated by these "tricks" of nature will find thousands of useful and amazing pieces of information. Hundreds of observational experiments are suggested which require no special equipment. 200 illustrations; 42 photos. xvi + 362pp. 5⅜ x 8.   T196 Paperbound **$1.95**

THE UNIVERSE OF LIGHT, W. Bragg. Sir William Bragg, Nobel Laureate and great modern physicist, is also well known for his powers of clear exposition. Here he analyzes all aspects of light for the layman: lenses, reflection, refraction, the optics of vision, x-rays, the photoelectric effect, etc. He tells you what causes the color of spectra, rainbows, and soap bubbles, how magic mirrors work, and much more. Dozens of simple experiments are described. Preface. Index. 199 line drawings and photographs, including 2 full-page color plates. x + 283pp. 5⅜ x 8.   T538 Paperbound **$1.85**

SOAP-BUBBLES: THEIR COLOURS AND THE FORCES THAT MOULD THEM, C. V. Boys. For continuing popularity and validity as scientific primer, few books can match this volume of easily-followed experiments, explanations. Lucid exposition of complexities of liquid films, surface tension and related phenomena, bubbles' reaction to heat, motion, music, magnetic fields. Experiments with capillary attraction, soap bubbles on frames, composite bubbles, liquid cylinders and jets, bubbles other than soap, etc. Wonderful introduction to scientific method; natural laws that have many ramifications in areas of modern physics. Only complete edition in print. New Introduction by S. Z. Lewin, New York University. 83 illustrations; 1 full-page color plate. xii + 190pp. 5⅜ x 8½.   T542 Paperbound **95¢**

CATALOGUE OF DOVER BOOKS

THE STORY OF X-RAYS FROM RONTGEN TO ISOTOPES, A. R. Bleich, M.D. This book, by a member of the American College of Radiology, gives the scientific explanation of x-rays, their applications in medicine, industry and art, and their danger (and that of atmospheric radiation) to the individual and the species. You learn how radiation therapy is applied against cancer, how x-rays diagnose heart disease and other ailments, how they are used to examine mummies for information on diseases of early societies, and industrial materials for hidden weaknesses. 54 illustrations show x-rays of flowers, bones, stomach, gears with flaws, etc. 1st publication. Index. xix + 186pp. 5⅜ x 8. T622 Paperbound **$1.35**

SPINNING TOPS AND GYROSCOPIC MOTION, John Perry. A classic elementary text of the dynamics of rotation — the behavior and use of rotating bodies such as gyroscopes and tops. In simple, everyday English you are shown how quasi-rigidity is induced in discs of paper, smoke rings, chains, etc., by rapid motions; why a gyrostat falls and why a top rises; precession; how the earth's motion affects climate; and many other phenomena. Appendix on practical use of gyroscopes. 62 figures. 128pp. 5⅜ x 8. T416 Paperbound **$1.00**

SNOW CRYSTALS, W. A. Bentley, M. J. Humphreys. For almost 50 years W. A. Bentley photographed snow flakes in his laboratory in Jericho, Vermont; in 1931 the American Meteorological Society gathered together the best of his work, some 2400 photographs of snow flakes, plus a few ice flowers, windowpane frosts, dew, frozen rain, and other ice formations. Pictures were selected for beauty and scientific value. A very valuable work to anyone in meteorology, cryology; most interesting to layman; extremely useful for artist who wants beautiful, crystalline designs. All copyright free. Unabridged reprint of 1931 edition. 2453 illustrations. 227pp. 8 x 10½. T287 Paperbound **$3.00**

A DOVER SCIENCE SAMPLER, edited by George Barkin. A collection of brief, non-technical passages from 44 Dover Books Explaining Science for the enjoyment of the science-minded browser. Includes work of Bertrand Russell, Poincaré, Laplace, Max Born, Galileo, Newton; material on physics, mathematics, metallurgy, anatomy, astronomy, chemistry, etc. You will be fascinated by Martin Gardner's analysis of the sincere pseudo-scientist, Moritz's account of Newton's absentmindedness, Bernard's examples of human vivisection, etc. Illustrations from the Diderot Pictorial Encyclopedia and De Re Metallica. 64 pages. **FREE**

THE STORY OF ATOMIC THEORY AND ATOMIC ENERGY, J. G. Feinberg. A broader approach to subject of nuclear energy and its cultural implications than any other similar source. Very readable, informal, completely non-technical text. Begins with first atomic theory, 600 B.C. and carries you through the work of Mendelejeff, Röntgen, Madame Curie, to Einstein's equation and the A-bomb. New chapter goes through thermonuclear fission, binding energy, other events up to 1959. Radioactive decay and radiation hazards, future benefits, work of Bohr, moderns, hundreds more topics. "Deserves special mention . . . not only authoritative but thoroughly popular in the best sense of the word," Saturday Review. Formerly, "The Atom Story." Expanded with new chapter. Three appendixes. Index. 34 illustrations. vii + 243pp. 5⅜ x 8. T625 Paperbound **$1.45**

THE STRANGE STORY OF THE QUANTUM, AN ACCOUNT FOR THE GENERAL READER OF THE GROWTH OF IDEAS UNDERLYING OUR PRESENT ATOMIC KNOWLEDGE, B. Hoffmann. Presents lucidly and expertly, with barest amount of mathematics, the problems and theories which led to modern quantum physics. Dr. Hoffmann begins with the closing years of the 19th century, when certain trifling discrepancies were noticed, and with illuminating analogies and examples takes you through the brilliant concepts of Planck, Einstein, Pauli, Broglie, Bohr, Schroedinger, Heisenberg, Dirac, Sommerfeld, Feynman, etc. This edition includes a new, long postscript carrying the story through 1958. "Of the books attempting an account of the history and contents of our modern atomic physics which have come to my attention, this is the best," H. Margenau, Yale University, in "American Journal of Physics." 32 tables and line illustrations. Index. 275pp. 5⅜ x 8. T518 Paperbound **$1.50**

SPACE AND TIME, E. Borel. Written by a versatile mathematician of world renown with his customary lucidity and precision, this introduction to relativity for the layman presents scores of examples, analogies, and illustrations that open up new ways of thinking about space and time. It covers abstract geometry and geographical maps, continuity and topology, the propagation of light, the special theory of relativity, the general theory of relativity, theoretical researches, and much more. Mathematical notes. 2 Indexes. 4 Appendices. 15 figures. xvi + 243pp. 5⅜ x 8. T592 Paperbound **$1.45**

FROM EUCLID TO EDDINGTON: A STUDY OF THE CONCEPTIONS OF THE EXTERNAL WORLD, Sir Edmund Whittaker. A foremost British scientist traces the development of theories of natural philosophy from the western rediscovery of Euclid to Eddington, Einstein, Dirac, etc. The inadequacy of classical physics is contrasted with present day attempts to understand the physical world through relativity, non-Euclidean geometry, space curvature, wave mechanics, etc. 5 major divisions of examination: Space; Time and Movement; the Concepts of Classical Physics; the Concepts of Quantum Mechanics; the Eddington Universe. 212pp. 5⅜ x 8. T491 Paperbound **$1.35**

CATALOGUE OF DOVER BOOKS

BRIDGES AND THEIR BUILDERS, D. B. Steinman & S. R. Watson. Engineers, historians, and every person who has ever been fascinated by great spans will find this book an endless source of information and interest. Greek and Roman structures, Medieval bridges, modern classics such as the Brooklyn Bridge, and the latest developments in the science are retold by one of the world's leading authorities on bridge design and construction. BRIDGES AND THEIR BUILDERS is the only comprehensive and accurate semi-popular history of these important measures of progress in print. New, greatly revised, enlarged edition. 23 photos; 26 line-drawings. Index. xvii + 401pp. 5⅜ x 8. T431 Paperbound **$2.00**

FAMOUS BRIDGES OF THE WORLD, D. B. Steinman. An up-to-the-minute new edition of a book that explains the fascinating drama of how the world's great bridges came to be built. The author, designer of the famed Mackinac bridge, discusses bridges from all periods and all parts of the world, explaining their various types of construction, and describing the problems their builders faced. Although primarily for youngsters, this cannot fail to interest readers of all ages. 48 illustrations in the text. 23 photographs. 99pp. 6⅛ x 9¼. T161 Paperbound **$1.00**

HOW DO YOU USE A SLIDE RULE? by A. A. Merrill. A step-by-step explanation of the slide rule that presents the fundamental rules clearly enough for the non-mathematician to understand. Unlike most instruction manuals, this work concentrates on the two most important operations: multiplication and division. 10 easy lessons, each with a clear drawing, for the reader who has difficulty following other expositions. 1st publication. Index. 2 Appendices. 10 illustrations. 78 problems, all with answers. vi + 36 pp. 6⅛ x 9¼. T62 Paperbound **60¢**

HOW TO CALCULATE QUICKLY, H. Sticker. A tried and true method for increasing your "number sense" — the ability to see relationships between numbers and groups of numbers. Addition, subtraction, multiplication, division, fractions, and other topics are treated through techniques not generally taught in schools: left to right multiplication, division by inspection, etc. This is not a collection of tricks which work only on special numbers, but a detailed well-planned course, consisting of over 9,000 problems that you can work in spare moments. It is excellent for anyone who is inconvenienced by slow computational skills. 5 or 10 minutes of this book daily will double or triple your calculation speed. 9,000 problems, answers. 256pp. 5⅜ x 8. T295 Paperbound **$1.00**

MATHEMATICAL FUN, GAMES AND PUZZLES, Jack Frohlichstein. A valuable service for parents of children who have trouble with math, for teachers in need of a supplement to regular upper elementary and junior high math texts (each section is graded—easy, average, difficult —for ready adaptation to different levels of ability), and for just anyone who would like to develop basic skills in an informal and entertaining manner. The author combines ten years of experience as a junior high school math teacher with a method that uses puzzles and games to introduce the basic ideas and operations of arithmetic. Stress on everyday uses of math: banking, stock market, personal budgets, insurance, taxes. Intellectually stimulating and practical, too. 418 problems and diversions with answers. Bibliography. 120 illustrations. xix + 306pp. 5⅝ x 8½. T789 Paperbound **$1.75**

GREAT IDEAS OF MODERN MATHEMATICS: THEIR NATURE AND USE, Jagjit Singh. Reader with only high school math will understand main mathematical ideas of modern physics, astronomy, genetics, psychology, evolution, etc. better than many who use them as tools, but comprehend little of their basic structure. Author uses his wide knowledge of non-mathematical fields in brilliant exposition of differential equations, matrices, group theory, logic, statistics, problems of mathematical foundations, imaginary numbers, vectors, etc. Original publication. 2 appendixes. 2 indexes. 65 illustr. 322pp. 5⅜ x 8. S587 Paperbound **$1.75**

***MATHEMATICS IN ACTION, O. G. Sutton.** Everyone with a command of high school algebra will find this book one of the finest possible introductions to the application of mathematics to physical theory. Ballistics, numerical analysis, waves and wavelike phenomena, Fourier series, group concepts, fluid flow and aerodynamics, statistical measures, and meteorology are discussed with unusual clarity. Some calculus and differential equations theory is developed by the author for the reader's help in the more difficult sections. 88 figures. Index. viii + 236pp. 5⅜ x 8. T440 Clothbound **$3.50**

***INTRODUCTION TO SYMBOLIC LOGIC AND ITS APPLICATIONS, Rudolph Carnap.** One of the clearest, most comprehensive, and rigorous introductions to modern symbolic logic, by perhaps its greatest living master. Not merely elementary theory, but demonstrated applications in mathematics, physics, and biology. Symbolic languages of various degrees of complexity are analyzed, and one constructed. "A creation of the rank of a masterpiece," Zentralblatt für Mathematik und Ihre Grenzgebiete. Over 300 exercises. 5 figures. Bibliography. Index. xvi + 241pp. 5⅜ x 8. S453 Paperbound **$1.85**

***HIGHER MATHEMATICS FOR STUDENTS OF CHEMISTRY AND PHYSICS, J. W. Mellor.** Not abstract, but practical, drawing its problems from familiar laboratory material, this book covers theory and application of differential calculus, analytic geometry, functions with singularities, integral calculus, infinite series, solution of numerical equations, differential equations, Fourier's theorem and extensions, probability and the theory of errors, calculus of variations, determinants, etc. "If the reader is not familiar with this book, it will repay him to examine it," CHEM. & ENGINEERING NEWS. 800 problems. 189 figures. 2 appendices; 30 tables of integrals, probability functions, etc. Bibliography. xxi + 641pp. 5⅜ x 8. S193 Paperbound **$2.25**

Entertainments, Humor

ODDITIES AND CURIOSITIES OF WORDS AND LITERATURE, C. Bombaugh, edited by M. Gardner. The largest collection of idiosyncratic prose and poetry techniques in English, a legendary work in the curious and amusing bypaths of literary recreations and the play technique in literature—so important in modern works. Contains alphabetic poetry, acrostics, palindromes, scissors verse, centos, emblematic poetry, famous literary puns, hoaxes, notorious slips of the press, hilarious mistranslations, and much more. Revised and enlarged with modern material by Martin Gardner. 368pp. 5⅜ x 8.   T759 Paperbound **$1.50**

A NONSENSE ANTHOLOGY, collected by Carolyn Wells. 245 of the best nonsense verses ever written, including nonsense puns, absurd arguments, mock epics and sagas, nonsense ballads, odes, "sick" verses, dog-Latin verses, French nonsense verses, songs. By Edward Lear, Lewis Carroll, Gelett Burgess, W. S. Gilbert, Hilaire Belloc, Peter Newell, Oliver Herford, etc., 83 writers in all plus over four score anonymous nonsense verses. A special section of limericks, plus famous nonsense such as Carroll's "Jabberwocky" and Lear's "The Jumblies" and much excellent verse virtually impossible to locate elsewhere. For 50 years considered the best anthology available. Index of first lines specially prepared for this edition. Introduction by Carolyn Wells. 3 indexes: Title, Author, First lines. xxxiii + 279pp.
T499 Paperbound **$1.35**

THE BAD CHILD'S BOOK OF BEASTS, MORE BEASTS FOR WORSE CHILDREN, and A MORAL ALPHABET, H. Belloc. Hardly an anthology of humorous verse has appeared in the last 50 years without at least a couple of these famous nonsense verses. But one must see the entire volumes—with all the delightful original illustrations by Sir Basil Blackwood—to appreciate fully Belloc's charming and witty verses that play so subacidly on the platitudes of life and morals that beset his day—and ours. A great humor classic. Three books in one. Total of 157pp. 5⅜ x 8.   T749 Paperbound **$1.00**

THE DEVIL'S DICTIONARY, Ambrose Bierce. Sardonic and irreverent barbs puncturing the pomposities and absurdities of American politics, business, religion, literature, and arts, by the country's greatest satirist in the classic tradition. Epigrammatic as Shaw, piercing as Swift, American as Mark Twain, Will Rogers, and Fred Allen, Bierce will always remain the favorite of a small coterie of enthusiasts, and of writers and speakers whom he supplies with "some of the most gorgeous witticisms of the English language" (H. L. Mencken). Over 1000 entries in alphabetical order. 144pp. 5⅜ x 8.   T487 Paperbound **$1.00**

THE PURPLE COW AND OTHER NONSENSE, Gelett Burgess. The best of Burgess's early nonsense, selected from the first edition of the "Burgess Nonsense Book." Contains many of his most unusual and truly awe-inspiring pieces: 36 nonsense quatrains, the Poems of Patagonia, Alphabet of Famous Goops, and the other hilarious (and rare) adult nonsense that place him in the forefront of American humorists. All pieces are accompanied by the original Burgess illustrations. 123 illustrations. xiii + 113pp. 5⅜ x 8.   T772 Paperbound **$1.00**

MY PIOUS FRIENDS AND DRUNKEN COMPANIONS and MORE PIOUS FRIENDS AND DRUNKEN COMPANIONS, Frank Shay. Folksingers, amateur and professional, and everyone who loves singing: here, available for the first time in 30 years, is this valued collection of 132 ballads, blues, vaudeville numbers, drinking songs, sea chanties, comedy songs. Songs of pre-Beatnik Bohemia; songs from all over America, England, France, Australia; the great songs of the Naughty Nineties and early twentieth-century America. Over a third with music. Woodcuts by John Held, Jr. convey perfectly the brash insouciance of an era of rollicking unabashed song. 12 illustrations by John Held, Jr. Two indexes (Titles and First lines and Choruses). Introductions by the author. Two volumes bound as one. Total of xvi + 235pp. 5⅜ x 8½.
T946 Paperbound **$1.00**

HOW TO TELL THE BIRDS FROM THE FLOWERS, R. W. Wood. How not to confuse a carrot with a parrot, a grape with an ape, a puffin with nuffin. Delightful drawings, clever puns, absurd little poems point out far-fetched resemblances in nature. The author was a leading physicist. Introduction by Margaret Wood White. 106 illus. 60pp. 5⅜ x 8.
T523 Paperbound **75¢**

PECK'S BAD BOY AND HIS PA, George W. Peck. The complete edition, containing both volumes, of one of the most widely read American humor books. The endless ingenious pranks played by bad boy "Hennery" on his pa and the grocery man, the outraged pomposity of Pa, the perpetual ridiculing of middle class institutions, are as entertaining today as they were in 1883. No pale sophistications or subtleties, but rather humor vigorous, raw, earthy, imaginative, and, as folk humor often is, sadistic. This peculiarly fascinating book is also valuable to historians and students of American culture as a portrait of an age. 100 original illustrations by True Williams. Introduction by E. F. Bleiler. 347pp. 5⅜ x 8.
T497 Paperbound **$1.35**

CATALOGUE OF DOVER BOOKS

THE HUMOROUS VERSE OF LEWIS CARROLL. Almost every poem Carroll ever wrote, the largest collection ever published, including much never published elsewhere: 150 parodies, burlesques, riddles, ballads, acrostics, etc., with 130 original illustrations by Tenniel, Carroll, and others. "Addicts will be grateful . . . there is nothing for the faithful to do but sit down and fall to the banquet," N. Y. Times. Index to first lines. xiv + 446pp. 5⅜ x 8.
T654 Paperbound **$1.85**

DIVERSIONS AND DIGRESSIONS OF LEWIS CARROLL. A major new treasure for Carroll fans! Rare privately published humor, fantasy, puzzles, and games by Carroll at his whimsical best, with a new vein of frank satire. Includes many new mathematical amusements and recreations, among them the fragmentary Part III of "Curiosa Mathematica." Contains "The Rectory Umbrella," "The New Belfry," "The Vision of the Three T's," and much more. New 32-page supplement of rare photographs taken by Carroll. x + 375pp. 5⅜ x 8.
T732 Paperbound **$1.65**

THE COMPLETE NONSENSE OF EDWARD LEAR. This is the only complete edition of this master of gentle madness available at a popular price. A BOOK OF NONSENSE, NONSENSE SONGS, MORE NONSENSE SONGS AND STORIES in their entirety with all the old favorites that have delighted children and adults for years. The Dong With A Luminous Nose, The Jumblies, The Owl and the Pussycat, and hundreds of other bits of wonderful nonsense. 214 limericks, 3 sets of Nonsense Botany, 5 Nonsense Alphabets, 546 drawings by Lear himself, and much more. 320pp. 5⅜ x 8.
T167 Paperbound **$1.00**

THE MELANCHOLY LUTE, The Humorous Verse of Franklin P. Adams ("FPA"). The author's own selection of light verse, drawn from thirty years of FPA's column, "The Conning Tower," syndicated all over the English-speaking world. Witty, perceptive, literate, these ninety-six poems range from parodies of other poets, Millay, Longfellow, Edgar Guest, Kipling, Masefield, etc., and free and hilarious translations of Horace and other Latin poets, to satiric comments on fabled American institutions—the New York Subways, preposterous ads, suburbanites, sensational journalism, etc. They reveal with vigor and clarity the humor, integrity and restraint of a wise and gentle American satirist. Introduction by Robert Hutchinson. vi + 122pp. 5⅜ x 8½.
T108 Paperbound **$1.00**

SINGULAR TRAVELS, CAMPAIGNS, AND ADVENTURES OF BARON MUNCHAUSEN, R. E. Raspe, with 90 illustrations by Gustave Doré. The first edition in over 150 years to reestablish the deeds of the Prince of Liars exactly as Raspe first recorded them in 1785—the genuine Baron Munchausen, one of the most popular personalities in English literature. Included also are the best of the many sequels, written by other hands. Introduction on Raspe by J. Carswell. Bibliography of early editions. xliv + 192pp. 5⅜ x 8.
T698 Paperbound **$1.00**

THE WIT AND HUMOR OF OSCAR WILDE, ed. by Alvin Redman. Wilde at his most brilliant, in 1000 epigrams exposing weaknesses and hypocrisies of "civilized" society. Divided into 49 categories—sin, wealth, women, America, etc.—to aid writers, speakers. Includes excerpts from his trials, books, plays, criticism. Formerly "The Epigrams of Oscar Wilde." Introduction by Vyvyan Holland, Wilde's only living son. Introductory essay by editor. 260pp. 5⅜ x 8.
T602 Paperbound **$1.00**

MAX AND MORITZ, Wilhelm Busch. Busch is one of the great humorists of all time, as well as the father of the modern comic strip. This volume, translated by H. A. Klein and other hands, contains the perennial favorite "Max and Moritz" (translated by C. T. Brooks), Plisch and Plum, Das Rabennest, Eispeter, and seven other whimsical, sardonic, jovial, diabolical cartoon and verse stories. Lively English translations parallel the original German. This work has delighted millions, since it first appeared in the 19th century, and is guaranteed to please almost anyone. Edited by H. A. Klein, with an afterword. x + 205pp. 5⅜ x 8½.
T181 Paperbound **$1.00**

HYPOCRITICAL HELENA, Wilhelm Busch. A companion volume to "Max and Moritz," with the title piece (Die Fromme Helena) and 10 other highly amusing cartoon and verse stories, all newly translated by H. A. Klein and M. C. Klein: Adventure on New Year's Eve (Abenteuer in der Neujahrsnacht), Hangover on the Morning after New Year's Eve (Der Katzenjammer am Neujahrsmorgen), etc. English and German in parallel columns. Hours of pleasure, also a fine language aid. x + 205pp. 5⅜ x 8½.
T184 Paperbound **$1.00**

THE BEAR THAT WASN'T, Frank Tashlin. What does it mean? Is it simply delightful wry humor, or a charming story of a bear who wakes up in the midst of a factory, or a satire on Big Business, or an existential cartoon-story of the human condition, or a symbolization of the struggle between conformity and the individual? New York Herald Tribune said of the first edition: ". . . a fable for grownups that will be fun for children. Sit down with the book and get your own bearings." Long an underground favorite with readers of all ages and opinions. v + 51pp. Illustrated. 5⅜ x 8½.
T939 Paperbound **75¢**

RUTHLESS RHYMES FOR HEARTLESS HOMES and MORE RUTHLESS RHYMES FOR HEARTLESS HOMES, Harry Graham ("Col. D. Streamer"). Two volumes of Little Willy and 48 other poetic disasters, A bright, new reprint of oft-quoted, never forgotten, devastating humor by a precursor of today's "sick" joke school. For connoisseurs of wicked, wacky humor and all who delight in the comedy of manners. Original drawings are a perfect complement. 61 illustrations. Index. vi + 69pp. Two vols. bound as one. 5⅜ x 8½.
T930 Paperbound **75¢**

Chess, Checkers, Games, Go

THE ADVENTURE OF CHESS, Edward Lasker. A lively history of chess, from its ancient beginnings in the Indian 4-handed game of Chaturanga, through to the great players of our day, as told by one of America's finest masters. He introduces such unusual sidelights and amusing oddities as Maelzel's chess-playing automaton that beat Napoleon 3 times. Major discussion of chess-playing machines and personal memories of Nimzovich, Capablanca, etc. 5-page chess primer. 11 illustrations, 53 diagrams. 296pp. 5⅜ x 8. **S510 Paperbound $1.45**

A TREASURY OF CHESS LORE, edited by Fred Reinfeld. A delightful collection of anecdotes, short stories, aphorisms by and about the masters, poems, accounts of games and tournaments, photography. Hundreds of humorous, pithy, satirical, wise, and historical episodes, comments, and word portraits. A fascinating "must" for chess players; revealing and perhaps seductive to those who wonder what their friends see in the game. 48 photographs (14 full page plates) 12 diagrams. xi + 306pp. 5⅜ x 8. **T458 Paperbound $1.75**

HOW DO YOU PLAY CHESS? by Fred Reinfeld. A prominent expert covers every basic rule of chess for the beginner in 86 questions and answers: moves, powers of pieces, rationale behind moves, how to play forcefully, history of chess, and much more. Bibliography of chess publications. 11 board diagrams. 48 pages. **FREE**

THE PLEASURES OF CHESS, Assiac. Internationally known British writer, influential chess columnist, writes wittily about wide variety of chess subjects: Anderssen's "Immortal Game;" only game in which both opponents resigned at once; psychological tactics of Reshevsky, Lasker; varieties played by masters for relaxation, such as "losing chess;" sacrificial orgies; etc. These anecdotes, witty observations will give you fresh appreciation of game. 43 problems. 150 diagrams. 139pp. 5⅜ x 8. **T597 Paperbound $1.25**

WIN AT CHESS, F. Reinfeld. 300 practical chess situations from actual tournament play to sharpen your chess eye and test your skill. Traps, sacrifices, mates, winning combinations, subtle exchanges, show you how to WIN AT CHESS. Short notes and tables of solutions and alternative moves help you evaluate your progress. Learn to think ahead playing the "crucial moments" of historic games. 300 diagrams. Notes and solutions. Formerly titled CHESS QUIZ. vi + 120pp. 5⅜ x 8. **T438 Paperbound $1.00**

THE ART OF CHESS, James Mason. An unabridged reprinting of the latest revised edition of the most famous general study of chess ever written. Also included, a complete supplement by Fred Reinfeld, "How Do You Play Chess?", invaluable to beginners for its lively question and answer method. Mason, an early 20th century master, teaches the beginning and intermediate player more than 90 openings, middle game, end game, how to see more moves ahead, to plan purposefully, attack, sacrifice, defend, exchange, and govern general strategy. Supplement. 448 diagrams. 1947 Reinfeld-Bernstein text. Bibliography. xvi + 340pp. 5⅜ x 8. **T463 Paperbound $1.85**

THE PRINCIPLES OF CHESS, James Mason. This "great chess classic" (N. Y. Times) is a general study covering all aspects of the game: basic forces, resistance, obstruction, opposition, relative values, mating, typical end game situations, combinations, much more. The last section discusses openings, with 50 games illustrating modern master play of Rubinstein, Spielmann, Lasker, Capablanca, etc., selected and annotated by Fred Reinfeld. Will improve the game of any intermediate-skilled player, but is so forceful and lucid that an absolute beginner might use it to become an accomplished player. 1946 Reinfeld edition. 166 diagrams. 378pp. 5⅜ x 8. **T646 Paperbound $1.85**

LASKER'S MANUAL OF CHESS, Dr. Emanuel Lasker. Probably the greatest chess player of modern times, Dr. Emanuel Lasker held the world championship 28 years, independent of passing schools or fashions. This unmatched study of the game, chiefly for intermediate to skilled players, analyzes basic methods, combinations, position play, the aesthetics of chess, dozens of different openings, etc., with constant reference to great modern games. Contains a brilliant exposition of Steinitz's important theories. Introduction by Fred Reinfeld. Tables of Lasker's tournament record. 3 indices. 308 diagrams. 1 photograph. xxx + 349pp. 5⅜ x 8. **T640 Paperbound $2.00**

THE ART OF CHESS COMBINATION, E. Znosko-Borovsky. Proves that combinations, perhaps the most aesthetically satisfying, successful technique in chess, can be an integral part of your game, instead of a haphazard occurrence. Games of Capablanca, Rubinstein, Nimzovich, Bird, etc. grouped according to common features, perceptively analyzed to show that every combination begins in certain simple ideas. Will help you to plan many moves ahead. Technical terms almost completely avoided. "In the teaching of chess he may claim to have no superior," P. W. Sergeant. Introduction. Exercises. Solutions. Index. 223pp. 5⅜ x 8. **T583 Paperbound $1.45**

CATALOGUE OF DOVER BOOKS

THE HASTINGS CHESS TOURNAMENT, 1895, edited by Horace F. Cheshire. This is the complete tournament book of the famous Hastings 1895 tournament. One of the most exciting tournaments ever to take place, it evoked the finest play from such players as Dr. Lasker, Steinitz, Tarrasch, Harry Pillsbury, Mason, Tchigorin, Schlecter, and others. It was not only extremely exciting as an event, it also created first-rate chess. This book contains fully annotated all 230 games, full information about the playing events, biographies of the players, and much other material that makes it a chess classic. 22 photos, 174 diagrams. x + 370pp. 5⅝ x 8½. T288 Paperbound **$2.00**

THE BOOK OF THE NOTTINGHAM INTERNATIONAL CHESS TOURNAMENT, 1936, Annotated by Dr. Alexander Alekhine. The Nottingham 1936 tournament is regarded by many chess enthusiasts as the greatest tournament of recent years. It brought together all the living former world champions, the current chess champion, and the future world champion: Dr. Lasker, Capablanca, Alekhine, Euwe, Botvinnik, and Reshevsky, Fine, Flohr, Tartakover, Vidmar, and Bogoljubov. The play was brilliant throughout. This volume contains all 105 of the games played, provided with the remarkable annotations of Alekhine. 1 illustration, 121 diagrams. xx + 291pp. 5⅜ x 8½. T189 Paperbound **$1.85**

CHESS FOR FUN AND CHESS FOR BLOOD, Edward Lasker. A genial, informative book by one of century's leading masters. Incisive comments on chess as a form of art and recreation, on how a master prepares for and plays a tournament. Best of all is author's move-by-move analysis of his game with Dr. Emanuel Lasker in 1924 World Tournament, a charming and thorough recreation of one of the great games in history: the author's mental processes; how his calculations were upset; how both players blundered; the surprising outcome. Who could not profit from this study-in-depth? For the enthusiast who likes to read about chess as well as play it. Corrected (1942) edition. Preface contains 8 letters to author about the fun of chess. 95 illustrations by Maximilian Mopp. 224pp. 5⅜ x 8½. T146 Paperbound **$1.25**

HOW NOT TO PLAY CHESS, Eugene A. Znosko-Borovsky. Sticking to a few well-chosen examples and explaining every step along the way, an outstanding chess expositor shows how to avoid playing a hit-or-miss game and instead develop general plans of action based on positional analysis: weak and strong squares, the notion of the controlled square, how to seize control of open lines, weak points in the pawn structure, and so on. Definition and illustration of typical chess mistakes plus 20 problems (from master games) added by Fred Reinfeld for the 1949 edition and a number of good-to-memorize tips make this a lucid book that can teach in a few hours what might otherwise take years to learn. 119pp. 5⅜ x 8. T920 Paperbound **$1.00**

THE SOVIET SCHOOL OF CHESS, A. Kotov and M. Yudovich. 128 master games, most unavailable elsewhere, by 51 outstanding players, including Botvinnik, Keres, Smyslov, Tal, against players like Capablanca, Euwe, Reshevsky. All carefully annotated, analyzed. Valuable biographical information about each player, early history of Russian chess, careers and contributions of Chigorin and Alekhine, development of Soviet school from 1920 to present with full over-all study of main features of its games, history of Russian chess literature. The most comprehensive work on Russian chess ever printed, the richest single sourcebook for up-to-date Russian theory and strategy. New introduction. Appendix of Russian Grandmasters, Masters, Master Composers. Two indexes (Players, Games). 30 photographs. 182 diagrams. vi + 390pp. 5⅜ x 8. T26 Paperbound **$2.00**

THE ART OF THE CHECKMATE, Georges Renaud and Victor Kahn. Two former national chess champions of France examine 127 games, identify 23 kinds of mate, and show the rationale for each. These include Legal's pseudo sacrifice, the double check, the smothered mate, Greco's mate, Morphy's mate, the mate of two bishops, two knights, many, many more. Analysis of ideas, not memorization problems. Review quizzes with answers help readers gauge progress. 80 quiz examples and solutions. 299 diagrams. vi + 208pp. T106 Paperbound **$1.35**

HOW TO SOLVE CHESS PROBLEMS, K. S. Howard. Full of practical suggestions for the fan or the beginner—who knows only the moves of the chessmen. Contains preliminary section and 58 two-move, 46 three-move, and 8 four-move problems composed by 27 outstanding American problem creators in the last 30 years. Explanation of all terms and exhaustive index. "Just what is wanted for the student," Brian Harley. 112 problems, solutions. vi +171pp. 5⅜ x 8. T748 Paperbound **$1.00**

CHESS STRATEGY, Edward Lasker. Keres, Fine, and other great players have acknowledged their debt to this book, which has taught just about the whole modern school how to play forcefully and intelligently. Covers fundamentals, general strategic principles, middle and end game, objects of attack, etc. Includes 48 dramatic games from master tournaments, all fully analyzed. "Best textbook I know in English," J. R. Capablanca. New introduction by author. Table of openings. Index. 167 illustrations. vii + 282pp. 5⅜ x 8. T528 Paperbound **$1.50**

REINFELD ON THE END GAME IN CHESS, F. Reinfeld. Formerly titled PRACTICAL END-GAME PLAY, this book contains clear, simple analyses of 62 end games by such masters as Alekhine, Tarrasch, Marshall, Morphy, Capablanca, and many others. Primary emphasis is on the general principles of transition from middle play to end play. This book is unusual in analyzing weak or incorrect moves to show how error occurs and how to avoid it. Covers king and pawn, minor piece, queen endings, weak squares, centralization, tempo moves, and many other vital factors. 62 diagrams. vi + 177pp. 5⅜ x 8. T417 Paperbound **$1.25**

CATALOGUE OF DOVER BOOKS

THE HASTINGS CHESS TOURNAMENT, 1895, edited by Horace F. Cheshire. This is the complete tournament book of the famous Hastings 1895 tournament. One of the most exciting tournaments ever to take place, it evoked the finest play from such players as Dr. Lasker, Steinitz, Tarrasch, Harry Pillsbury, Mason, Tchigorin, Schlecter, and others. It was not only extremely exciting as an event, it also created first-rate chess. This book contains fully annotated all 230 games, full information about the playing events, biographies of the players, and much other material that makes it a chess classic. 22 photos, 174 diagrams. x + 370pp. 5⅝ x 8½. T288 Paperbound **$2.00**

THE BOOK OF THE NOTTINGHAM INTERNATIONAL CHESS TOURNAMENT, 1936, Annotated by Dr. Alexander Alekhine. The Nottingham 1936 tournament is regarded by many chess enthusiasts as the greatest tournament of recent years. It brought together all the living former world champions, the current chess champion, and the future world champion: Dr. Lasker, Capablanca, Alekhine, Euwe, Botvinnik, and Reshevsky, Fine, Flohr, Tartakover, Vidmar, and Bogoljubov. The play was brilliant throughout. This volume contains all 105 of the games played, provided with the remarkable annotations of Alekhine. 1 illustration, 121 diagrams. xx + 291pp. 5⅝ x 8½. T189 Paperbound **$1.85**

CHESS FOR FUN AND CHESS FOR BLOOD, Edward Lasker. A genial, informative book by one of century's leading masters. Incisive comments on chess as a form of art and recreation, on how a master prepares for and plays a tournament. Best of all is author's move-by-move analysis of his game with Dr. Emanuel Lasker in 1924 World Tournament, a charming and thorough recreation of one of the great games in history: the author's mental processes; how his calculations were upset; how both players blundered; the surprising outcome. Who could not profit from this study-in-depth? For the enthusiast who likes to read about chess as well as play it. Corrected (1942) edition. Preface contains 8 letters to author about the fun of chess. 95 illustrations by Maximilian Mopp. 224pp. 5⅜ x 8½. T146 Paperbound **$1.25**

HOW NOT TO PLAY CHESS, Eugene A. Znosko-Borovsky. Sticking to a few well-chosen examples and explaining every step along the way, an outstanding chess expositor shows how to avoid playing a hit-or-miss game and instead develop general plans of action based on positional analysis: weak and strong squares, the notion of the controlled square, how to seize control of open lines, weak points in the pawn structure, and so on. Definition and illustration of typical chess mistakes plus 20 problems (from master games) added by Fred Reinfeld for the 1949 edition and a number of good-to-memorize tips make this a lucid book that can teach in a few hours what might otherwise take years to learn. 119pp. 5⅜ x 8. T920 Paperbound **$1.00**

THE SOVIET SCHOOL OF CHESS, A. Kotov and M. Yudovich. 128 master games, most unavailable elsewhere, by 51 outstanding players, including Botvinnik, Keres, Smyslov, Tal, against players like Capablanca, Euwe, Reshevsky. All carefully annotated, analyzed. Valuable biographical information about each player, early history of Russian chess, careers and contributions of Chigorin and Alekhine, development of Soviet school from 1920 to present with full over-all study of main features of its games, history of Russian chess literature. The most comprehensive work on Russian chess ever printed, the richest single sourcebook for up-to-date Russian theory and strategy. New introduction. Appendix of Russian Grandmasters, Masters, Master Composers. Two indexes (Players, Games). 30 photographs. 182 diagrams. vi + 390pp. 5⅜ x 8. T26 Paperbound **$2.00**

THE ART OF THE CHECKMATE, Georges Renaud and Victor Kahn. Two former national chess champions of France examine 127 games, identify 23 kinds of mate, and show the rationale for each. These include Legal's pseudo sacrifice, the double check, the smothered mate, Greco's mate, Morphy's mate, the mate of two bishops, two knights, many, many more. Analysis of ideas, not memorization problems. Review quizzes with answers help readers gauge progress. 80 quiz examples and solutions. 299 diagrams. vi + 208pp. T106 Paperbound **$1.35**

HOW TO SOLVE CHESS PROBLEMS, K. S. Howard. Full of practical suggestions for the fan or the beginner—who knows only the moves of the chessmen. Contains preliminary section and 58 two-move, 46 three-move, and 8 four-move problems composed by 27 outstanding American problem creators in the last 30 years. Explanation of all terms and exhaustive index. "Just what is wanted for the student," Brian Harley. 112 problems, solutions. vi +171pp. 5⅜ x 8. T748 Paperbound **$1.00**

CHESS STRATEGY, Edward Lasker. Keres, Fine, and other great players have acknowledged their debt to this book, which has taught just about the whole modern school how to play forcefully and intelligently. Covers fundamentals, general strategic principles, middle and end game, objects of attack, etc. Includes 48 dramatic games from master tournaments, all fully analyzed. "Best textbook I know in English," J. R. Capablanca. New introduction by author. Table of openings. Index. 167 illustrations. vii + 282pp. 5⅜ x 8. T528 Paperbound **$1.50**

REINFELD ON THE END GAME IN CHESS, F. Reinfeld. Formerly titled PRACTICAL END-GAME PLAY, this book contains clear, simple analyses of 62 end games by such masters as Alekhine, Tarrasch, Marshall, Morphy, Capablanca, and many others. Primary emphasis is on the general principles of transition from middle play to end play. This book is unusual in analyzing weak or incorrect moves to show how error occurs and how to avoid it. Covers king and pawn, minor piece, queen endings, weak squares, centralization, tempo moves, and many other vital factors. 62 diagrams. vi + 177pp. 5⅜ x 8. T417 Paperbound **$1.25**

CATALOGUE OF DOVER BOOKS

THE AMERICAN TWO-MOVE CHESS PROBLEM, Kenneth S. Howard. One of this country's foremost contemporary problem composers selects an interesting, diversified collection of the best two-movers by 58 top American composers. Involving complete blocks, mutates, line openings and closings, other unusual moves, these problems will help almost any player improve his strategic approach. Probably has no equal for all around artistic excellence, surprising keymoves, interesting strategy. Includes 30-page history of development of American two-mover from Loyd, its founder, to the present. Index of composers. vii + 99pp. 5⅜ x 8½.
T997 Paperbound **$1.00**

WIN AT CHECKERS, M. Hopper. (Formerly CHECKERS). The former World's Unrestricted Checker Champion discusses the principles cf the game, expert's shots and traps, problems for the beginner, standard openings, locating your best move, the end game, opening "blitzkrieg" moves, ways to draw when you are behind your opponent, etc. More than 100 detailed questions and answers anticipate your problems. Appendix. 75 problems with solutions and diagrams. Index. 79 figures. xi + 107pp. 5⅜ x 8.
T363 Paperbound **$1.00**

GAMES ANCIENT AND ORIENTAL, AND HOW TO PLAY THEM, E. Falkener. A connoisseur's selection of exciting and different games: Oriental varieties of chess, with unusual pieces and moves (including Japanese shogi); the original pachisi; go; reconstructions of lost Roman and Egyptian games; and many more. Full rules and sample games. Now play at home the games that have entertained millions, not on a fad basis, but for millennia. 345 illustrations and figures. iv + 366pp. 5⅜ x 8.
T739 Paperbound **$2.00**

GO AND GO-MOKU, Edward Lasker. A fascinating Oriental game, Go, is winning new devotees in America daily. Rules that you can learn in a few minutes—a wealth of combinations that makes it more profound than chess! This is an easily followed step-by-step explanation of this 2000-year-old game, beginning with fundamentals. New chapter on advanced strategy in this edition! Also contains rules for Go-Moku, a very easy sister game. 72 diagrams. xix + 215pp. 5⅜ x 8.
T613 Paperbound **$1.50**

HOW TO FORCE CHECKMATE, F. Reinfeld. Formerly titled CHALLENGE TO CHESSPLAYERS, this is an invaluable collection of 300 lightning strokes selected from actual masters' play, which will demonstrate how to smash your opponent's game with strong decisive moves. No board needed — clear, practical diagrams and easy-to-understand solutions. Learn to plan up to three moves ahead and play a superior end game. 300 diagrams. 111pp. 5⅜ x 8.
T439 Paperbound **$1.25**

CHESSBOARD MAGIC! A COLLECTION OF 160 BRILLIANT ENDINGS, I. Chernev. Contains 160 endgame compositions, all illustrating not only ingenuity of composition, but inherent beauty of solution. In one, five Knights are needed to force mate; in another White forces stalemate though Black finishes eight passed pawns ahead; 150 more, all remarkable, all will sharpen your imagination and increase your skill. "Inexhaustible source of entertainment, an endless feast of delight," Reuben Fine, Grandmaster. Introduction. 160 diagrams. Index of composers. vii + 172pp. 5⅜ x 8.
T607 Paperbound **$1.00**

LEARN CHESS FROM THE MASTERS, F. Reinfeld. Formerly titled CHESS BY YOURSELF, this book contains 10 games which you play against such masters as Marshall, Bronstein, Najdorf, and others, and an easy system for grading each move you make against a variety of other possible moves. Detailed annotations reveal the principles of the game through actual play. 91 diagrams. viii + 144pp. 5⅜ x 8.
T362 Paperbound **$1.00**

MORPHY'S GAMES OF CHESS, edited by Philip W. Sergeant. You can put boldness into your game by following the brilliant, forceful moves of the man who has been called the greatest chess player of all time. Here are 300 of Morphy's best games carefully annotated to reveal Morphy's principles. 54 classics against masters like Anderssen, Harrwitz, Bird, Paulsen, and others. 52 games at odds; 54 blindfold games; plus over 100 others. Unabridged reissue of the latest revised edition. Bibliography. New introduction by Fred Reinfeld. Annotations and introduction by Sergeant. Index. 235 diagrams. x + 352pp. 5⅜ x 8. T386 Paperbound **$1.75**

CHESS PRAXIS, Aron Nimzovich. Nimzovich was the stormy petrel of chess in the first decades of this century, and his system, known as hypermodern chess, revolutionized all play since his time. Casting aside the classical chess theory of Steinitz and Tarrasch, he created his own analysis of chess, considering dynamic patterns as they emerge during play. This is the fullest exposition of his ideas, and it is easily one of the dozen greatest books ever written on chess. Nimzovich illustrates each of his principles with at least two games, and shows how he applied his concepts successfully in games against such masters as Alekhine, Tarrasch, Reti, Rubinstein, Capablanca, Spielmann and others. Indispensable to every serious chess player. Translated by J. DuMont. 135 diagrams, 1 photo. xi + 364pp. 5½ x 8⅝.
T296 Paperbound **$2.00**

CHESS AND CHECKERS: THE WAY TO MASTERSHIP, Edward Lasker. Complete, lucid instructions for the beginner—and valuable suggestions for the advanced player! For both games the great master and teacher presents fundamentals, elementary tactics, and steps toward becoming a superior player. He concentrates on general principles rather than a mass of rules, comprehension rather than brute memory. Historical introduction. 118 diagrams. xiv + 167pp. 5⅜ x 8.
T657 Paperbound **$1.15**

Puzzles, Mathematical Recreations

SYMBOLIC LOGIC and THE GAME OF LOGIC, Lewis Carroll. "Symbolic Logic" is not concerned with modern symbolic logic, but is instead a collection of over 380 problems posed with charm and imagination, using the syllogism, and a fascinating diagrammatic method of drawing conclusions. In "The Game of Logic" Carroll's whimsical imagination devises a logical game played with 2 diagrams and counters (included) to manipulate hundreds of tricky syllogisms. The final section, "Hit or Miss" is a lagniappe of 101 additional puzzles in the delightful Carroll manner. Until this reprint edition, both of these books were rarities costing up to $15 each. Symbolic Logic: Index. xxxi + 199pp. The Game of Logic: 96pp. 2 vols. bound as one. 5⅜ x 8.   **T492 Paperbound $1.50**

PILLOW PROBLEMS and A TANGLED TALE, Lewis Carroll. One of the rarest of all Carroll's works, "Pillow Problems" contains 72 original math puzzles, all typically ingenious. Particularly fascinating are Carroll's answers which remain exactly as he thought them out, reflecting his actual mental process. The problems in "A Tangled Tale" are in story form, originally appearing as a monthly magazine serial. Carroll not only gives the solutions, but uses answers sent in by readers to discuss wrong approaches and misleading paths, and grades them for insight. Both of these books were rarities until this edition, "Pillow Problems" costing up to $25, and "A Tangled Tale" $15. Pillow Problems: Preface and Introduction by Lewis Carroll. xx + 109pp. A Tangled Tale: 6 illustrations. 152pp. Two vols. bound as one. 5⅜ x 8.   **T493 Paperbound $1.50**

AMUSEMENTS IN MATHEMATICS, Henry Ernest Dudeney. The foremost British originator of mathematical puzzles is always intriguing, witty, and paradoxical in this classic, one of the largest collections of mathematical amusements. More than 430 puzzles, problems, and paradoxes. Mazes and games, problems on number manipulation, unicursal and other route problems, puzzles on measuring, weighing, packing, age, kinship, chessboards, joiners', crossing river, plane figure dissection, and many others. Solutions. More than 450 illustrations. vii + 258pp. 5⅜ x 8.   **T473 Paperbound $1.25**

THE CANTERBURY PUZZLES, Henry Dudeney. Chaucer's pilgrims set one another problems in story form. Also Adventures of the Puzzle Club, the Strange Escape of the King's Jester, the Monks of Riddlewell, the Squire's Christmas Puzzle Party, and others. All puzzles are original, based on dissecting plane figures, arithmetic, algebra, elementary calculus and other branches of mathematics, and purely logical ingenuity. "The limit of ingenuity and intricacy," The Observer. Over 110 puzzles. Full Solutions. 150 illustrations. vii + 225pp. 5⅜ x 8.   **T474 Paperbound $1.25**

MATHEMATICAL EXCURSIONS, H. A. Merrill. Even if you hardly remember your high school math, you'll enjoy the 90 stimulating problems contained in this book and you will come to understand a great many mathematical principles with surprisingly little effort. Many useful shortcuts and diversions not generally known are included: division by inspection, Russian peasant multiplication, memory systems for pi, building odd and even magic squares, square roots by geometry, dyadic systems, and many more. Solutions to difficult problems. 50 illustrations. 145pp. 5⅜ x 8.   **T350 Paperbound $1.00**

MAGIC SQUARES AND CUBES, W. S. Andrews. Only book-length treatment in English, a thorough non-technical description and analysis. Here are nasik, overlapping, pandiagonal, serrated squares; magic circles, cubes, spheres, rhombuses. Try your hand at 4-dimensional magical figures! Much unusual folklore and tradition included. High school algebra is sufficient. 754 diagrams and illustrations. viii + 419pp. 5⅜ x 8.   **T658 Paperbound $1.85**

CALIBAN'S PROBLEM BOOK: MATHEMATICAL, INFERENTIAL AND CRYPTOGRAPHIC PUZZLES, H. Phillips (Caliban), S. T. Shovelton, G. S. Marshall. 105 ingenious problems by the greatest living creator of puzzles based on logic and inference. Rigorous, modern, piquant; reflecting their author's unusual personality, these intermediate and advanced puzzles all involve the ability to reason clearly through complex situations; some call for mathematical knowledge, ranging from algebra to number theory. Solutions. xi + 180pp. 5⅜ x 8.   **T736 Paperbound $1.25**

MATHEMATICAL PUZZLES FOR BEGINNERS AND ENTHUSIASTS, G. Mott-Smith. 188 mathematical puzzles based on algebra, dissection of plane figures, permutations, and probability, that will test and improve your powers of inference and interpretation. The Odic Force, The Spider's Cousin, Ellipse Drawing, theory and strategy of card and board games like tit-tat-toe, go moku, salvo, and many others. 100 pages of detailed mathematical explanations. Appendix of primes, square roots, etc. 135 illustrations. 2nd revised edition. 248pp. 5⅜ x 8.   **T198 Paperbound $1.00**

MATHEMAGIC, MAGIC PUZZLES, AND GAMES WITH NUMBERS, R. V. Heath. More than 60 new puzzles and stunts based on the properties of numbers. Easy techniques for multiplying large numbers mentally, revealing hidden numbers magically, finding the date of any day in any year, and dozens more. Over 30 pages devoted to magic squares, triangles, cubes, circles, etc. Edited by J. S. Meyer. 76 illustrations. 128pp. 5⅜ x 8.   **T110 Paperbound $1.00**

CATALOGUE OF DOVER BOOKS

MATHEMATICAL RECREATIONS, M. Kraitchik. One of the most thorough compilations of unusual mathematical problems for beginners and advanced mathematicians. Historical problems from Greek, Medieval, Arabic, Hindu sources. 50 pages devoted to pastimes derived from figurate numbers, Mersenne numbers, Fermat numbers, primes and probability. 40 pages of magic, Euler, Latin, panmagic squares. 25 new positional and permutational games of permanent value: fairy chess, latruncles, reversi, jinx, ruma, lasca, tricolor, tetrachrome, etc. Complete rigorous solutions. Revised second edition. 181 illustrations. 333pp. 5⅜ x 8.
T163 Paperbound **$1.75**

MATHEMATICAL PUZZLES OF SAM LOYD, selected and edited by M. Gardner. Choice puzzles by the greatest American puzzle creator and innovator. Selected from his famous collection, "Cyclopedia of Puzzles," they retain the unique style and historical flavor of the originals. There are posers based on arithmetic, algebra, probability, game theory, route tracing, topology, counter, sliding block, operations research, geometrical dissection. Includes the famous "14-15" puzzle which was a national craze, and his "Horse of a Different Color" which sold millions of copies. 117 of his most ingenious puzzles in all, 120 line drawings and diagrams. Solutions. Selected references. xx + 167pp. 5⅜ x 8. T498 Paperbound **$1.00**

MATHEMATICAL PUZZLES OF SAM LOYD, Vol. II, selected and edited by Martin Gardner. The outstanding 2nd selection from the great American innovator's "Cyclopedia of Puzzles": speed and distance problems, clock problems, plane and solid geometry, calculus problems, etc. Analytical table of contents that groups the puzzles according to the type of mathematics necessary to solve them. 166 puzzles, 150 original line drawings and diagrams. Selected references. xiv + 177pp. 5⅜ x 8. T709 Paperbound **$1.00**

ARITHMETICAL EXCURSIONS: AN ENRICHMENT OF ELEMENTARY MATHEMATICS, H. Bowers and J. Bowers. A lively and lighthearted collection of facts and entertainments for anyone who enjoys manipulating numbers or solving arithmetical puzzles: methods of arithmetic never taught in school, little-known facts about the most simple numbers, and clear explanations of more sophisticated topics; mysteries and folklore of numbers, the "Hin-dog-abic" number system, etc. First publication. Index. 529 numbered problems and diversions, all with answers. Bibliography. 60 figures. xiv + 320pp. 5⅜ x 8. T770 Paperbound **$1.65**

CRYPTANALYSIS, H. F. Gaines. Formerly entitled ELEMENTARY CRYPTANALYSIS, this introductory-intermediate level text is the best book in print on cryptograms and their solution. It covers all major techniques of the past, and contains much that is not generally known except to experts. Full details about concealment, substitution, and transposition ciphers; periodic mixed alphabets, multafid, Kasiski and Vigenere methods, Ohaver patterns, Playfair, and scores of other topics. 6 language letter and word frequency appendix. 167 problems, now furnished with solutions. Index. 173 figures. vi + 230pp. 5⅜ x 8.
T97 Paperbound **$2.00**

CRYPTOGRAPHY, L. D. Smith. An excellent introductory work on ciphers and their solution, the history of secret writing, and actual methods and problems in such techniques as transposition and substitution. Appendices describe the enciphering of Japanese, the Baconian biliteral cipher, and contain frequency tables and a bibliography for further study. Over 150 problems with solutions. 160pp. 5⅜ x 8. T247 Paperbound **$1.00**

PUZZLE QUIZ AND STUNT FUN, J. Meyer. The solution to party doldrums. 238 challenging puzzles, stunts and tricks. Mathematical puzzles like The Clever Carpenter, Atom Bomb; mysteries and deductions like The Bridge of Sighs, The Nine Pearls, Dog Logic; observation puzzles like Cigarette Smokers, Telephone Dial; over 200 others including magic squares, tongue twisters, puns, anagrams, and many others. All problems solved fully. 250pp. 5⅜ x 8. T337 Paperbound **$1.00**

101 PUZZLES IN THOUGHT AND LOGIC, C. R. Wylie, Jr. Brand new problems you need no special knowledge to solve! Take the kinks out of your mental "muscles" and enjoy solving murder problems, the detection of lying fishermen, the logical identification of color by a blindman, and dozens more. Introduction with simplified explanation of general scientific method and puzzle solving. 128pp. 5⅜ x 8. T367 Paperbound **$1.00**

MY BEST PROBLEMS IN MATHEMATICS, Hubert Phillips ("Caliban"). Only elementary mathematics needed to solve these 100 witty, catchy problems by a master problem creator. Problems on the odds in cards and dice, problems in geometry, algebra, permutations, even problems that require no math at all—just a logical mind, clear thinking. Solutions completely worked out. If you enjoy mysteries, alerting your perceptive powers and exercising your detective's eye, you'll find these cryptic puzzles a challenging delight. Original 1961 publication. 100 puzzles, solutions. x + 107pp. 5⅝ x 8. T91 Paperbound **$1.00**

MY BEST PUZZLES IN LOGIC AND REASONING, Hubert Phillips ("Caliban"). A new collection of 100 inferential and logical puzzles chosen from the best that have appeared in England, available for first time in U.S. By the most endlessly resourceful puzzle creator now living. All data presented are both necessary and sufficient to allow a single unambiguous answer. No special knowledge is required for problems ranging from relatively simple to completely original one-of-a-kinds. Guaranteed to please beginners and experts of all ages. Original publication. 100 puzzles, full solutions. x + 107pp. 5⅜ x 8. T119 Paperbound **$1.00**

THE BOOK OF MODERN PUZZLES, G. L. Kaufman. A completely new series of puzzles as fascinating as crossword and deduction puzzles but based upon different principles and techniques. Simple 2-minute teasers, word labyrinths, design and pattern puzzles, logic and observation puzzles — over 150 braincrackers. Answers to all problems. 116 illustrations. 192pp. 5⅜ x 8.
T143 Paperbound **$1.00**

NEW WORD PUZZLES, G. L. Kaufman. 100 ENTIRELY NEW puzzles based on words and their combinations that will delight crossword puzzle, Scrabble and Jotto fans. Chess words, based on the moves of the chess king; design-onyms, symmetrical designs made of synonyms; rhymed double-crostics; syllable sentences; addle letter anagrams; alphagrams; linkograms; and many others all brand new. Full solutions. Space to work problems. 196 figures. vi + 122pp. 5⅜ x 8.
T344 Paperbound **$1.00**

MAZES AND LABYRINTHS: A BOOK OF PUZZLES, W. Shepherd. Mazes, formerly associated with mystery and ritual, are still among the most intriguing of intellectual puzzles. This is a novel and different collection of 50 amusements that embody the principle of the maze: mazes in the classical tradition; 3-dimensional, ribbon, and Möbius-strip mazes; hidden messages; spatial arrangements; etc.—almost all built on amusing story situations. 84 illustrations. Essay on maze psychology. Solutions. xv + 122pp. 5⅜ x 8.
T731 Paperbound **$1.00**

MAGIC TRICKS & CARD TRICKS, W. Jonson. Two books bound as one. 52 tricks with cards, 37 tricks with coins, bills, eggs, smoke, ribbons, slates, etc. Details on presentation, misdirection, and routining will help you master such famous tricks as the Changing Card, Card in the Pocket, Four Aces, Coin Through the Hand, Bill in the Egg, Afghan Bands, and over 75 others. If you follow the lucid exposition and key diagrams carefully, you will finish these two books with an astonishing mastery of magic. 106 figures. 224pp. 5⅜ x 8. T909 Paperbound **$1.00**

PANORAMA OF MAGIC, Milbourne Christopher. A profusely illustrated history of stage magic, a unique selection of prints and engravings from the author's private collection of magic memorabilia, the largest of its kind. Apparatus, stage settings and costumes; ingenious ads distributed by the performers and satiric broadsides passed around in the streets ridiculing pompous showmen; programs; decorative souvenirs. The lively text, by one of America's foremost professional magicians, is full of anecdotes about almost legendary wizards: Dede, the Egyptian; Philadelphia, the wonder-worker; Robert-Houdin, "the father of modern magic;" Harry Houdini; scores more. Altogether a pleasure package for anyone interested in magic, stage setting and design, ethnology, psychology, or simply in unusual people. A Dover original. 295 illustrations; 8 in full color. Index. viii + 216pp. 8⅜ x 11¼.
T774 Paperbound **$2.25**

HOUDINI ON MAGIC, Harry Houdini. One of the greatest magicians of modern times explains his most prized secrets. How locks are picked, with illustrated picks and skeleton keys; how a girl is sawed into twins; how to walk through a brick wall — Houdini's explanations of 44 stage tricks with many diagrams. Also included is a fascinating discussion of great magicians of the past and the story of his fight against fraudulent mediums and spiritualists. Edited by W.B. Gibson and M.N. Young. Bibliography. 155 figures, photos. xv + 280pp. 5⅜ x 8.
T384 Paperbound **$1.25**

MATHEMATICS, MAGIC AND MYSTERY, Martin Gardner. Why do card tricks work? How do magicians perform astonishing mathematical feats? How is stage mind-reading possible? This is the first book length study explaining the application of probability, set theory, theory of numbers, topology, etc., to achieve many startling tricks. Non-technical, accurate, detailed! 115 sections discuss tricks with cards, dice, coins, knots, geometrical vanishing illusions, how a Curry square "demonstrates" that the sum of the parts may be greater than the whole, and dozens of others. No sleight of hand necessary! 135 illustrations. xii + 174pp. 5⅜ x 8.
T335 Paperbound **$1.00**

EASY-TO-DO ENTERTAINMENTS AND DIVERSIONS WITH COINS, CARDS, STRING, PAPER AND MATCHES, R. M. Abraham. Over 300 tricks, games and puzzles will provide young readers with absorbing fun. Sections on card games; paper-folding; tricks with coins, matches and pieces of string; games for the agile; toy-making from common household objects; mathematical recreations; and 50 miscellaneous pastimes. Anyone in charge of groups of youngsters, including hard-pressed parents, and in need of suggestions on how to keep children sensibly amused and quietly content will find this book indispensable. Clear, simple text, copious number of delightful line drawings and illustrative diagrams. Originally titled "Winter Nights Entertainments." Introduction by Lord Baden Powell. 329 illustrations. v + 186pp. 5⅜ x 8½.
T921 Paperbound **$1.00**

STRING FIGURES AND HOW TO MAKE THEM, Caroline Furness Jayne. 107 string figures plus variations selected from the best primitive and modern examples developed by Navajo, Apache, pygmies of Africa, Eskimo, in Europe, Australia, China, etc. The most readily understandable, easy-to-follow book in English on perennially popular recreation. Crystal-clear exposition; step-by-step diagrams. Everyone from kindergarten children to adults looking for unusual diversion will be endlessly amused. Index. Bibliography. Introduction by A. C. Haddon. 17 full-page plates. 960 illustrations. xxiii + 401pp. 5⅜ x 8½.
T152 Paperbound **$2.00**

Language Books and Records

GERMAN: HOW TO SPEAK AND WRITE IT. AN INFORMAL CONVERSATIONAL METHOD FOR SELF STUDY, Joseph Rosenberg. Eminently useful for self study because of concentration on elementary stages of learning. Also provides teachers with remarkable variety of aids: 28 full- and double-page sketches with pertinent items numbered and identified in German and English; German proverbs, jokes; grammar, idiom studies; extensive practice exercises. The most interesting introduction to German available, full of amusing illustrations, photographs of cities and landmarks in German-speaking cities, cultural information subtly woven into conversational material. Includes summary of grammar, guide to letter writing, study guide to German literature by Dr. Richard Friedenthal. Index. 400 illustrations. 384pp. 5⅜ x 8½.
T271 Paperbound **$2.00**

FRENCH: HOW TO SPEAK AND WRITE IT. AN INFORMAL CONVERSATIONAL METHOD FOR SELF STUDY, Joseph Lemaitre. Even the absolute beginner can acquire a solid foundation for further study from this delightful elementary course. Photographs, sketches and drawings, sparkling colloquial conversations on a wide variety of topics (including French culture and custom), French sayings and quips, are some of aids used to demonstrate rather than merely describe the language. Thorough yet surprisingly entertaining approach, excellent for teaching and for self study. Comprehensive analysis of pronunciation, practice exercises and appendices of verb tables, additional vocabulary, other useful material. Index. Appendix. 400 illustrations. 416pp. 5⅜ x 8½.
T268 Paperbound **$2.00**

DICTIONARY OF SPOKEN SPANISH, Spanish-English, English-Spanish. Compiled from spoken Spanish, emphasizing idiom and colloquial usage in both Castilian and Latin-American. More than 16,000 entries containing over 25,000 idioms—the largest list of idiomatic constructions ever published. Complete sentences given, indexed under single words—language in immediately useable form, for travellers, businessmen, students, etc. 25 page introduction provides rapid survey of sounds, grammar, syntax, with full consideration of irregular verbs. Especially apt in modern treatment of phrases and structure. 17 page glossary gives translations of geographical names, money values, numbers, national holidays, important street signs, useful expressions of high frequency, plus unique 7 page glossary of Spanish and Spanish-American foods and dishes. Originally published as War Department Technical Manual TM 30-900. iv + 513pp. 5⅜ x 8.
T495 Paperbound **$1.75**

SPEAK MY LANGUAGE: SPANISH FOR YOUNG BEGINNERS, M. Ahlman, Z. Gilbert. Records provide one of the best, and most entertaining, methods of introducing a foreign language to children. Within the framework of a train trip from Portugal to Spain, an English-speaking child is introduced to Spanish by a native companion. (Adapted from a successful radio program of the N. Y. State Educational Department.) Though a continuous story, there are a dozen specific categories of expressions, including greetings, numbers, time, weather, food, clothes, family members, etc. Drill is combined with poetry and contextual use. Authentic background music is heard. An accompanying book enables a reader to follow the records, and includes a vocabulary of over 350 recorded expressions. Two 10" 33⅓ records, total of 40 minutes. Book. 40 illustrations. 69pp. 5¼ x 10½.
T890 The set **$4.95**

AN ENGLISH-FRENCH-GERMAN-SPANISH WORD FREQUENCY DICTIONARY, H. S. Eaton. An indispensable language study aid, this is a semantic frequency list of the 6000 most frequently used words in 4 languages—24,000 words in all. The lists, based on concepts rather than words alone, and containing all modern, exact, and idiomatic vocabulary, are arranged side by side to form a unique 4-language dictionary. A simple key indicates the importance of the individual words within each language. Over 200 pages of separate indexes for each language enable you to locate individual words at a glance. Will help language teachers and students, authors of textbooks, grammars, and language tests to compare concepts in the various languages and to concentrate on basic vocabulary, avoiding uncommon and obsolete words. 2 Appendixes. xxi + 441pp. 6½ x 9¼.
T738 Paperbound **$2.45**

NEW RUSSIAN-ENGLISH AND ENGLISH-RUSSIAN DICTIONARY, M. A. O'Brien. Over 70,000 entries in the new orthography! Many idiomatic uses and colloquialisms which form the basis of actual speech. Irregular verbs, perfective and imperfective aspects, regular and irregular sound changes, and other features. One of the few dictionaries where accent changes within the conjugation of verbs and the declension of nouns are fully indicated. "One of the best," Prof. E. J. Simmons, Cornell. First names, geographical terms, bibliography, etc. 738pp. 4½ x 6¼.
T208 Paperbound **$2.00**

96 MOST USEFUL PHRASES FOR TOURISTS AND STUDENTS in English, French, Spanish, German, Italian. A handy folder you'll want to carry with you. How to say "Excuse me," "How much is it?", "Write it down, please," etc., in four foreign languages. Copies limited, no more than 1 to a customer.
FREE

Say It language phrase books

These handy phrase books (128 to 196 pages each) make grammatical drills unnecessary for an elementary knowledge of a spoken foreign language. Covering most matters of travel and everyday life each volume contains:

Over 1000 phrases and sentences in immediately useful forms — foreign language plus English.

Modern usage designed for Americans. Specific phrases like, "Give me small change," and "Please call a taxi."

Simplified phonetic transcription you will be able to read at sight.

The only completely indexed phrase books on the market.

Covers scores of important situations: — Greetings, restaurants, sightseeing, useful expressions, etc.

These books are prepared by native linguists who are professors at Columbia, N.Y.U., Fordham and other great universities. Use them independently or with any other book or record course. They provide a supplementary living element that most other courses lack. Individual volumes in:

Russian 75¢	Italian 75¢	Spanish 75¢	German 75¢
Hebrew 75¢	Danish 75¢	Japanese 75¢	Swedish 75¢
Dutch 75¢	Esperanto 75¢	Modern Greek 75¢	Portuguese 75¢
Norwegian 75¢	Polish 75¢	French 75¢	Yiddish 75¢
Turkish 75¢		English for German-speaking people 75¢	
English for Italian-speaking people 75¢		English for Spanish-speaking people 75¢	

Large clear type. 128-196 pages each. 3½ x 5¼. Sturdy paper binding.

Listen and Learn language records

LISTEN & LEARN is the only language record course designed especially to meet your travel and everyday needs. It is available in separate sets for FRENCH, SPANISH, GERMAN, JAPANESE, RUSSIAN, MODERN GREEK, PORTUGUESE, ITALIAN and HEBREW, and each set contains three 33⅓ rpm long-playing records—1½ hours of recorded speech by eminent native speakers who are professors at Columbia, New York University, Queens College.

Check the following special features found only in LISTEN & LEARN:

● **Dual-language recording.** 812 selected phrases and sentences, over 3200 words, spoken first in English, then in their foreign language equivalents. A suitable pause follows each foreign phrase, allowing you time to repeat the expression. You learn by unconscious assimilation.

● **128 to 206-page manual** contains everything on the records, plus a simple phonetic pronunciation guide.

● **Indexed for convenience. The only set on the market** that is completely indexed. No more puzzling over where to find the phrase you need. Just look in the rear of the manual.

● **Practical.** No time wasted on material you can find in any grammar. LISTEN & LEARN covers central core material with phrase approach. Ideal for the person with limited learning time.

● **Living, modern expressions,** not found in other courses. Hygienic products, modern equipment, shopping—expressions used every day, like "nylon" and "air-conditioned."

● **Limited objective.** Everything you learn, no matter where you stop, is immediately useful. You have to finish other courses, wade through grammar and vocabulary drill, before they help you.

● **High-fidelity recording.** LISTEN & LEARN records equal in clarity and surface-silence any record on the market costing up to $6.

"Excellent . . . the spoken records . . . impress me as being among the very best on the market," **Prof. Mario Pei,** Dept. of Romance Languages, Columbia University. "Inexpensive and well-done . . . it would make an ideal present," CHICAGO SUNDAY TRIBUNE. "More genuinely helpful than anything of its kind which I have previously encountered," **Sidney Clark,** well-known author of "ALL THE BEST" travel books.

UNCONDITIONAL GUARANTEE. Try LISTEN & LEARN, then return it within 10 days for full refund if you are not satisfied.

Each set contains three twelve-inch 33⅓ records, manual, and album.

SPANISH	the set $5.95	GERMAN	the set $5.95
FRENCH	the set $5.95	ITALIAN	the set $5.95
RUSSIAN	the set $5.95	JAPANESE	the set $5.95
PORTUGUESE	the set $5.95	MODERN GREEK	the set $5.95
MODERN HEBREW	the set $5.95		

Trubner Colloquial Manuals

These unusual books are members of the famous Trubner series of colloquial manuals. They have been written to provide adults with a sound colloquial knowledge of a foreign language, and are suited for either class use or self-study. Each book is a complete course in itself, with progressive, easy to follow lessons. Phonetics, grammar, and syntax are covered, while hundreds of phrases and idioms, reading texts, exercises, and vocabulary are included. These books are unusual in being neither skimpy nor overdetailed in grammatical matters, and in presenting up-to-date, colloquial, and practical phrase material. Bilingual presentation is stressed, to make thorough self-study easier for the reader.

COLLOQUIAL HINDUSTANI, A. H. Harley, formerly Nizam's Reader in Urdu, U. of London. 30 pages on phonetics and scripts (devanagari & Arabic-Persian) are followed by 29 lessons, including material on English and Arabic-Persian influences. Key to all exercises. Vocabulary. 5 x 7½. 147pp. Clothbound **$1.75**

COLLOQUIAL PERSIAN, L. P. Elwell-Sutton. Best introduction to modern Persian, with 90 page grammatical section followed by conversations, 35-page vocabulary. 139pp.
Clothbound **$1.75**

COLLOQUIAL ARABIC, DeLacy O'Leary. Foremost Islamic scholar covers language of Egypt, Syria, Palestine, & Northern Arabia. Extremely clear coverage of complex Arabic verbs & noun plurals; also cultural aspects of language. Vocabulary. xviii + 192pp. 5 x 7½.
Clothbound **$2.50**

COLLOQUIAL GERMAN, P. F. Doring. Intensive thorough coverage of grammar in easily-followed form. Excellent for brush-up, with hundreds of colloquial phrases. 34 pages of bilingual texts. 224pp. 5 x 7½. Clothbound **$1.75**

COLLOQUIAL SPANISH, W. R. Patterson. Castilian grammar and colloquial language, loaded with bilingual phrases and colloquialisms. Excellent for review or self-study. 164pp. 5 x 7½.
Clothbound **$1.75**

COLLOQUIAL FRENCH, W. R. Patterson. 16th revision of this extremely popular manual. Grammar explained with model clarity, and hundreds of useful expressions and phrases; exercises, reading texts, etc. Appendixes of new and useful words and phrases. 223pp. 5 x 7½.
Clothbound **$1.75**

COLLOQUIAL CZECH, J. Schwarz, former headmaster of Lingua Institute, Prague. Full easily followed coverage of grammar, hundreds of immediately useable phrases, texts. Perhaps the best Czech grammar in print. "An absolutely successful textbook," JOURNAL OF CZECHO-SLOVAK FORCES IN GREAT BRITAIN. 252pp. 5 x 7½. Clothbound **$3.00**

COLLOQUIAL RUMANIAN, G. Nandris, Professor of University of London. Extremely thorough coverage of phonetics, grammar, syntax; also included 70-page reader, and 70-page vocabulary. Probably the best grammar for this increasingly important language. 340pp. 5 x 7½.
Clothbound **$2.50**

COLLOQUIAL ITALIAN, A. L. Hayward. Excellent self-study course in grammar, vocabulary, idioms, and reading. Easy progressive lessons will give a good working knowledge of Italian in the shortest possible time. 5 x 7½. Clothbound **$1.75**

COLLOQUIAL TURKISH, Yusuf Mardin. Very clear, thorough introduction to leading cultural and economic language of Near East. Begins with pronunciation and statement of vowel harmony, then 36 lessons present grammar, graded vocabulary, useful phrases, dialogues, reading, exercises. Key to exercises at rear. Turkish-English vocabulary. All in Roman alphabet. x + 288pp. 4¾ x 7¼. Clothbound **$4.00**

DUTCH-ENGLISH AND ENGLISH-DUTCH DICTIONARY, F. G. Renier. For travel, literary, scientific or business Dutch, you will find this the most convenient, practical and comprehensive dictionary on the market. More than 60,000 entries, shades of meaning, colloquialisms, idioms, compounds and technical terms. Dutch and English strong and irregular verbs. This is the only dictionary in its size and price range that indicates the gender of nouns. New orthography. xvii + 571pp. 5½ x 6¼. T224 Clothbound **$2.75**

LEARN DUTCH, F. G. Renier. This book is the most satisfactory and most easily used grammar of modern Dutch. The student is gradually led from simple lessons in pronunciation, through translation from and into Dutch, and finally to a mastery of spoken and written Dutch. Grammatical principles are clearly explained while a useful, practical vocabulary is introduced in easy exercises and readings. It is used and recommended by the Fulbright Committee in the Netherlands. Phonetic appendices. Over 1200 exercises; Dutch-English, English-Dutch vocabularies. 181pp. 4¼ x 7¼. T441 Clothbound **$2.25**

Art, History of Art, Antiques, Graphic Arts, Handcrafts

ART STUDENTS' ANATOMY, E. J. Farris. Outstanding art anatomy that uses chiefly living objects for its illustrations. 71 photos of undraped men, women, children are accompanied by carefully labeled matching sketches to illustrate the skeletal system, articulations and movements, bony landmarks, the muscular system, skin, fasciae, fat, etc. 9 x-ray photos show movement of joints. Undraped models are shown in such actions as serving in tennis, drawing a bow in archery, playing football, dancing, preparing to spring and to dive. Also discussed and illustrated are proportions, age and sex differences, the anatomy of the smile, etc. 8 plates by the great early 18th century anatomic illustrator Siegfried Albinus are also included. Glossary. 158 figures, 7 in color. x + 159pp. 5⅝ x 8⅜. T744 Paperbound **$1.50**

AN ATLAS OF ANATOMY FOR ARTISTS, F Schider. A new 3rd edition of this standard text enlarged by 52 new illustrations of hands, anatomical studies by Cloquet, and expressive life studies of the body by Barcsay. 189 clear, detailed plates offer you precise information of impeccable accuracy. 29 plates show all aspects of the skeleton, with closeups of special areas, while 54 full-page plates, mostly in two colors, give human musculature as seen from four different points of view, with cutaways for important portions of the body. 14 full-page plates provide photographs of hand forms, eyelids, female breasts, and indicate the location of muscles upon models. 59 additional plates show how great artists of the past utilized human anatomy. They reproduce sketches and finished work by such artists as Michelangelo, Leonardo da Vinci, Goya, and 15 others. This is a lifetime reference work which will be one of the most important books in any artist's library. "The standard reference tool," AMERICAN LIBRARY ASSOCIATION. "Excellent," AMERICAN ARTIST. Third enlarged edition. 189 plates, 647 illustrations. xxvi + 192pp. 7⅞ x 10⅝. T241 Clothbound **$6.00**

AN ATLAS OF ANIMAL ANATOMY FOR ARTISTS, W. Ellenberger, H. Baum, H. Dittrich. The largest, richest animal anatomy for artists available in English. 99 detailed anatomical plates of such animals as the horse, dog, cat, lion, deer, seal, kangaroo, flying squirrel, cow, bull, goat, monkey, hare, and bat. Surface features are clearly indicated, while progressive beneath-the-skin pictures show musculature, tendons, and bone structure. Rest and action are exhibited in terms of musculature and skeletal structure and detailed cross-sections are given for heads and important features. The animals chosen are representative of specific families so that a study of these anatomies will provide knowledge of hundreds of related species. "Highly recommended as one of the very few books on the subject worthy of being used as an authoritative guide," DESIGN. "Gives a fundamental knowledge," AMERICAN ARTIST. Second revised, enlarged edition with new plates from Cuvier, Stubbs, etc. 288 illustrations. 153pp. 11⅜ x 9. T82 Clothbound **$6.00**

THE HUMAN FIGURE IN MOTION, Eadweard Muybridge. The largest selection in print of Muybridge's famous high-speed action photos of the human figure in motion. 4789 photographs illustrate 162 different actions: men, women, children—mostly undraped—are shown walking, running, carrying various objects, sitting, lying down, climbing, throwing, arising, and performing over 150 other actions. Some actions are shown in as many as 150 photographs each. All in all there are more than 500 action strips in this enormous volume, series shots taken at shutter speeds of as high as 1/6000th of a second! These are not posed shots, but true stopped motion. They show bone and muscle in situations that the human eye is not fast enough to capture. Earlier, smaller editions of these prints have brought $40 and more on the out-of-print market. "A must for artists," ART IN FOCUS. "An unparalleled dictionary of action for all artists," AMERICAN ARTIST. 390 full-page plates, with 4789 photographs. Printed on heavy glossy stock. Reinforced binding with headbands. xxi + 390pp. 7⅞ x 10⅝. T204 Clothbound **$10.00**

ANIMALS IN MOTION, Eadweard Muybridge. This is the largest collection of animal action photos in print. 34 different animals (horses, mules, oxen, goats, camels, pigs, cats, guanacos lions, gnus, deer, monkeys, eagles—and 21 others) in 132 characteristic actions. The horse alone is shown in more than 40 different actions. All 3919 photographs are taken in series at speeds up to 1/6000th of a second. The secrets of leg motion, spinal patterns, head movements, strains and contortions shown nowhere else are captured. You will see exactly how a lion sets his foot down; how an elephant's knees are like a human's—and how they differ; the position of a kangaroo's legs in mid-leap; how an ostrich's head bobs; details of the flight of birds—and thousands of facets of motion only the fastest cameras can catch. Photographed from domestic animals and animals in the Philadelphia zoo, it contains neither semiposed artificial shots nor distorted telephoto shots taken under adverse conditions. Artists, biologists, decorators, cartoonists, will find this book indispensable for understanding animals in motion. "A really marvelous series of plates," NATURE (London). "The dry plate's most spectacular early use was by Eadweard Muybridge," LIFE. 3919 photographs; 380 full pages of plates. 440pp. Printed on heavy glossy paper. Deluxe binding with headbands. 7⅞ x 10⅝. T203 Clothbound **$10.00**

CATALOGUE OF DOVER BOOKS

ART ANATOMY, William Rimmer, M.D. Often called one of America's foremost contributions to art instruction, a work of art in its own right. More than 700 line drawings by the author, first-rate anatomist and dissector as well as artist, with a non-technical anatomical text. Impeccably accurate drawings of muscles, skeletal structure, surface features, other aspects of males and females, children, adults and aged persons show not only form, size, insertion and articulation but personality and emotion as reflected by physical features usually ignored in modern anatomical works. Complete unabridged reproduction of 1876 edition slightly rearranged. Introduction by Robert Hutchinson. 722 illustrations. xiii + 153pp. 7¾ x 10¾.
T908 Paperbound **$2.00**

ANIMAL DRAWING: ANATOMY AND ACTION FOR ARTISTS, C. R. Knight. The author and illustrator of this work was "the most distinguished painter of animal life." This extensive course in animal drawing discusses musculature, bone structure, animal psychology, movements, habits, habitats. Innumerable tips on proportions, light and shadow play, coloring, hair formation, feather arrangement, scales, how animals lie down, animal expressions, etc., from great apes to birds. Pointers on avoiding gracelessness in horses, deer; on introducing proper power and bulk to heavier animals; on giving proper grace and subtle expression to members of the cat family. Originally titled "Animal Anatomy and Psychology for the Artist and Layman." Over 123 illustrations. 149pp. 8¼ x 10½.
T426 Paperbound **$2.00**

DESIGN FOR ARTISTS AND CRAFTSMEN, L. Wolchonok. The most thorough course ever prepared on the creation of art motifs and designs. It teaches you to create your own designs out of things around you — from geometric patterns, plants, birds, animals, humans, landscapes, and man-made objects. It leads you step by step through the creation of more than 1300 designs, and shows you how to create design that is fresh, well-founded, and original. Mr. Wolchonok, whose text is used by scores of art schools, shows you how the same idea can be developed into many different forms, ranging from near representationalism to the most advanced forms of abstraction. The material in this book is entirely new, and combines full awareness of traditional design with the work of such men as Miro, Léger, Picasso, Moore, and others. 113 detailed exercises, with instruction hints, diagrams, and details to enable you to apply Wolchonok's methods to your own work. "A great contribution to the field of design and crafts," N. Y. SOCIETY OF CRAFTSMEN. More than 1300 illustrations. xv + 207pp. 7⅞ x 10¾.
T274 Clothbound **$4.95**

HAWTHORNE ON PAINTING. A vivid recreation, from students' notes, of instruction by Charles W. Hawthorne, given for over 31 years at his famous Cape Cod School of Art. Divided into sections on the outdoor model, still life, landscape, the indoor model, and water color, each section begins with a concise essay, followed by epigrammatic comments on color, form, seeing, etc. Not a formal course, but comments of a great teacher-painter on specific student works, which will solve problems in your own painting and understanding of art. "An excellent introduction for laymen and students alike," Time. Introduction. 100pp. 5⅜ x 8.
T653 Paperbound **$1.00**

THE ENJOYMENT AND USE OF COLOR, Walter Sargent. This book explains fascinating relations among colors, between colors in nature and art; describes experiments that you can perform to understand these relations more thoroughly; points out hundreds of little known facts about color values, intensities, effects of high and low illumination, complementary colors, color harmonies. Practical hints for painters, references to techniques of masters, questions at chapter ends for self-testing all make this a valuable book for artists, professional and amateur, and for general readers interested in world of color. Republication of 1923 edition. 35 illustrations, 6 full-page plates. New color frontispiece. Index. xii + 274pp. 5⅜ x 8.
T944 Paperbound **$2.25**

DECORATIVE ALPHABETS AND INITIALS, ed. by Alexander Nesbitt. No payment, no permission needed to reproduce any one of these 3924 different letters, covering 1000 years. Crisp, clear letters all in line, from Anglo-Saxon mss., Luebeck Cathedral, 15th century Augsburg; the work of Dürer, Holbein, Cresci, Beardsley, Rossing Wadsworth, John Moylin, etc. Every imaginable style. 91 complete alphabets. 123 full-page plates. 192pp. 7¾ x 10¾.
T544 Paperbound **$2.25**

THREE CLASSICS OF ITALIAN CALLIGRAPHY, edited by Oscar Ogg. Here, combined in a single volume, are complete reproductions of three famous calligraphic works written by the greatest writing masters of the Renaissance: Arrighi's OPERINA and IL MODO, Tagliente's LO PRESENTE LIBRO, and Palatino's LIBRO NUOVO. These books present more than 200 complete alphabets and thousands of lettered specimens. The basic hand is Papal Chancery, but scores of other alphabets are also given: European and Asiatic local alphabets, foliated and art alphabets, scrolls, cartouches, borders, etc. Text is in Italian. Introduction. 245 plates. x + 272pp. 6⅛ x 9¼.
T212 Paperbound **$2.25**

CALLIGRAPHY, J. G. Schwandner. One of the legendary books in the graphic arts, copies of which brought $500 each on the rare book market, now reprinted for the first time in over 200 years. A beautiful plate book of graceful calligraphy, and an inexhaustible source of first-rate material copyright-free, for artists and directors, craftsmen, commercial artists, etc. More than 300 ornamental initials forming 12 complete alphabets, over 150 ornate frames and panels, over 200 flourishes, over 75 calligraphic pictures including a temple, cherubs, cocks, dodos, stags, chamois, foliated lions, greyhounds, etc. Thousand of calligraphic elements to be used for suggestions of quality, sophistication, antiquity, and sheer beauty. Historical introduction. 158 full-page plates. 368pp. 9 x 13.
T475 Clothbound **$10.00**

THE HISTORY AND TECHNIQUE OF LETTERING, A. Nesbitt. The only thorough inexpensive history of letter forms from the point of view of the artist. Mr. Nesbitt covers every major development in lettering from the ancient Egyptians to the present and illustrates each development with a complete alphabet. Such masters as Baskerville, Bell, Bodoni, Caslon, Koch, Kilian, Morris, Garamont, Jenson, and dozens of others are analyzed in terms of artistry and historical development. The author also presents a 65-page practical course in lettering, besides the full historical text. 89 complete alphabets; 165 additional lettered specimens. xvii + 300pp. 5⅜ x 8.   T427 Paperbound **$2.00**

FOOT-HIGH LETTERS: A GUIDE TO LETTERING (A PRACTICAL SYLLABUS FOR TEACHERS), M. Price. A complete alphabet of Classic Roman letters, each a foot high, each on a separate 16 x 22 plate—perfect for use in lettering classes. In addition to an accompanying description, each plate also contains 9 two-inch-high forms of letter in various type faces, such as "Caslon," "Empire," "Onyx," and "Neuland," illustrating the many possible derivations from the standard classical forms. One plate contains 21 additional forms of the letter A. The fully illustrated 16-page syllabus by Mr. Price, formerly of the Pratt Institute and the Rhode Island School of Design, contains dozens of useful suggestions for student and teacher alike. An indispensable teaching aid. Extensively revised. 16-page syllabus and 30 plates in slip cover, 16 x 22.   T239 Clothbound **$6.00**

THE STYLES OF ORNAMENT, Alexander Speltz. Largest collection of ornaments in print—3765 illustrations of prehistoric, Lombard, Gothic, Frank, Romanesque, Mohammedan, Renaissance, Polish, Swiss, Rococo, Sheraton, Empire, U. S. Colonial, etc., ornament. Gargoyles, dragons, columns, necklaces, urns, friezes, furniture, buildings, keyholes, tapestries, fantastic animals, armor, religious objects, much more, all in line. Reproduce any one free. Index. Bibliography. 400 plates. 656pp. 5⅝ x 8⅜.   T557 Paperbound **$2.50**

HANDBOOK OF DESIGNS AND DEVICES, C. P. Hornung. This unique book is indispensable to the designer, commercial artist, and hobbyist. It is not a textbook but a working collection of 1836 basic designs and variations, carefully reproduced, which may be used without permission. Variations of circle, line, band, triangle, square, cross, diamond, swastika, pentagon, octagon, hexagon, star, scroll, interlacement, shields, etc. Supplementary notes on the background and symbolism of the figures. "A necessity to every designer who would be original without having to labor heavily," ARTIST AND ADVERTISER. 204 plates. 240pp. 5⅜ x 8.
T125 Paperbound **$1.90**

THE UNIVERSAL PENMAN, George Bickham. This beautiful book, which first appeared in 1743, is the largest collection of calligraphic specimens, flourishes, alphabets, and calligraphic illustrations ever published. 212 full-page plates are drawn from the work of such 18th century masters of English roundhand as Dove, Champion, Bland, and 20 others. They contain 22 complete alphabets, over 2,000 flourishes, and 122 illustrations, each drawn with a stylistic grace impossible to describe. This book is invaluable to anyone interested in the beauties of calligraphy, or to any artist, hobbyist, or craftsman who wishes to use the very best ornamental handwriting and flourishes for decorative purposes. Commercial artists, advertising artists, have found it unexcelled as a source of material suggesting quality. "An essential part of any art library, and a book of permanent value," AMERICAN ARTIST. 212 plates. 224pp. 9 x 13¾.   T20 Clothbound **$10.00**

1800 WOODCUTS BY THOMAS BEWICK AND HIS SCHOOL. Prepared by Dover's editorial staff, this is the largest collection of woodcuts by Bewick and his school ever compiled. Contains the complete engravings from all his major works and a wide range of illustrations from lesser-known collections, all photographed from clear copies of the original books and reproduced in line. Carefully and conveniently organized into sections on Nature (animals and birds, scenery and landscapes, plants, insects, etc.), People (love and courtship, social life, school and domestic scenes, misfortunes, costumes, etc.), Business and Trade, and illustrations from primers, fairytales, spelling books, frontispieces, borders, fables and allegories, etc. In addition to technical proficiency and simple beauty, Bewick's work is remarkable as a mode of pictorial symbolism, reflecting rustic tranquility, an atmosphere of rest, simplicity, idyllic contentment. A delight for the eye, an inexhaustible source of illustrative material for art studios, commercial artists, advertising agencies. Individual illustrations (up to 10 for any one use) are copyright free. Classified index. Bibliography and sources. Introduction by Robert Hutchinson. 1800 woodcuts. xiv + 247pp. 9 x 12.
T766 Clothbound **$10.00**

A HANDBOOK OF EARLY ADVERTISING ART, C. P. Hornung. The largest collection of copyright-free early advertising art ever compiled. Vol. I contains some 2,000 illustrations of agricultural devices, animals, old automobiles, birds, buildings, Christmas decorations (with 7 Santa Clauses by Nast), allegorical figures, fire engines, horses and vehicles, Indians, portraits, sailing ships, trains, sports, trade cuts — and 30 other categories! Vol. II, devoted to typography, has over 4000 specimens: 600 different Roman, Gothic, Barnum, Old English faces; 630 ornamental type faces; 1115 initials, hundreds of scrolls, flourishes, etc. This third edition is enlarged by 78 additional plates containing all new material. "A remarkable collection," PRINTERS' INK. "A rich contribution to the history of American design," GRAPHIS. Volume I, Pictorial. Over 2000 illustrations. xiv + 242pp. 9 x 12. T122 Clothbound **$10.00** Volume II, Typographical. Over 4000 specimens. vii + 312pp. 9 x 12. T123 Clothbound **$10.00**
Two volume set, T121 Clothbound, only **$18.50**

DESIGN MOTIFS OF ANCIENT MEXICO, J. Enciso. This unique collection of pre-Columbian stamps for textiles and pottery contains 766 superb designs from Aztec, Olmec, Totonac, Maya, and Toltec origins. Plumed serpents, calendrical elements, wind gods, animals, flowers, demons, dancers, monsters, abstract ornament, and other designs. More than 90% of these illustrations are completely unobtainable elsewhere. Use this work to bring new barbaric beauty into your crafts or drawing. Originally $17.50. Printed in three colors. 766 illustrations, thousands of motifs. 192pp. 7⅞ x 10¾.　　　　　　　**T84 Paperbound $1.85**

DECORATIVE ART OF THE SOUTHWEST INDIANS, D. S. Sides. A magnificent album of authentic designs (both pre- and post-Conquest) from the pottery, textiles, and basketry of the Navaho, Hopi, Mohave, Santo Domingo, and over 20 other Southwestern groups. Designs include birds, clouds, butterflies, quadrupeds, geometric forms, etc. A valuable book for folklorists, and a treasury for artists, designers, advertisers, and craftsmen, who may use without payment or permission any of the vigorous, colorful, and strongly rhythmic designs. Aesthetic and archeological notes. 50 plates. Bibliography of over 50 items. xviii + 101pp. 5⅝ x 8⅜.　　　　　　　**T139 Paperbound $1.00**

PAINTING IN THE FAR EAST, Laurence Binyon. Excellent introduction by one of greatest authorities on subject studies 1500 years of oriental art (China, Japan; also Tibet, Persia), over 250 painters. Examines works, schools, influence of Wu Tao-tzu, Kanaoka, Toba Sojo, Masanobu, Okio, etc.; early traditions; Kamakura epoch; the Great Decorators; T'ang Dynasty; Matabei, beginnings of genre; Japanese woodcut, color print; much more, all chronological, in cultural context. 42 photos. Bibliography. 317pp. 6 x 9¼.　　　　**T520 Paperbound $2.00**

ON THE LAWS OF JAPANESE PAINTING, H. Bowie. This unusual book, based on 9 years of profound study-experience in the Late Kano art of Japan, remains the most authentic guide in English to the spirit and technique of Japanese painting. A wealth of interesting and useful data on control of the brush; practise exercises; manufacture of ink, brushes, colors; the use of various lines and dots to express moods. It is the best possible substitute for a series of lessons from a great oriental master. 66 plates with 220 illustrations. Index. xv + 177pp. 6⅛ x 9¼.　　　　　　　**T30 Paperbound $1.95**

THE MATERIALS AND TECHNIQUES OF MEDIEVAL PAINTING, D. V. Thompson. Based on years of study of medieval manuscripts and laboratory analysis of medieval paintings, this book discusses carriers and grounds, binding media, pigments, metals used in painting, etc. Considers relative merits of painting al fresco and al secco, the procession of coloring materials, burnishing, and many other matters. Preface by Bernard Berenson. Index. 239pp. 5⅜ x 8.　　　　　　　**T327 Paperbound $1.85**

THE CRAFTSMAN'S HANDBOOK, Cennino Cennini. This is considered the finest English translation of IL LIBRO DELL' ARTE, a 15th century Florentine introduction to art technique. It is both fascinating reading and a wonderful mirror of another culture for artists, art students, historians, social scientists, or anyone interested in details of life some 500 years ago. While it is not an exact recipe book, it gives directions for such matters as tinting papers, gilding stone, preparation of various hues of black, and many other useful but nearly forgotten facets of the painter's art. As a human document reflecting the ideas of a practising medieval artist it is particularly important. 4 illustrations. xxvii + 142pp. D. V. Thompson translator. 6⅛ x 9¼.　　　　　　　**T54 Paperbound $1.35**

VASARI ON TECHNIQUE, G. Vasari. Pupil of Michelangelo and outstanding biographer of the Renaissance artists, Vasari also wrote this priceless treatise on the technical methods of the painters, architects, and sculptors of his day. This is the only English translation of this practical, informative, and highly readable work. Scholars, artists, and general readers will welcome these authentic discussions of marble statues, bronze casting, fresco painting, oil painting, engraving, stained glass, rustic fountains and grottoes, etc. Introduction and notes by G. B. Brown. Index. 18 plates, 11 figures. xxiv + 328pp. 5⅜ x 8.

T717 Paperbound $2.00

METHODS AND MATERIALS OF PAINTING OF THE GREAT SCHOOLS AND MASTERS, C. L. Eastlake. A vast, complete, and authentic reconstruction of the secret techniques of the masters of painting, collected from hundreds of forgotten manuscripts by the eminent President of the British Royal Academy: Greek, Roman, and medieval techniques; fresco and tempera; varnishes and encaustics; the secrets of Leonardo, Van Eyck, Raphael, and many others. Art historians, students, teachers, critics, and laymen will gain new insights into the creation of the great masterpieces; while artists and craftsmen will have a treasury of valuable techniques. Index. Two volume set. Total of 1025pp. 5⅜ x 8.　　　　**T718 Paperbound $2.00**
T719 Paperbound $2.00
The set $4.00

BYZANTINE ART AND ARCHAEOLOGY, O. M. Dalton. Still the most thorough work in English— both in breadth and in depth—on the astounding multiplicity of Byzantine art forms throughout Europe, North Africa, and Western Asia from the 4th to the 15th century. Analyzes hundreds of individual pieces from over 160 public and private museums, libraries, and collections all over the world. Full treatment of Byzantine sculpture, painting, mosaic, jewelry, textiles, etc., including historical development, symbolism, and aesthetics. Chapters on iconography and ornament. Indispensable for study of Christian symbolism and medieval art. 457 illustrations, many full-page. Bibliography of over 2500 references. 4 Indexes. xx + 727pp. 6⅛ x 9¼.　　　　　　　**T776 Clothbound $8.50**